Unusual Environments and Human Behavior

Edited by

NEAL M. BURNS

Space and Armaments Systems
Honeywell Aeronautical Division
Minneapolis, Minnesota

RANDALL M. CHAMBERS

Aviation Medical Acceleration Laboratory
Naval Air Development Center
Johnsville, Pennsylvania

EDWIN HENDLER

Air Crew Equipment Laboratory
Naval Air Equipment Center
Philadelphia, Pennsylvania

THE FREE PRESS OF GLENCOE
Collier-Macmillan Limited, London

Unusual

Environments

and Human

Behavior

PHYSIOLOGICAL AND PSYCHOLOGICAL

PROBLEMS OF MAN IN SPACE

ACKNOWLEDGMENTS

We wish to thank Sondra Burns for her help in every phase of the compilation. Another debt, which we happily acknowledge, is to Douglas Kimura for his criticism and guidance during the preparation of the text. Deborah L. Snyder and others at the Decker Corporation and the Honeywell Aeronautical Division also deserve our appreciation. Finally, we wish to thank the authors for their contributions and their indulgence through the delays seemingly inherent in a book of this nature.

Neal M. Burns
Randall M. Chambers
Edwin Hendler

Preface

Stress represents a special aspect of the relationships man establishes between himself and his environment. The exacting nature of the aerospace milieu and the environmental extremes it presents has served only to bring into sharper focus this aspect of the relationship. Problems of temperature, for example, are encountered routinely by all of us and are dealt with in a direct fashion. A window is opened, a thermostat adjusted, or a sweater is worn under a jacket. On the other hand, temperature control in a manned space capsule represents a totally different type of problem, and new concepts and techniques are needed to cope with these problems. Changes in acceleration have also been experienced by those of us who have ridden an elevator directed by an overly inspired operator. The changes in g that result from this situation can be met with nicely by deft knee flexion or rail grabbing. The acceleration profiles of launch and re-entry are far more severe than those encountered in elevators, and to cope with them requires extremely complicated devices. The study of man's responses to stress forms one of the major efforts of the manned space-flight program. The purpose of this volume is to describe the ranges of these environmental variables that enable us to categorize them as stressful or unusual and to arrange the data concerning these variables into a presentation that describes the effects of exposure to them.

Each of the twelve chapters comprising the main sections of this volume treats an aspect of the general problems facing man as he ventures beyond his normal, everyday environment. The first six chapters of the book are concerned with the general problem of the response of the human organism to unusual environmental conditions. In Chapter 1, Lawton reviews the physiological mechanisms that operate to maintain homeostasis under environmental stresses. Adaptive processes, particularly their time course and limitations, are discussed with reference to cardiovascular, thermal, visual, and respiratory stress conditions. The problems of detecting more generalized stress states, such as anxiety, are discussed, and the areas requiring further investigation delineated.

The chapter by Ruff analyses the problem of developing psychological indexes of stress. Ruff's contention is that definitions of stress must reflect the actions of physiological and psychological compensatory mechanisms. A preliminary model is offered in which stress inputs to the system are evaluated in terms of the behavioral and physiological outputs. The measures used to detect and evaluate the level of stress are discussed in detail, and the results of many experimental papers are organized in a theoretical schema.

In Chapter 3, Siegel and Wolf describe a mathematical model of man-machine interactions that can provide human performance information on optimization. Actual operational characteristics of a given configuration, such as interactions under various stress conditions, can be simulated and quantified by digital computers.

The fourth chapter, by Weybrew, is a summary of the many biological, psychological, and engineering factors involved in maintaining viable a small society of men living in the closed ecological system contained within the hull of a nuclear submarine. The problems of interpersonal relationships, morale, vibration, and so on, are directly comparable to those anticipated on extended space voyages. This chapter also reminds us that a great deal of exploration, demanding incomparable courage as well as the most advanced techniques available, still remains to be done on our own planet. The ocean, particularly its currents, temperature, and ecology, as well as the topography of the ocean bottom, remains largely unknown and awaits further study.

Chapter 5, by Simons, Flinn, and Hartman, describes the problems involved in maintaining men at high altitudes. Balloon ascents are useful in providing information on such factors as responses to hazard, acceleration, and temperature changes. The duration of exposure to the stress conditions can also be varied. The treatment of the data obtained is also discussed in detail.

The second part of this work consists of six chapters on specific problem areas. In Chapter 6, on isolation and sensory deprivation, Burns and Kimura discuss the psychological and physiological changes following the deprivation of normal environmental stimulation and social interactions. These include hallucinations, disorientation in space and time, metabolic alterations, and modifications of many physiological functions.

Ameliorative measures, such as the programming of meaningful tasks and adequate communications, are suggested; but the need for systematic and long-term studies in this area is emphasized.

A comprehensive treatment of the problems of acceleration is offered by Chambers in Chapter 7. The effects of acceleration stress on many dimensions of operator performance are thoroughly discussed. Studies conducted on the Project Mercury astronauts are reviewed, as are a number of investigations on hand controllers, displays, and restraint systems that were designed to extend man's acceleration tolerance. The analysis of the results of all the studies reviewed is complemented by the author's appreciation of the psychological factors (personality, emotional state, motivation) that affect performance.

The importance of temperature regulation is discussed by Hendler in Chapter 8. The presentation is enhanced by a concise review of the basic physical concepts of temperature and emphasizes the way in which performance is affected by exposure to temperature extremes. The complicated nature of this reaction is reflected throughout the organism, from biochemical to cardiovascular changes. The problem of the simultaneous interaction of a variety of stresses is well illustrated in Hendler's chapter and is also referred to in other presentations in the volume.

Loftus and Hammer review the effects of exposure to weightlessness in Chapter 9. A description of the three techniques most commonly used to produce or simulate weightlessness—parabolic maneuvers in aircraft, frictionless platforms, and water immersion—is given, and the effects on physiological function and behavior are analyzed. The authors' conclusion, that man can function well under weightless conditions, is supported by the results of manned orbital flights. Longer exposure to this unique condition will be needed, however, before the final statement on the hazards of prolonged weightlessness can be written.

The effects of vibratory forces upon animals and man have often been neglected as a form of stress by experimenters. Nadel, in Chapter 10, describes the physiological and structural changes that have been observed in experimental subjects following exposure to vibration. Tolerance limits for vibration, drawn from a variety of studies, are presented in tabular form. Protective devices are also analyzed.

The final chapter in this section is concerned with the effects of radiation on integrated behavior. Tobias has taken care to introduce the language and units of radiation to his audience. His review of the effects of radiation covers the earlier animal work as well as a number of Russian studies. The often subtle and cumulative effects of radiation on biological systems is regarded by Tobias as being, at least minimally, deleterious. Accordingly, he concludes his chapter by proposing a new standard for radiation exposure.

Common to all of these chapters are a number of problem areas that require the attention of the scientific community as a whole. These are fundamental not only to the man-in-space effort, but also to the more general problem of adapting man to unusual environments.

First, there is the question of human tolerance limits in an unusual environment. New efforts must be directed towards improving ways of specifying these limits. Most experiments on the effects of stress have employed rather limited stress intensities, so that there is little information on the end points of the responses to stress. Approaches for studying the effects of combinations and the cumulative effects of stress must also be developed.

A problem perhaps unique to aerospace biology is the preparation of a few individuals for specific missions. This has required an important shift of scientific method. Traditionally, generalizations are made from the study of several samples to the larger group from which the samples were derived. In this field, in contrast, it is necessary to apply group data to an individual. The trend is toward the preparation of intensive case history studies, which attempt to describe and predict the performance of a particular individual in a specific situation. The methodology involved should be validated and standardized.

Finally, more research on methods of extending physiological and psychological limits is needed. This is desirable not only to utilize with increased efficiency the unique systems capabilities of man but also to provide him with the best possible protective equipment.

In their concluding remarks the editors consider some methodological problems which remain to be solved, and some social problems brought about by the rapid advance of space science. Such problems promise to become more acute in the decade ahead.

Contents

Preface   v

Part I. **OVERVIEWS**

1. The Physiological Effects of Unusual
   Environments   *Richard W. Lawton*   3

2. Psychological and Psychophysiological Indices of
   Stress   *George E. Ruff*   33

3. Computor Simulation of Man-Machine Systems
   Arthur I. Siegel and *J. J. Wolf*   61

4. Psychological Problems of Prolonged Marine
   Submergence   *Benjamin B. Weybrew*   87

5. Psychophysiology of High-Altitude Experience
   David G. Simons, Don E. Flinn, and
   Bryce Hartman   127

Part II. SPECIFIC PROBLEM AREAS

6. Isolation and Sensory Deprivation
   Neal M. Burns and *Douglas Kimura*   167

7. Operator Performance in Acceleration
   Environments   *Randall M. Chambers*   193

8. Temperature Effects on Operator Performance
   Edwin Hendler   321

9. Weightlessness   *J. P. Loftus, Jr.,* and
   Lois R. Hammer   353

10. Vibration   *Aaron B. Nadel*   379

11. The Effects of Radiation on Integrated Behavior
    Paul R. Tobias   395

12. The Decade Ahead   *The Editors*   419

Index   427

I

OVERVIEWS

I

THE PHYSIOLOGICAL EFFECTS OF UNUSUAL ENVIRONMENTS

Richard W. Lawton

General Electric Space Technology Center
Valley Forge, Pennsylvania

THE physiologist regards the study of stress as a major experimental approach to the understanding of the regulation of biological function. Under relatively constant conditions a disturbance in an appropriate environmental variable will often produce compensatory behavior on the part of the organism. It is the mechanism of this regulatory behavior that is of primary interest. Small variations are of importance not only for theoretical reasons but also because such variations are likely to occur most commonly during normal daily life and activity. If the variation is sufficiently large, regulation may fail, and the organism

The author is grateful to Dr. J. L. Brown for assistance in the preparation of the section on visual stress.

is overwhelmed. The mechanism of failure itself is significant for the determination of human tolerance criteria and for the development of the means of protecting and supporting man in systems such as aircraft, submarines, and space vehicles.

The physiologist accepts the physical analog of stress, that is, as a forcing function. Experimental studies are then directed at the resulting strains or restorative forces called forth by particular internal or external environmental configurations. It is only through the disturbance of homeostasis that the equilibrium-seeking response can be studied. In experiments involving the intact organism, particularly man, the variables of cognition and motivation are frequently present and often poorly controlled (Chiles, 1957). During extreme stress states these and other psychological variables are of considerable importance and will be dealt with elsewhere in this volume.

In order to effectively study the physiology of stress, it is necessary to control the amplitude and temporal relations of the stimulus. Only in this way can dynamic input-output relations be established. Theoretically, it is assumed that a linear relationship obtains over a somewhat limited range of small stresses. In the discussion that follows, stresses arising from carefully controlled variations in the environment will be examined, and experiments dealing with small variations will be contrasted with those employing large variations. It will be seen that these two types of studies complement and supplement each other and broaden our understanding of response mechanisms.

In order to illustrate this approach to the physiology of stress, examples can be drawn from the fields of cardiovascular, respiratory, thermal and sensory physiology. Thus, the pressure-volume changes induced in the vascular system by normal cardiac ejection excite vascular regulatory mechanisms, and this forms the basis for the interpretation of the response of the organism to the massive redistribution of blood which occurs during high acceleration. Controlled observations on the effects of local heating of small areas of skin has resulted in data on warmth sensation, the peripheral mechanisms for the control of body temperature, and the relation between pain threshold and thermal burns. Such data form the basis of our understanding of the regulatory mechanisms and responses of the body to superclimatic heat exposure. Illumination of the retina results in pupillary constriction, and the careful study of this phenomenon has defined its properties in terms of servomechanism theory. In flash blindness, pupillary size determines in part the time-intensity relations for injurious exposure. Finally, recent studies of the respiratory system have suggested that the arterial blood stream serves as a communication link between the neural respiratory centers and the environment.

In addition to the specific regulatory responses set in motion by environmental disturbances, the body exhibits certain generalized responses that are reflected in biochemical or hormonal changes. Such responses are often nonspecific and accompany psychological as well as physical threats to the well-being of the individual. Among such changes are autonomic responses of various types and changes in circulating hormone levels, particularly those of the adrenal gland. Excretory levels of hormonal metabolic products thus may serve as a qualitative index of the stress state but usually throw no light on the nature of the precipitating agent. Although considerable literature and some controversy has developed in this area of study, the lack of established relations between specific causes and these effects has impaired the general usefulness of this approach in the understanding of regulatory mechanisms. The phenomenon of biological rhythmicity, now under intensive study, is a new area where the relation of biological processes to the environment can be studied.

Cardiovascular Stress

Every heart beat excites regulatory activity in the vascular system. Cardiac ejection results in a pressure and a flow pulse that is propagated to the extremes of the system. The vascular walls, which are distensible, are thus distorted, and nerve nets within them are accordingly stimulated. Such nerve discharges, which occur rhythmically with the pulse, are highly complex and play a major role in regulatory activity. The relation between the pressure pulse and the vessel wall distension, and between the distension of the wall (containing the nerve net) and the nerve discharge, are critical to an understanding of the regulation of the caliber and the mechanical properties of blood vessels.

The shape of the pressure wave is a complex product of cardiac ejection and the physical characteristics of the blood. The shape of this wave is continuously altered as it progresses along the vascular tree by the physical nature of the blood vessel walls themselves. The normal pulse wave thus represents an uncontrolled variable, and this fact alone has markedly impeded experimental studies.

Peterson (1954) has examined the relation between the flow pulse and the resulting pressure wave by interpolating small square-wave flow pulses during various parts of the cardiac cycle. His analysis identified resulting pressure deflections that are related to acceleration of the blood, the opposing forces of viscous friction, and the elasticity of blood vessel walls. The arterial pressure pulse is conceived of as the instantaneous sum of these forces. The initial peak of the pressure wave is the

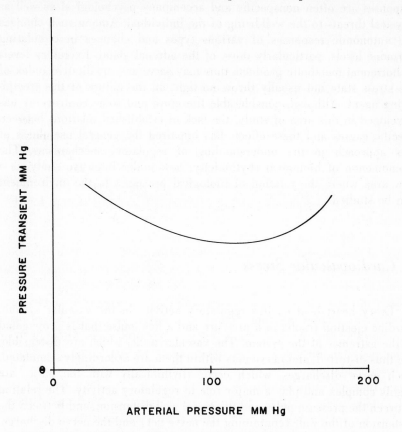

Figure 1. Amplitude of induced pressure transient as a function of the arterial pressure at the transient onset. After Peterson (1954).

sum of forces principally related to acceleration and viscous friction, and its amplitude is a function of the total pressure. Figure 1 shows the amplitude of this transient plotted against the arterial pressure present at the moment the artificial flow pulse was introduced. The curve exhibits a minimum in the region of the normal mean arterial pressure value. Other studies (King, 1957) have suggested that under both static and dynamic conditions arterial distensibility is a maximum at similar pressure values. It appears that the major effective opposing forces are minimal at normal pressure values and that a null operational level exists at which there is maximum power transfer. The circulatory system should automatically seek this level of optimal operation unless driven and held outside this range by other forces. This mechanism represents a major passive regulatory feature of the arterial system and may be offered as an explanation for normal blood pressure (Peterson and Shepard, 1955).

Regulatory nerve discharges from blood vessels are directly related to the stretch of the nerve endings in the vessel walls to which they are attached. Until recently the relation between internal pressure and blood vessel wall distension was poorly understood. Although the data of Bronk and Stella (1932) suggest that the over-all intensity of the sinus nerve discharge is nearly linearly related to mean arterial pressure, recent studies (Peterson, *et al.*, 1960) indicate that while some fibers may increase in discharge rate, others decrease in response to pressure increases. There is presumptive evidence that the discharge rate is related in part to the rate of change of pressure as well. The available data suggest that the peripheral inputs to the central nervous system for the regulation of arterial pressure are therefore extremely complex. The nerve nets of the arterial tree are intimately related to the smooth muscle of the arterial wall. A major regulatory response of the homeostatic mechanism regulating the arterial system is smooth muscle contraction or relaxation. The regulatory loop is thus closed: arterial pressure distends the smooth muscle of vessel walls and stretches the associated nerve nets; complex afferent neural discharges result in efferent impulses altering the physical characteristics of vessel walls. Other neural discharges alter the character of the cardiac ejection.

The elucidation of this mechanism under the dynamic conditions of normal function requires that the normal pressure or flow pulse be used as the independent variable. These pulses are complex functions of time, and Fourier analyses have been used to analyse these relations (Farrow and Stacy, 1961; Warner, 1959). By the use of such powerful analytical tools and with the aid of modern computers, we may expect large strides in our understanding of the regulatory mechanisms of circulation in terms of transfer functions between flow, pressure, vessel wall distention, and regulatory nerve discharge.

The arterial blood pressure response in man and other mammals to acceleration along the arterial axis is a consequence of the complex interaction of hydrostatic forces and an alteration in the dynamic inflow-outflow relations in the arterial tree with a resulting decrease in arterial blood volume. For extremely short accelerations system inertia prevents

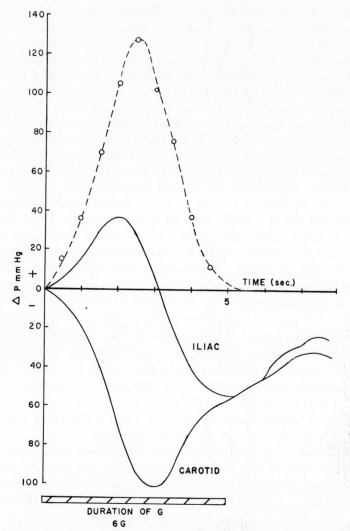

Figure 2. The pressure contribution of the fluid column (dotted line), the difference between iliac and carotid pressure curves, compared with the radial acceleration curve (open circles). After Lawton (1958).

important cardiovascular effects. For accelerations lasting of the order of 5 sec, however, the blood pressure responses may be interpreted in terms of physical analogies. For longer accelerations the arterial pressure disturbance excites cardiovascular reflex responses. The time lag of reflex response thus plays an important role in tolerance to positive

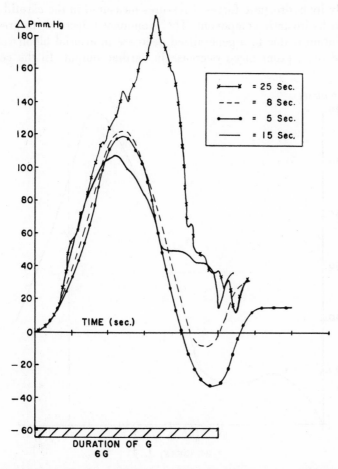

Figure 3. Effect of varying the period of acceleration on the blood pressure response (tibial artery). All records have been normalized to a common representation for the duration of the acceleration. After Lawton (1958).

acceleration and modifies the intensity-time curves, beginning in the region of 10-sec exposure.

Modern computer-controlled centrifuges offer an opportunity to control the amplitude and temporal course of the acceleration transient so that the response can be analyzed. For a 5-sec 6-g peak exposure, having the form $A(1 - \cos \omega t)$, diastolic blood pressure as measured from catheters placed in the carotid and iliac arteries varied as shown in

Figure 2. The pressure difference between these two curves is accounted for entirely by hydrostatic forces. Pressures measured in the carotid have little or no hydrostatic component. The pronounced decrease in pressure in this location is due to a generalized decrease in arterial blood volume occasioned by a pronounced decrease in cardiac output. In the central

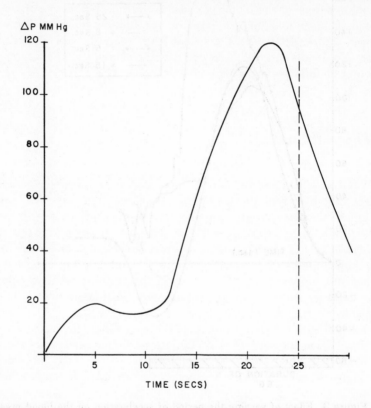

Figure 4. Pressure difference due to reflex effects (26-sec curve minus 5-sec curve of Figure 3).

portion of the arterial tree the hydrostatic and volume effects are transiently in balance, so that little or no blood pressure change occurs for one or more of the 5 sec. Even in the extremes of the arterial system, however, where the hydrostatic forces are greatest, the blood pressure ultimately falls below preacceleration values.

When exposure is prolonged, the blood pressure response is altered by cardiovascular reflexes. These take the form of cardiac acceleration and peripheral vasoconstriction. For accelerations of 6-*g* peak applied for periods varying between 5 and 25 sec diastolic blood pressure varies as shown in Figure 3. If we assume that the 5-sec blood pressure curve is equivalent to a 25-sec curve with no reflex effects, subtraction of the actual 25-sec curve from it yields the curve of Figure 4. Although the difference blood pressure oscillates initially, fully developed reflex effects are not apparent in the blood pressure record until 10 sec or more have elapsed. Human tolerance to positive acceleration indeed reflects such changes (Stark, 1959). In the seated man, using the loss of peripheral vision as an endpoint, the positive *g*-tolerance curve shows a minimum at the onset of full cardiovascular reflex response.

Thermal Stress

When a small area of skin is irradiated with infrared energy, the subject first perceives the sensation of warmth and secondly, pain, if energy of sufficient strength is applied for an appropriate period. Studies of the thresholds for warmth sensation have had an important role in the elucidation of the mechanisms of temperature regulation present in the skin, while studies of pain threshold have thrown light not only on the mechanisms of pain sensation but upon the relation between pain and tissue damage. Thermal energy, falling upon small areas of skin, initially evokes local vascular responses. When pain occurs, a wide variety of general autonomic reactions take place, depending upon the strength and duration of the sensation. As larger and larger surfaces of the body are irradiated, the general thermal balance of the body becomes increasingly threatened and widespread tissue damage may ultimately occur.

One of the most interesting explorations of warmth and cold sensations in man is that of Ebaugh and Thauer (1950). These workers exposed subjects to heat and cold sources at a variety of environmental temperatures. Subjects, nude to the waist, sat at the end of a long table blindfolded. A heat source (an electric hot plate) or a cold source (a block of dry ice) was moved nearer or farther away from the subject until he detected warmth or cold. A radiometer was then used to measure the radiant characteristics of the source. Experimental data were obtained for both warmth and cold thresholds over a range of room temperatures (Figure 5). It was shown that man is three times more sensitive to cold when the skin is cold. Notice the extreme sensitivity of the skin to warmth where changes in skin temperature of $0.001°C$ may be detected.

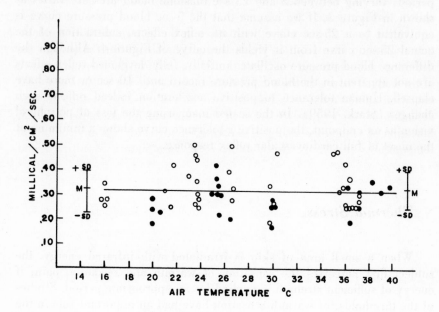

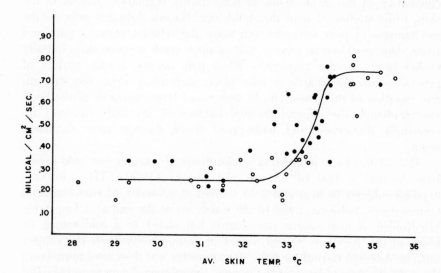

Figure 5.(a) Warmth threshold as a function of environmental temperature (Hardy, 1951).

(b) Cold threshold as a function of average skin temperature (Hardy, 1951).

Notice also that the warmth and cold sensitivity curves cross at the so-called "comfort zone."

On the basis of this and other studies in the general field of temperature regulation Hardy (1951) proposed a critical role for the skin in the detection of warmth and cold, and thus the control of the thermal balance of the body. The use of the temperature range where the warmth and cold sensation curves cross as a baseline provides a sensitive method for the detection of temperature changes in the skin and for studying the local initiation of vasomotor changes, sweating, or shivering. As environmental temperatures rise above the comfort zone, vasodilation is initiated and

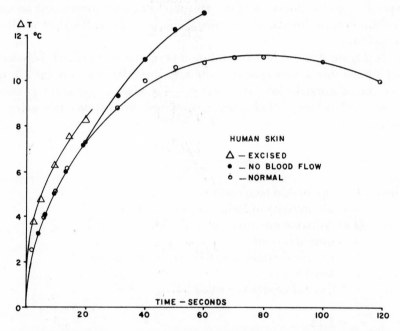

Figure 6. Change in skin temperature with time during irradiation (Lipkin and Hardy, 1954).

finally sweating occurs, the latter tending to restore normal skin temperature by evaporative cooling. For environmental temperatures falling from the comfort zone, vasoconstriction and ultimately shivering result, the latter tending to raise skin temperatures. Such mechanisms of body temperature control, although active in the regulation of skin temperature under conditions of small changes, are integrated with central mechanisms and are generally subservient to them during extreme heat stress. For instance, if the mechanisms of vasodilatation and sweating fail, the individual may die in hyperprexia. If, on the other hand, vasodilatation and sweating persist for long periods, the circulatory system may fail and produce a shocklike state.

The role of the skin in the detection of changes in the environment, as well as of the more extreme stresses of pain and thermal burns, depends to a great extent on its physical characteristics. When the skin is irradiated, the skin temperature rises, and the temperature-time curve produced depends upon the product of the thermal conductivity (k), the density (ρ), and the thermal capacity (c) of the skin. The "inertia for surface heating," or the $k\rho c$ value, is not constant for living skin but depends upon the thickness of the avascular stratum corneum, the amount of blood flow in the underlying tissue, and possibly on the state of tissue hydration.

In Figure 6 the skin temperature-time curves for excised, bloodless, and normal skin are compared. Irradiance was 0.055 cal/sec/cm². In the presence of normal blood flow the curve reaches a maximum at about 80 sec and begins to fall despite continued irradiation. The value of $k\rho c$ is:

$$k\rho c = \frac{4a^2 Q^2 t}{\pi (\Delta T)^2}$$

where ΔT = rise in skin temperature, °C
    a = absorptivity of India-inked skin (0.94)
    Q = radiation intensity, cal/cm²–/sec
    t = time in seconds
    k = specific thermal conductivity, g–cal/cm/sec/°C
    ρ = density, g/cm³
    c = thermal capacity, g cal/g/°C
$\dfrac{4a^2}{\pi} = 1.13$

The application of this equation requires a careful control of the physical variables in the experiment. A source providing a uniform field of irradiation (Hardy, 1951), blackening of the skin with India ink to provide a known value of a, and a method for the accurate measurement of skin temperature are required. This latter measurement must be made radiometrically in order that the measurement device itself not interfere with the radiation falling on the skin. The Golay detector has proved of value for this measurement, providing a correction is made for reflected visible and near infrared radiation.

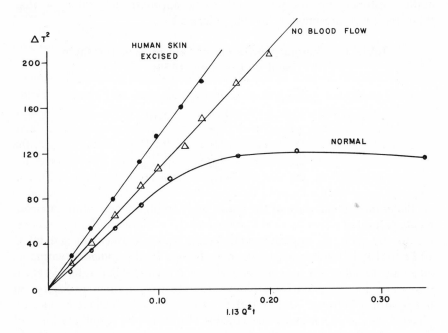

Figure 7. Thermal inertia parameters computed from Figure 6.

The $k\rho c$ value can be determined from the curves in Figure 7 when ΔT^2 is plotted against $1.13 Q^2 t$. For excised skin the value slope is 66×10^{-5} cal^2/cm^4/°C/sec, while for living skin with blood flow occluded it is 90×10^{-5}. In normal intact skin the $k\rho c$ value is not constant, but becomes progressively larger as heating continues, reaching values as high as 400–500×10^5.

With sufficiently intense radiation, skin pain will be experienced in the irradiated area and tissue damage in the form of a skin burn or blister will occur. The $k\rho c$ values at pain threshold vary depending upon the irradiance (Table 1). In Table 2 skin temperature and exposure times associated with the nonburning pain threshold, burning pain threshold, and stages of blister formation are given for a number of irradiances. From the nonburning pain threshold data, Stoll and Greene (1959) have estimated the firing temperature of the pain receptors and their average depth, using the equations of Henriques (1937). The pain receptor temperature averages 43.2 ± 0.4°C throughout the range of irradiances studied, a value that is in good agreement with other estimates. Using a number of estimates of k, ρ, and c for the epidermis and the dermis, these authors estimate the receptor depth to be approximately 200μ, so that these receptors presumably lie subepidermally.

Table 1. Thermal Inertia $k\rho c$ of Skin at Pain Threshold (Stoll and Greene, 1959)

Irradiance mc/cm²–sec	kpc (10⁻⁵) cal²/cm⁴/°C/sec	
	Average	Range
100	96	75–117
150	110	89–142
200	127	95–158
300	139	115–168
400	159	144–181

Tolerance to exposure of the entire body to high-temperature environments is limited either by heat storage and the elevation of body temperature or by pain. At environmental temperatures between 50 and 60°C (122 to 140°F) tolerance is given in hours. In this range sweating is adequate to maintain heat storage at low levels, and body temperature limits are not exceeded for prolonged periods. Continuous exposures to temperatures between 70 and 120°C (158 to 248°F) cannot be met by physiological compensatory mechanisms (for example, vasodilatation and sweating). Heat storage then occurs, causing an elevation in body temperature and pulse rate, and exposure time becomes limited to 20 to 80 min (Blockley, et al., 1954). Webb (1961) has recently reported human exposures to operative temperatures between 115 and 260°C (240 to 500°F) and has demonstrated that such exposures are pain-limited. In these latter exposures careful attention was given to the control of the thermal environment. Exposures in some cases were abrupt. A preheated chamber, mounted on rails, was rolled to surround the subject in a period of 2 sec. Other exposures employed slow heat pulses and consisted of a linear increase in wall temperature at rates between 8 and 55°C per minute (15 to 100°F per minute) until pain occurred. The data on heat storage-limited and pain-limited tolerances are sum-

Table 2. Thermal Inertia $(k\rho c)$ for Whole-Body Heating at Pain Threshold

Wall, T°C, T_w	Air, T°C, T_a	q_r, cal/m²hr	Q, cal/m²hr	kpc (10⁻⁵) cal²/m⁴/sec°/C
149	121	399	988	83
204	177	745	1885	80
260	232	1262	2924	66

q_r = radiant heat transfer T_w = wall temperature

Q = total heat transfer T_a = air temperature

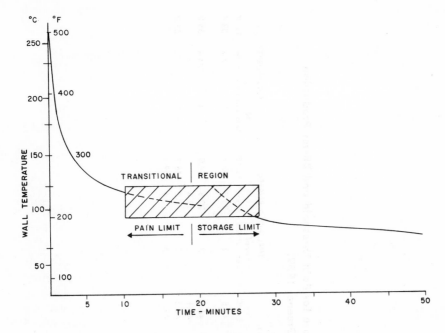

Figure 8. Pain-limited versus heat storage-limited heat tolerance. After Webb (1961).

marized in Figure 8. A broad transitional zone between the two tolerance-limiting mechanisms is evident and reflects the present experimental uncertainty as to the exact limiting mechanism in individual cases.

Webb has computed $k\rho c$ values on the basis of exposures of this type and these agree well with data on small skin areas. The time-to-pain threshold has been computed at several heating levels, and these also fall within the same ranges as given for small skin areas. Heat storage-limited rather than pain-limited thermal tolerance, which is more often encountered in operational conditions, is discussed in Chapter 7.

Visual Stress

The human eye performs effectively over a range of illumination of greater than 100 million to one. It does not adjust to such changes in illumination instantaneously, and this gives rise to practical problems at the extreme ranges. When the illumination level is suddenly raised within

Table 3. Irradiance, Time, and Temperature for Pain Threshold and Blister Production (Stoll and Greene, 1959)

Radiation Intensity, mcal/cm²–sec	PAIN THRESHOLD CONTROLS			PAIN THRESHOLD (During Burning)			THRESHOLD BLISTER			FULL BLISTER		
	No. of Observations	t, sec	Ts, °C	No. of Observations	t, sec	Ts, °C	No. of Observations	t, sec	Ts, °C	No. of Observations	t, sec	Ts, °C
100	49	13.5	45.1	6	12.4	45.8	2	33.8	52.9	1	37.2	53.4
125	31	10.1	45.3									
150	67	7.8	45.9	12	8.2	46.5	3	20.8	54.0	4	24.4	55.3
200	22	5.5	46.5	3	5.6	47.1	1	13.4				
300	36	2.9	47.1	10	2.6	46.5	2	7.8	56.7	1	8.6	57.9
400	13	2.2	48.3	8	2.2	49.7	5	5.6	59.1			

the normal range, there is a brief interval of dazzling sensation but within less than a minute it is possible to see quite effectively. When the illumination level is reduced from a high value to a very low value, 30 minutes or more may be needed for the achievement of maximum visual sensitivity.

The relatively long time required for dark adaptation has been recognized as a problem in military operations at night. For occupants of orbiting space vehicles, the problem of adaptation may be complicated by the relatively short day-night cycle. There will be alternating periods of approximately 45 minutes of daylight and 45 minutes of night for vehicles in the 100- to 500-mile altitude range. If an occupant is required to view objects outside the vehicle during both the light and dark phases of flight, precautions must be taken to compensate for the change in illumination in order to preserve the low-luminance sensitivity that will be required during the dark phase. Because there is no atmosphere at these altitudes to attenuate or scatter illumination from the sun, the level of illumination will be somewhat higher than that at the surface of the earth and there will be greater contrast within the visual field.

With the advent of space flight, and with the development of atomic weapons, it has become possible to expose the eye to extremely high levels of illumination. These may render the eye virtually blind for a time after the illumination has returned to normal levels. This transient or flash blindness is generally reversible. Irreversible damage may result, however, if the amount of radiation received is sufficiently great. It has been estimated that a direct view of the sun from the surface of the earth for less than a minute may cause a retinal burn (Cordes, 1948). Beyond the earth's atmosphere, the time will be shorter, perhaps 15 sec or less (Henriques, 1937). The actual danger of irreversible damage to the eye under these conditions is small because there is ample time to avert the eyes voluntarily.

Energy flux levels encountered when atomic weapons are detonated are many times higher than the flux levels that reach the earth from the sun. In consequence, only very short exposures may be sufficient to cause serious damage to the eyes (Byrnes, *et al.*, 1955). Because of the focusing action of the eyes, this damage may occur at ranges well beyond those at which any other kind of injury is to be expected. Although the linear size of the image will reduce directly with distance, flux density (that is, the amount of energy reaching a unit area in unit time) and hence the capacity for burning are minimally reduced by atmospheric attenuation. In certain atomic tests it was demonstrated that retinal burns may occur in the eyes of rabbits at a range of 370 miles if the animal's head is fixed and no protective filtering is used. The actual energy threshold for a retinal burn has been estimated to be approximately 0.017 cal/cm^2 from experimental work with animals.

In order to evaluate the possible ways of preventing damage as a result of exposures to extremes of illumination, the available body defenses must be examined. These are limited and consist only of voluntary movements of the eyes, the pupillary reflex, and the blink reflex. Under a variety of normal circumstances the pupil of the eye acts as a regulator of the light impinging on the retina, and the transfer function and noise characteristics of this servomechanism have been well described (Stark, 1959). The pupillary mechanism has many advantages from an experimental point of view because its motor component, the iris, is exposed for easy observation and can be driven by changes in the intensity of visible light, a form of energy easy to control. Thus, experiments can be performed on awake, unanesthetized humans without pain or discomfort. The technique used by Stark consists of the continuous measurement of pupillary area by reflecting infrared light from the iris onto a photocell. The stimulus light is controlled electronically so that sinusoidal or stepwise variations can be obtained and is focused so that an image of a small disk is formed on the pupil whose diameter is smaller than the smallest diameter of the disk of light. Under these conditions changes in pupillary size obviously have no effect on the flux on the retina. If the light source is placed at the edge of the iris, small changes in the iris position result in large changes in light intensity at the retina. These high-gain conditions result in instability of the mechanism and oscillation. In some experiments a diffuse light source is used so that changes in pupillary diameter affect retinal flux. Under the latter condition the pupillary servomechanism operates in a closed-loop fashion as opposed to the open-loop method previously described.

If small sinusoidal light stimuli of varying frequency are applied, the sinusoidal response amplitude and phase relationship may be determined. Typical data are shown in Figure 9. From this plot certain features of the pupil system are seen: low gain, steep attenuation of gain at high frequencies, and a large phase shift. Another method of displaying system behavior is the Nyquist diagram (Figure 10). This vector plot of gain and phase angle shows the stability or instability of operation and range of frequencies over which the system will operate. The critical point (gain $= 1.0$ at 180 degree phase shift) is not enclosed and indicates the system is stable. When the pupillary mechanism is driven by a light at the edge of the iris (high-gain mode), this point is enclosed and the system occillates.

For sudden exposure to an intensive source, such as the sun or an atomic explosion, the pupillary mechanism has little to offer in the way

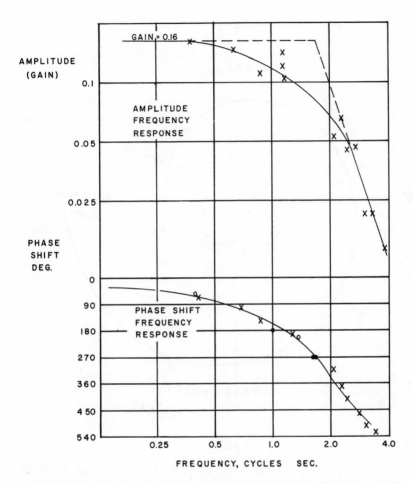

Figure 9. Open-loop frequency response. Amplitude plotted on log-log scale; phase shift on log-linear scale. Points are experimental; continuous line fitted; dashed lines are asymptote. After Stark (1959).

of protection. Pupillary size at the moment of exposure is of considerable importance in limiting the total retinal flux, however. The smaller diameter characteristic of daylight will afford more protection than the larger diameter to be expected at night. According to Spector (1956) pupillary contraction will begin following a latency of approximately 100 msec. It will reach 50 per cent completion in another 300 msec and finally be completed after an additional 600 msec. Davson (1949) gives a latency of 500 msec, however, and states that maximum con-

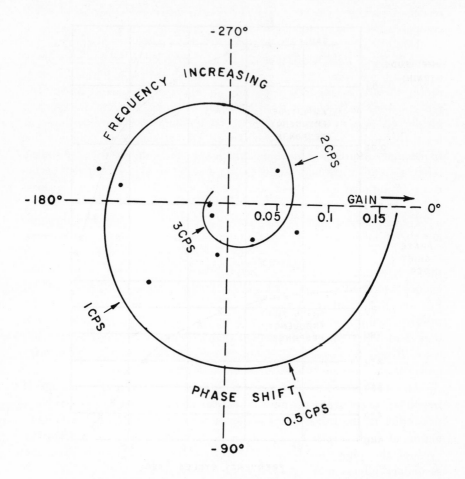

Figure 10. Nyquist diagram of pupil response. Points are experimental; curve derived from fitted lines from gain and phase frequency response graphs. After Stark (1959).

traction to a moderate stimulus may require as long as 5 sec. The speed of response is known to be related to the intensity level of the stimulating light and this may afford an explanation of discrepancies in the values presented by different authors. The amount of constriction is also related to the intensity level of the stimulating light. The maximum reduction of pupillary diameter to be expected under even extreme conditions is probably a factor of three to one (from 9 to 3 mm). This factor represents a reduction in area by a factor of nine, a relatively small effect compared with the protection afforded by blinking.

The blinking reflex occurs either upon direct stimulation of the cornea or upon light stimulation and may follow almost any other sudden or unexpected stimulus. The response to corneal stimulation is most rapid, closure of the eye occurring in approximately 100 msec. The reflex begins in response to stimulation by a bright light in approximately 40 msec (Whiteside, 1960), but complete closure requires at least 100 msec and probably closer to 150–200 msec. Irving (1949) found that closure is more rapid for higher luminance stimuli. The blink reflex is readily trained, as is clearly indicated by its frequent occurrence in anticipation of loud sounds and bright flashes even when these do not occur.

The closed lid will afford excellent protection of the eye throughout the range associated with an atomic blast. The important concern is whether closure in 150 msc is sufficiently rapid. The nature of the distribution of nuclear energy and the time interval during which energy is emitted will vary with the size of the weapon (U.S. AEC, 1957). For one in the kiloton range, 54 per cent of the total energy may be released within 300 msec. For a megaton weapon, on the other hand, only 2 to 3 per cent of the energy may be emitted within the first 300 msec. It may be possible, therefore, to receive more serious eye injuries under certain circumstances from smaller weapons.

Although it is true that the eye may suffer irreversible damage if irradiated excessively, in most situations this will not be as serious a possibility as the transient reduction in sensitivity which follows illumination at high levels. For example, if reduced sensitivity renders the eyes of the pilot incapable of performing essential visual tasks, the secondary effects may be fatal even though the reduced sensitivity is only a manifestation of a normal, reversible, physiological process. Although there is a wealth of literature on dark adaptation, much of it concerned with the relation of sensitivity and time in the dark to the photochemical regeneration process, and to the relation between the time course of recovery of sensitivity and the duration and intensity of light adaptation, little of this work is relevant to the problem of flash blindness. There has been little concern with sensitivity changes in the first minute following the termination of the adapting light, and almost no concern with events occurring in the first few seconds of dark adaptation. This interval is critical for the pilot of a supersonic aircraft; if he is without vision for as long as 5 or 10 sec, the results may be fatal. The seriousness of the problem of flash blindness for the pilot in the region of an atomic blast hinges on many variables. The problem is ably discussed from a relatively optimistic point of view in a recent paper by Whiteside (1960).

Respiratory Stress

Of all the homeostatic mechanisms in the body the biochemical are the most difficult to quantitate under dynamic conditions. Generally, steady-state equilibrium conditions alone are treated. Thus, for a given level of some biochemical constituent in the arterial blood, a certain response is expected. Constituents may seem invariant because of inadequate methodology, when in reality small variations may have important effects on extremely sensitive detector mechanisms. When the blood stream is considered as a communication channel for physiological regulation, it is apparent that the relevant information that is transmitted must in many cases be embodied in a time series. The usual process of blood sampling thus will destroy such a temporally structured message.

Carbon dioxide is ubiquitous in the body and plays an important role in the regulation of a number of physiological systems. A system of particular interest is respiration. Increases in metabolic activity as the result of exercise elevates the CO_2 load in the blood and brings about a regulatory response—hyperventilation. Elevations in the inspired CO_2 concentration beyond a certain level also brings about respiratory responses. The study of these stresses—internal and environmental— has been the subject of a great deal of literature (Comroe, 1957). Only recently has an attempt been made to treat the regulatory mechanisms in terms of relatively explicit servomechanism models (Grodins, *et al.*, 1954).

A system with no regulatory capability would permit its internal composition (CO_2 load) to rise to a steady state at which the excretion rate equals the loading rate, with no increase in ventilation. In an ideal regulator ventilation increases until excretion rate equals the loading rate with no change in the internal concentration. Other regulators would show some increase in ventilation and some rise in CO_2 concentration, so that a steady-state error signal is generated. In the hyperpnea of exercise, ventilation is proportional to metabolism while the arterial PCO_2 is constant or, if anything, a decreasing function of metabolism. When carbon dioxide enters the system from the environment, ventila-

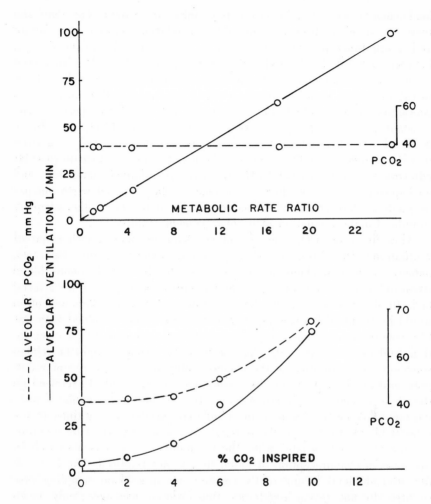

Figure 11. Alveolar gas computations for internal CO_2 stress (upper curves) and external CO_2 stress (lower curves). After Yamamoto and Edwards (1960).

tion is a hyperbolic function of the inspired CO_2 concentration (at constant metabolic production), and the arterial CO_2 rises roughly in proportion to the ventilation.

Yamamoto and Edwards (1960) perfused rats with variable quantities of CO_2-loaded blood via the inferior vena cava using a heart-lung machine. The anesthetized CO_2-infused animal is thought to be equivalent to the exercising animal except that exercise cues other than the CO_2

load, such as neural inflow from the limbs, are absent. The data and their statistical analysis indicate a linear relation between CO_2 output and ventilation and the absence of a statistically significant relation between arterial PCO_2 and ventilation (Figure 11). The increased oxygen uptake associated with the hyperventilation seems to be related to the increased work of breathing. Over the range of CO_2 outputs and ventilatory rates studied, homeostasis of CO_2 is nearly perfect. The constant quantity is the mean (time average) arterial PCO_2. At extreme levels of CO_2, loading cardiovascular changes are observed suggesting that the regulation of PCO_2 involves both pulmonary and cardiovascular adjustments. Such arterial PCO_2 and pH are relatively unaltered, and no hyposia occurs; and, because evidence is lacking that perfusion per se produces hyperpnea, it seems reasonable that CO_2 is the adequate stimulus for the regulation of its own concentration.

How then does CO_2 exert an influence on the neural mechanisms of ventilation? Of a number of hypotheses, Yamomoto discusses two, namely, peripheral chemorecptors exposed to the mixed venous blood stream (Lambertson, et al., 1953) and a control mechanism in the arterial bed. In the former case mechanoreception as well as chemoreception would be required because equivalent responses were obtained with low CO_2 concentrations and high perfusion rates as with high CO_2 concentrations and low perfusion rates. The respiratory response might be related somehow to the product of the chemorecptor and mechanoreceptor outputs, and homeostasis would be a consequence of a control exercised on the whole animal. The arterial concentration could thus be regulated without our knowing the status of the regulated variable at any time. In the arterial blood stream hypothesis regulation is accomplished by monitoring the regulated variable after the regulatory action has occurred. In this case mechanoreception of blood flow is not required. The PCO_2 in the arterial blood is apparently constant because blood sampling procedures do not reveal regulatory time-ordered messages, only mean values. In the unsteady state, temporal fluctuations in arterial PCO_2 provide the signal for ventilatory regulation, although such fluctuations may have a constant mean value.

Using a time-dependent dilution equation Yamamoto (1960) has developed a mathematical analysis of the time course of alveolar CO_2. When excess CO_2 arrives at the lung, whether the cause be high venous blood content or an increased blood flow, some CO_2 will pass through because of the relative hypoventilation. Arterial chemoreceptors are thus stimulated; and ventilation is increased, thereby lowering the arterial CO_2 content. Oscillations of PCO_2 in the arterial blood are thus induced (Figure 12), and the time average of ventilation would be an hyperpnea

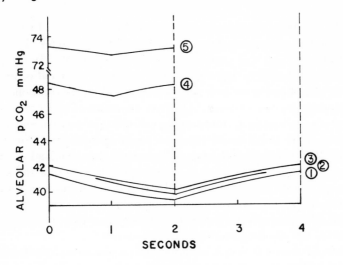

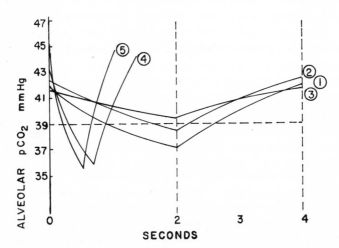

Figure 12. Alveolar gas composition calculations during one cycle of steady state under conditions of increasing metabolic CO_2 stress (lower curve) and CO_2 inhalation (upper curve). Numbers refer to selected parameters of Yamamoto and Edwards (1960).

suited to the CO_2 load. Oscillatory rates, amplitudes, and phase relations would be conditioned by the length of the circulatory paths to the chemoreceptors (Guyton, *et al.*, 1956) and by recirculation, but is bounded by the fixed blood volume and the finite volume of the organism.

The error signal that results in regulation is generated at chemoreceptors which may be widely located peripherally (Pi Suner, 1947). The
most sensitive detector is centrally located in the medulla. In the process
of controlling its own environment, the internal environment of the whole
organism is controlled because all arterial blood stems from one source.
As Yamamoto points out, the CO_2-sensitive areas of the brain may be
regarded as possessing memory and performing a comparison between
its present state and the consequences of its past actions. How such a
center might deal with the time difference in communication between
central and peripheral detectors is not known, although this and all other
time-series information must ultimately be translated into nonpropagated
potentials in the brain stem. The electrical slow potentials thus far
observed have not been recorded by systems adapted to detect frequencies as fast as the respiratory cycle.

It has been noted that the ventilation response to inspiratory CO_2
loading is different from that associated with metabolic stress (Figure
11). In this case the system does not maintain a constant mean composition. The arterial PCO_2 rises roughly in proportion to the ventilation
response. Theoretically, the shift in the arterial PCO_2 mean is associated
with diminution in the amplitude of the fluctuations of PCO_2 in the
blood stream.

Conclusions

Man during his lifetime encounters many stresses, both internal and
external. He reacts to these stresses and often adapts. Adaptations vary
widely, from the development of bacteriological immunity to the formation of new behavioral patterns. For adaptations to be effective, their time
constants must bear an appropriate relation to the time course of the
environmental stress. When adaptations occur on the same time scale
as the development of stress, there may be no manifestation of the stress
state. In stress states, regulatory activity is often unimpaired, although
regulation now takes place around a new level. For instance, in hyper-
tension, cardiovascular regulatory activity takes place around a new
mean blood pressure value, just as in fever, where body temperature
regulation occurs at a new mean body temperature.

When compensation is complete and the normal mean value is pre-
served, there may be little or no physiological evidence that the organism is strained. In environmental stress the alteration in the environment

is generally detected, so that the presence of a stressor is established. In the case of internal stresses, particularly in the compensated state, detection may be more difficult, and recourse to more general correlates of strain are required. This is often the case in various psychic states such as anxiety. The degree of engagement of the autonomic nervous system, as detected by the GSR or by catecholamine excretion, is often used as a criteria for the presence of the stress state in such cases. Such methods may allow standardization of stress states for purposes of personnel selection.

There may, however, be changes in the environment which go undetected because of a lack of appreciation of these changes as stressing agents. Two such environment alterations currently undergoing intensive study are the presence or absence of magnetic fields and innate biological rhythms. Although there is little evidence at present that either high or low magnetic fields represent an environmental stress, such changes, if they occur, may have importance in the field of space flight. An equally complex and poorly understood field of research related to environmental stress is that of biological rhythms. When organisms are deprived of all environmental influences (for example, light-dark relations, sound, and temperature fluctuations), "free-running" rhythms are observed in a variety of biological processes. Such innate rhythmic activity extends down to the cellular level. Generally, such free-running rhythms are entrained to the rhythms of the environment and to each other. Entrainment occurs when the environmental frequencies do not depart remarkably from the natural free-running frequencies or its submultiples. Failure to entrain may be demonstrated by direct experimental manipulation in the laboratory. For instance, the organism may be driven at atypical frequencies or rapid shifts in phase induced. In the latter case the transient period associated with the adjustment to the new phase relation may be prolonged and particularly stressful. In the free-running state, dissociation of cellular processes and their rhythms may occur. The absence of the terrestrial environmental rhythms and the imposition of new rhythms related to orbital periods or work-rest cycles as well as their relationships to the free-running rhythms of man require careful investigation.

The spectrum of biological responses to environmental stress thus extends from the moment-to-moment physiological regulatory behavior associated with daily activity to the regulatory breakdown due to the overwhelming stresses of environments—such as acceleration and superclimatic heat—that markedly diverge from the normal. Adaptation may bring about permanent alterations in biological responses. The responses may be limited only to compensation, however, and special analytical methods may be required to detect stress in the presence of successful compensation. Finally, the distortion of biological rhythms of organisms and its possible relation to stress emphasizes the complexity of the links of man to his environment.

References

Blockley, W. V., McCutchan, J. W., and Taylor, C. L. *WADC Tech. Rept.* 53–346, May, 1954; *J. Aviation Med., 25*:515, 1954.

Bronk, D. W., and G. Stella. *J. Comp. Cell. Physiol., 1*:113, 1932.

Byrnes, V. A., Brown, D. V. L., Rose, H. W., and Cibis, P. A. *A.M.A. Arch. of Ophthal., 53*:351, 1955.

Chiles, W. D. *WADC Tech. Rept.* 57–457, July, 1957.

Comroe, J. H., Jr., *Physiol. Rev., 24*:319, 1944.

Cordes, F. C. *Am. J. Ophthal., 31*:101, 1948.

Davson, H. *The Physiology of the Eye,* New York: McGraw-Hill, 1949.

Ebaugh, F. G., Jr., and Thauer, R. *J. Applied Physiol., 3*:173, 1950.

Farrow, R. L., and Stacy, R. W. *Circulation Res., 9*:395, 1961.

Grodins, F. S., Gray, J. S., Shroeder, K. R., Norins, A. L., and Jones, R. W. *J. Applied Physiol., 7*:283, 1954.

Guyton, A. C., Crowell, J. W., and Moore, J. W. *Am. J. Physiol., 187*:395, 1956.

Hardy, J. D. *Science, 114*:149, 1951.

————. Harvey Lectures, Series XLIX, 1953–54, p. 242.

Henriques, F. C., Jr. *Arch. Path., 43*:489, 1937.

Irving, A. Air Ministry Flying Personnel Research Committee, Memo 101, 1949.

King, A. L. In *Tissue Elasticity,* Am. Physiol. Soc., Washington, 1957, p. 123.

Lambertson, C. J., Keough, R. H., Cooper, D. Y., and Emmel, G. R. *J. Applied Physiol., 5*:803, 1953.

Lawton, R. W., Greene, L. C., Kydd, G. H., Peterson, L. H., and Crosbie, R. J. *J. Aviation Med. 29*:97, 1958.

Lipkin, M. and Hardy, J. D. *J. Applied Physiol., 7*:212, 1954.

Peterson, L. H. *Circulation Res., 2*:127, 1954.

————, Feigl, E., and Gouras, P. *Fed. Proc. 19*:40, 1960.

———— and Shepard, R. B. *Surg. Clin. No. Am., 35*:1613, 1955.

Pi Suner, A. *Physiol. Rev., 27*:1, 1947.

Spector, W. S. *Handbook of Biological Data, WADC Tech. Rept.* 56–273, October, 1956.

Stark, L. *Proc. IRE, 47*:1925, 1959.

Stoll, A. *U.S. Naval Air Devel. Ctr., Rept. No.* NADC-MA-5508, August, 1955.

———— and L. C. Greene. *J. Applied Physiol., 14*:373, 1959.

Strughold, H. *Astronautica Acta, 5*:1960.

U.S. Atomic Energy Commission. *Effects of Nuclear Weapons*, 1954.

Warner, H. *Proc. IRE*, 47:1913, 1959.

Webb, P. In *Symposium on Temperature: Its Measurement and Control in Science and Industry*. New York: Reinhold, 1962.

Whiteside, T. C. D. Air Ministry Flying Personnel Research Committee Report 1075.1, March, 1960.

Yamamoto, W. S. *J. Applied Physiol.*, 15:215, 1960.

—— and M. W. Edwards, Jr. *J. Applied Physiol.*, 15:807, 1960.

2

PSYCHOLOGICAL AND PSYCHOPHYSIOLOGICAL INDICES OF STRESS

George E. Ruff

School of Medicine
University of Pennsylvania
Philadelphia, Pennsylvania

Introduction

THE term *stress* usually implies a change in the conditions affecting an organism that requires an expenditure of effort so that essential functions are maintained at a desired level. Because a load is placed upon the organism, it must modify its behavior to continue operating; that is, an adaptation, or a compensatory response, enables the organism to continue functioning in spite of the load.

Although the concept of stress may be useful, it lacks sufficient precision for research. A more explicit definition is not difficult in physics, where "stress" is the force applied to an object and "strain" is the change in the properties of the object induced by the stress. In physiology and psychology, however, there is no universally accepted definition. "Stress" may refer either to the conditions that affect the organism or to the change induced by these conditions. Perhaps the most widely used terminology is that of Selye (1950), who refers to stress-producing agents as "stressors," and to the resulting state of the organism as "stress."

Providing definitions for these terms, however, is far from easy. The problem may be approached by describing a model of the organism in which it is viewed as a system with inputs and outputs of energy and information. Information refers to energy inputs organized in such a way that they can be decoded by the system. Information outputs are organized to allow decoding by other systems.* Each system tends to maintain steady states of many variables through homeostatic mechanisms. These confine within a limited range the variables that are crucial for continued existence of the system. Inputs that force the variables beyond this range are called *stressors*.

Stress can be defined in terms of inputs, outputs, or both. "Input" definitions state conditions that are known to produce stress within the system. "Output" definitions are based on variables that the system normally maintains within a certain range. When a variable exceeds this range, "stress" is said to exist. For example, an input definition of acceleration would involve the number of g's and other factors of centrifugation. An output definition might involve a tracking task, where failure to track, increased errors, or erratic performance would be indicators of stress.

Unfortunately, input definitions may be inadequate in biological research, where responses of different systems to the same input vary more widely than in the physical sciences. Moreover, simple output definitions may be misleading for many reasons. In the acceleration example, performance decrements may occur without stress—as when motivation declines. Furthermore, if compensatory mechanisms are effective, performance may be maintained at a high level even while the subject is under extreme stress.

It is often desirable, therefore, to base the definition of stress on those outputs that can indicate the utilization of a compensatory mechanism. This mechanism involves a reorganization of subsystems within the system that opposes failure of other subsystems required for continued survival. If the compensatory mechanism is activated, the system is considered to be under stress. A definition of this type requires not only the choice of measurable outputs that are characteristic of the compensatory response, but also requires an agreement on the range within

---

* A detailed discussion of the General Systems Theory concepts on which this model is based has recently been prepared by Miller (1962).

which these outputs are normal and beyond which they indicate stress.

To return to acceleration, it can be demonstrated that increased positive g impairs function of the central nervous system by forcing blood from the head. Centrifugation would rapidly impair performance on a tracking task if no compensatory mechanism existed. But insofar as constriction of a subject's peripheral blood vessels enables him to maintain adequate cerebral circulation, he may continue to track normally until higher g levels are imposed. By demonstrating compensatory responses within the cardiovascular subsystem, we can show that the subject is under stress before a tracking decrement appears.

Further discussion of our model will clarify the importance of the compensatory mechanism in the definition of stress. The system, it will be remembered, has inputs of energy and information. An additional factor is the meaning or implication of the information input—the coding of the information—which involves conditioning or learning, so that the system responds to the information according to past experience. Where stress arises from the implication or meaning of information to the system, it cannot be defined in terms of the input or stressor, or in terms of simple output variables. Because of differences in past experience, what is stressful for one system may not be stressful for another. We can define stress, therefore, only by demonstrating changes in output that show that compensatory mechanisms have been called into play within the system.

This can be illustrated by an acceleration study in which subjects were placed in the centrifuge and prepared to undergo high G loads (Berman and Pettitt, 1960). On two trials they were run as expected, but on one trial the centrifuge remained motionless. Subsequent urinalyses revealed that outputs of adrenaline and noradrenaline—often used as stress indicators—rose as high on the mock trial as on the others. This could not have been defined by the energy input—acceleration— since none occurred. The degree of stress would not necessarily have been revealed by a tracking task, since subjects often maintain performance in spite of their anticipatory anxiety. It was revealed only by the evidence of a compensatory response, in this case indicated by catecholamine excretion.

Psychological Effects of Unusual Environments

Three aspects of behavior in unusual environments may be approached from the standpoint of psychology. According to the stress model that has been described, we may consider the effects of a change in energy inputs, the effects of a change in information inputs, and the effects of a change in the meaning of information inputs. Each of these three parameters must be studied in a somewhat different manner.

CHANGE IN ENERGY INPUT

By a change in energy input, we mean, in this case, any physical change which interferes with the functions of the central nervous system. Insofar as stressors such as low oxygen tension, acceleration, vibration, heat, and radiation may impair central nervous system functioning, they can be studied psychologically, as well as physiologically. The difference, as indicated in the previous chapter, is that the physiologist is interested primarily in the response of subsystems, while the psychologist is interested in the response of the whole organism.

The psychologist may contribute to the study of physical stressors imposed by unusual environments when either of two types of questions are asked. The first concerns the ability to perform a given task under the environmental conditions being investigated. We may wish to know, for example, if an operator can manually control the attitude of a re-entry vehicle at 8 G. This can best be determined by simulating the control task on the centrifuge. If exact simulation is not feasible, psychomotor tests analogous to the control task may be used. In either case, psychological measures are essential for answering questions on performance capability under adverse conditions.

It should be pointed out that the concept of "stress" need not be used to study performance capability in an unusual environment. The problem can be viewed simply as an effort to determine relationships between those variables which define the environment and those which define performance. The choice of output variables depends entirely on what job an operator must do, and no attempt to deal with compensatory mechanisms need be made.

On the other hand, viewing a problem of this kind as a stress experiment may be heuristic. By planning and interpreting studies within the framework of a concept of stress, the results of one study can be related to others based on a similar concept. Furthermore, by asking what degree of stress is imposed by the environment on the operator of the task, it is possible to discover the cost of maintaining performance. Thus, we may be able not only to choose operators who can carry out the task at minimum cost, but also to protect the health and optimize performance of those who are selected.

A second type of question on physical stressors is asked of the psychologist with increasing frequency. This involves use of psychological techniques as tools to learn more about the stressor. A subject is asked to perform a task not because we are interested in the task, *per se,* but because it yields data on his environment. A common example is the use of peripheral visual acuity in studies of acceleration. Failure of peripheral vision is employed as a dependent variable for comparing rates of *G* onset, subject position, protective equipment, and the like.

The choice of variables used in a study of the effects of physical stressors depends on many factors. The nature of the stressor must be considered first. Peripheral vision, for example, can be used more effectively in studies of positive acceleration—where retinal blood flow

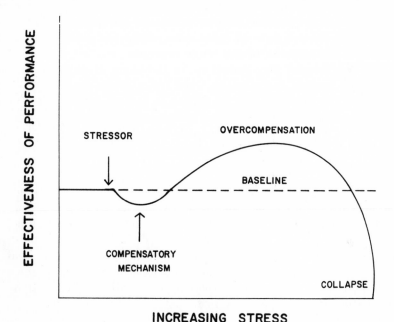

Figure 1. Schematic representation of the relationship between stress and performance.

is quickly affected—than in studies on heat—where it is affected much later. In addition, information on the subject's position and activity must be considered in the experimental design. If impairment of central nervous system functions is to be used as a measure of the changes produced by a physical stressor, the task cannot involve a motor response that the subject could not make after the stressor has been applied.

A more important issue, however, concerns the sensitivity of psychological measures to subtle changes in energy input. It is pointless to choose an output variable which will not be measurably affected during the period of stress. This can be illustrated by a diagram adapted from Selye (Figure 1). The stressor, represented by the descending arrow, tends to displace a function of the subsystem under study away from its equilibrium point. (This function can be anything we choose to measure, let us say a tracking task.) The compensatory response, represented by the ascending arrow, may actually lead to improved performance until the experiment has ended. Unless we choose to continue until the point of collapse is reached, it will be necessary either to measure the compensatory response to show the effect of the stressor or to choose another variable that will be more sensitive.

CHANGE IN INFORMATION INPUT

Stress arises from a change in information input when the quantity of information to be processed becomes too great or too small for the system to maintain an optimal output. A telephone operator whose switchboard suddenly is covered by flashing lights may be under stress even when the energy input of the lights presents no problem whatever. Similarly, individuals carrying out tasks may show performance decrements and signs of stress because too little is happening.

Another problem of the unusual environment is the occurrence of unaccustomed information input. Even where no physical stressors or threatening implications are involved, subjects may be unable to function properly when novel information is presented. Everyone tends to structure his behavior according to certain expectations about the kind of events he is used to. It is as if each individual makes his environment less chaotic by organizing his experiences according to a hierarchy of probabilities. If this expectancy is disrupted, he may be unable to function even when the principles underlying the task he is to perform remain unaltered.

CHANGE IN MEANING

Perhaps nothing is more difficult to study than stress arising from the meaning of information inputs to the system. Yet, since humans tend to react to inputs according to their implications, investigators who focus only on the physical or quantitative aspects of these inputs can easily be misled. Studies of unusual environments must deal not only with the physical characteristics of the environment, but also with what these characteristics may symbolize. Furthermore, the personalities and past experience of those persons placed in the environment must be taken into account.

It would be impossible to catalog all aspects of an environment that might symbolically threaten any individual. Certain generalizations, however, may serve as guide lines and can be derived by considering the ways in which an environment may permit or interfere with gratification of human needs. Most readers would agree that some needs are fundamental—such as food, water, and exchange of certain gases. Other needs usually viewed as basic involve outlets for sexual and aggressive drives. Furthermore, man must be protected against energy inputs from the environment that are too small or too large. Because of unpleasant past experiences with lacks or excesses of supplies or stimuli, he has learned to respond to the threat of pain before he begins to suffer. There are also secondary needs for contact with other people, for achievement, for status, and for other requirements derived from the primary needs.

Whenever a man is placed in an environment that blocks gratification of such needs, stress may arise. Furthermore, it is not essential that gratification actually be blocked. Men respond to symbols or threats of frustration before it exists in fact—or even when there are no realistic grounds for assuming that it will exist. Any potential cause of deprivation may be looked upon as a source of danger and will elicit a response, depending on the need that is blocked and on the individual. The fear of anoxia, for example, will lead to responses that are more immediate and less varied than responses to the fear of failure.

Where danger is external, realistic, and immediate, uncomplicated fight-or flight-mechanisms may be seen. But when danger is internal, symbolic, and anticipated, a variety of psychological defense mechanisms are called into play. These mechanisms have usually been learned in early life and are often inappropriate for handling adult problems. The result may be a breakdown in performance that would be unpredicted if the total meaning of an unusual environment were not considered.

Indices of Stress

It has been pointed out that stress can be defined either by inputs to a system or by outputs from a system. Where input definitions are used, the stressor is usually physical, and psychological measures are used to determine the relationship of the stressor to performance of a particular task. Choice of measures then depends on the nature of the task to be studied.

Where output definitions are used, psychological measures may serve as indices of stress. The variables chosen for measurement are usually those which the unstressed system can maintain within a defined range. The existence of stress is demonstrated when a variable under study fails to stay inside this range.

Whenever there is reason to suspect that stress can exist without a change in output or that outputs can change without stress, other outputs must be chosen as indices of possible compensatory responses. Such outputs may be related to psychological defense mechanisms or to physiological variables that either reveal the functioning of homeostatic mechanisms or show a change in the "state of arousal" of the organism.

PSYCHOLOGICAL MEASURES

Since it is not possible to consider more than a small fraction of the available psychological assessment techniques, those interested in further information on this topic are referred to reference works such as those edited by Stevens (1951), Woodworth and Schlosberg (1954), French (1954), or Buros (1959). Critical treatment of these can also be found periodically in the *Annual Reviews of Psychology*. The measures to be discussed here are those which have been found useful either in studies of real-life situations threatening an individual's safety or in laboratory stress experiments. The vast literature resulting from such studies has been reviewed by Horvath (1959); Lazarus, *et al.* (1952); and Holtzman and Bitterman. No attempt will be made here to deal with the entire subject, but emphasis will be placed on illustrative examples of techniques and studies. Although any scheme of classification is partly arbitrary, measures will be grouped under the following categories.

PERCEPTUAL TESTS

Threshold. The intensity at which a stimulus can just be perceived has been shown to be altered by a variety of stressors. Many of these are cues that threaten the individual in some way. Under such circumstances, thresholds are often raised. If avoidance is possible, however, different results may be obtained. Rosen (1954), for example, found that where correct identification of a nonsense syllable presented tachistoscopically enabled the subject to avoid a shock, recognition time decreased. Where punishment could not be avoided, however, no adaptation was possible, and no more than a normal practice effect was seen.

Flicker Fusion. The frequency is determined at which a subject perceives an intermittently flashing light as a steady one. Although considerable care must be taken in measuring the critical flicker fusion frequency (CFF), it is still well adapted for stress experiments. It appears most sensitive either to prolonged periods of stress (Brozek and Keys, 1944) or to conditions favoring the development of anxiety (Ross, *et al.*, 1954; Krugman, 1947).

Perceptual Speed. A variety of techniques are available for studying this parameter. Perhaps the most common is the test developed by Thurstone, in which the subject is presented with two pages of numbers taken from a table of random numbers. The left-hand number of each row is circled. The subject's task is to cross out each digit in a row that is like the one circled in that row (French, 1954).

Perceptual Retention. This is a test of the number of units in a series of stimuli that can be retained. A measure of perceptual span, it involves attention and immediate memory. It is usually tested by giving the Digit Span subtest of the Wechsler Adult Intelligence Scale, where lists of increasing length are read, and the subject is asked to repeat them, both forward and backward. A similar, but nonverbal, task is presented by the Knox cubes, where the subject is required to repeat the experimenter's sequence of taps on four cubes, while the pattern of tapping increases in length and complexity. Although reports of the stress sensitivity of perceptual retention tasks vary (Mandler and Sarason, 1952), digit span has been found to decrease in situations that provoke anxiety (Woodworth and Schlosberg, 1954). It has been found to decrease and become more variable in subjects with high anxiety levels than those with lower levels (Mandler and Sarason, 1952).

Attention. Several aspects of attention have been studied. One aspect refers to the capacity to maintain attention, or vigilance. This has been intensively investigated by Mackworth (1950). His technique involves a clock hand that usually moves in single steps, but occasionally gives a double jump. The subject responds only to the double jump. Missed signals have been found to increase as a result of both monotony and fatigue. In using different tasks, Jerison (1957; Jerison and Wing, 1957) found that high-intensity noise failed to affect vigilance where a single stimulus was employed, but did impair performance where multiple stimuli were monitored.

Another aspect of this problem is the focus of attention. Narrowed attention refers to the subject's focusing on only one portion of the environment, excluding other stimuli. Broad attention implies the awareness of a wide spectrum of stimuli. Mild stress may lead to narrowing of attention, with improved performance resulting on those tasks requiring a subject to attend to only one portion of the environment (Silverman,

1954). On the other hand, stress may make it impossible for subjects to avoid distraction. Callaway and Band (1958) have suggested that different stressors may affect the focus of attention in different ways, thus improving performance on tasks which require one type of attention and disrupting it on others.

Discrimination. A variety of tasks have been used in which the subject is required to differentiate between two similar stimuli. One of the most stress-sensitive of these is the closure of C's interspersed in a field of O's. Korchin and Basowitz (1954) found that the number of closures was increased in parachute trainees, compared with a control group, as well as in trainees in a prejump period, compared with a postjump period. This finding is compatible with the concept that low levels of anxiety increase performance. This effect is shown by the elevated segment of the curve in Figure 1.

MOTOR TESTS

Steadiness. By testing the ability of a subject to hold a stylus in holes of decreasing diameter without touching the edge, a measure of steadiness can be obtained. Through the use of more elaborate equipment, it is also possible to measure body sway. Both have been shown to be affected by stress (Lewisohn, 1956; Roos, *et al.*, 1952).

Tracking. This task requires a coordinated motor response to a continuously varying display. For example, the subject may use an aircraft-type control to keep a marker centered on both horizontal and vertical axes of a cathode-ray oscilloscope. The position of the marker is changed in random fashion by a separate input to the oscilloscope. Performance has been shown to be impaired by many stressors including cold (Teichner and Wehrkamp, 1954), heat (Pepler, 1958), fatigue (Hauty and Payne, 1955), acceleration (Brown and Collins, 1958), and confinement (Burns and Gifford, 1961). Another technique commonly used is the pursuit rotor, where the subject attempts to maintain constant contact between a stylus held in his hand and a disk on a rotating turntable.

Coordination. Tests of coordination emphasize the speed and precision of motor behavior. They may involve either gross or fine movements. For measuring the speed of finer movements, a well-standardized task is the Purdue Pegboard, which involves the serial assembly of small objects on a perforated board. Another is mirror drawing, where the subject must follow with a pencil a pathway made by two parallel lines in the shape of a six-pointed star. He can observe his progress only by looking at a mirror image of the tracing. Vernon, *et al.* (1959), have demonstrated that this task is affected by sensory deprivation.

Reaction Time. While all of the measures described above include elements of both sensory and motor functions, reaction time tests involve such a balance of these elements that it is difficult to classify them according to either category. Because of its relative ease of measurement, reaction time has been extensively used in stress experiments. In simple reaction time tests, the subject is instructed to give a single response to a single stimulus. He can be either warned or not warned to alert himself before each stimulus appears. This has shown little sensitivity to a variety of stressors (Cooperman, *et al.*, 1934).

Where several signals are used, however, and the subject must choose the proper stimulus before reacting, stress sensitivity is increased. McFarland (1939) found, for example, that partial anoxia impairs complex reaction time, but has no effect on simple reaction time. As the resemblance of stimuli to each other becomes closer, the problem becomes increasingly one of discrimination. The stress sensitivity then appears to be raised. For studies on the School of Aviation Medicine Space Cabin Simulator, Hauty (personal communication) developed a task in which the subject responds only when a constantly changing geometric pattern matches a reference pattern. This is affected by both fatigue and changes in diurnal rhythm.

Problem Solving. Stress studies have utilized tests ranging from simple arithmetic to those involving complex inductive and deductive reasoning processes. The Number Facility Task devised by French, Coombs, and Humphreys (French, 1954), for example, gives the subject a series of problems requiring addition of one or two-digit numbers in sets of three. A more demanding task is provided by the PSI apparatus, where problems in logic of any desired degree of complexity are presented by an electronic device. This task has been found to be sensitive to fatigue and various drug effects.

Concept Formation. The subject is usually required to search for common elements in a series of stimuli and form appropriate generalizations. Tests of concept formation thus frequently involve classification. The subject is given cards or blocks of various kinds and instructed to sort them. An example is the Wisconsin card-sorting test, in which the subject has four stimulus cards and 64 response cards. Each card bears one to four identical figures of a single color. He begins to sort according to number, form, or color and is told only whether he is right or wrong.

After 10 consecutive successes, the instructions are changed. Roos, *et al.* (1952) have shown this method to be sensitive to stress induced by intermittent electric shocks. Another approach is provided by the Minnesota Paper Form Board Test, which requires the subject to identify the result of assembling a given group of isolated plane figures. Performance of the task has been shown to be impaired by noise (Smith, 1951).

Conditioning and Learning. Many tests fall into these broad categories. Subjects may be conditioned in a variety of ways, required to learn lists of nonsense syllables or to associate different responses to different verbal or non-verbal stimuli. Taylor (1951) found, for example, that the eyeblink could be conditioned more rapidly in high anxiety subjects than in low anxiety subjects. Using a measure of nonsense syllable learning, Silverman and Blitz (1956) found that performance of low anxiety subjects improved when they were told they *might* receive a shock and declined when they were told they *would* receive a shock, while the performance of high anxiety subjects was unchanged.

Flexibility Tests. The necessity of altering a previously learned set is a component of many tasks that primarily measure sensory or motor functions (Burns and Gifford, 1961). Since this requirement involves certain cognitive processes, tests of flexibility are conveniently grouped in this category. A good example is the Bourdon-Wiersma Stipple Test, in which the subject is presented with horizontal rows of three-, four-, and five-dot clusters. He is first instructed to place a horizontal line through five-dot clusters and a vertical line through four-dot clusters. After 20 lines, the instructions are reversed. The decrease in speed and increase in errors under the second or subsequent instructions, compared with the prior instructions, gives a measure of rigidity. This technique has been found sensitive to a variety of stressors employed by van Wulfften Palthe (personal communication).

TESTS OF EMOTIONAL RESPONSE

Measures in this category are designed to indicate the meaning of an environment to a subject, the nature of the threat the environment may present, the type of conflict aroused, and the style of the individual's attempts at mastery. In practice, measures of personality or emotion are seldom used in studies of stress, frequently because of the investigator's lack of interest in these areas. More often, the reason is the lack of objectivity and the difficulty of interpretation inherent in the measures available.

While such limitations undoubtedly exist, they should be viewed in their proper perspective. For one thing, data on personality and emotion may be used in conjunction with data on performance and physiological reactions. Stress can thus be defined in terms of variables that can be measured, while the less objective personality data are used to indicate what kind of emotional response the subject has made and why he has made it. In this way, the virtues of each type of test can be combined. Performance and physiological variables are well-suited for serving as criteria of stress and for measuring its magnitude, but they are usually nonspecific. For example, impaired tracking and decreased skin resistance might be used to indicate the extent to which a subject in isolation is under stress, but they rarely would tell either why he was under stress or why he might perceive this stressor as more or less threatening than some other. Personality variables, on the other hand, tell us what kind of stress, but seldom indicate its degree. By combining both categories of tests, we can learn something about the nature and degree of stress—both as imposed by the environment and as perceived by the subject.

Even though limitations on objectivity—coupled with scientific discretion—may usually make it desirable to employ personality data qualitatively, the quantitative use of such data is often possible, commonly through the use of rating scales or the development and validation of objective scoring systems. Examples of the use of such techniques will be discussed as individual measures are considered.

Direct Observation and Interviewing. Probably no other technique illustrates so clearly the advantages and disadvantages of methods to study personality as the clinical interview. While the observer's impression of the subject's behavior, followed by his account of his experience—catalyzed by appropriate questioning—are rich sources of data, they are often too complex and too subjective to be measurable. Few investigators neglect to use such techniques qualitatively. They can be used quantitatively only if the elements of the situation can be abstracted, defined explicitly, and incorporated into a rating which can be made by judges.

The studies by Funkenstein, *et al.* (1957) provide an excellent example of the combination of interview and other data. Stress was induced experimentally by requiring the subject to repeat a previously learned story while a feedback mechanism returned his speech, after a delay, through earphones. Interviews immediately after the stress situation were recorded and scored independently, according to whether the subject's reaction was one of anger directed outward, anger directed inward, anxiety, or combinations of these. The ratings thus obtained proved highly reliable and were significantly correlated with a battery of psychological and physiological measures.

Self-Ratings. The subject's thoughts and feelings can often be systematized and measured by tests in which he is given questions or asked to rate himself. Among the most popular are the Taylor Manifest Anxiety Scale, where yes-no answers to 65 questions are used as an index of anxiety, and the Nowlis Mood Scale, where the subject is asked to indicate the extent to which adjectives or brief descriptive statements apply to him. For example, the Nowlis includes such phrases as "rebellious," "startled," and "affectionate." For each of these, the subject is instructed to check whether "you definitely feel this way," "you feel slightly this way," "you can't decide whether or not you feel this way," or "you definitely don't feel this way." A score is then derived that indicates the strength of feeling in the following categories: concentration, aggression, pleasantness, activation-deactivation, social affection, depression, and anxiety.

A more complex type of measure is the personality inventory, where the subject's answers to questions or choice of responses are used as an index of his personality. Commonly used examples are the Minnesota Multiphasic Personality Inventory and the Edwards Personal Preference Schedule. The subject is exposed to the stressful situation and his response, as measured by other variables, is compared with the personality data. An indication of the role of individual differences is thus obtained. Findings from such studies may subsequently be applied in selection programs, where correlations between personality scores and successful adaptation to stress are used in predicting which candidates are best suited for a mission involving the stress that has been studied.

Projective Tests. Measures in this broad category are based upon what Rapaport (1946) has termed the "projective hypothesis." They allow the subject to structure unstructured material, thus revealing his structuring principles. Since important aspects of the individual's psychological structure are unconscious, projective procedures are particularly useful in gaining information on his unconscious motivations and drives.

All projective techniques have in common the presentation of an ambiguous stimulus. The subject presumably interprets the stimulus according to his experience, needs, and personality structure. Since two subjects seldom perceive these stimuli in the same manner, data on individual differences are obtained. But since the segment of behavior observed is limited, the patterns of response are similarly limited. Certain styles of response can thus be abstracted and scoring systems can be devised.

Perhaps the most widely known of the projective tests is the Rorschach. In this test, the subject is given successively 10 standard cards printed with bilaterally symmetrical inkblots, to which the subject responds by telling "what he sees on each card, or anything that might be presented there" (English and English, 1958). Analysis of the Rorschach test depends both on what is seen and how it is seen. Scores are obtained for variables such as the number of human figures reported, the amount of movement, or the use of color and texture.

The Rorschach can be employed in stress research in a variety of ways. One is to use it as part of the evaluation of the subject's personality —much as is done with the personality inventory. An illustration of this is provided by the isolation studies of Goldberger and Holt (1958), who used a scoring system to rank Rorschach protocols according to the method of dealing with primary process thinking. This is the prelogical thought pattern of the child that, according to the hypothesis developed by these investigators, would be expected to emerge when normal reality contact was impaired by isolation. Their experiments revealed the predicted relationship between scores indicating mature handling of the primary process and measures of response to isolation.

Another possibility is to administer the Rorschach before and after stress to provide information on the nature of the subject's reaction (Burch and Childers, 1961; Burns and Ziegler, 1960). Used in this way, projective techniques are more sensitive than personality inventories. Furthermore, they may reflect unconscious processes that are hard to reach through inventories. Since it is difficult to interpret changes in such tests if they are given both before and after an experience, it is often best to compare responses of subjects who have been under stress with responses of a control group treated in similar fashion except for the independent variable under study.

A second popular projective technique is the Thematic Apperception Test (TAT), where subjects are shown pictures of 20 ambiguous scenes and asked to tell stories based on what they think the pictures depict. Like the Rorschach, the TAT can be used either to evaluate personality or to measure responses to experimental conditions. A good example is a study by Walker and Atkinson (1958), who developed a form of the TAT and a scoring system to assess the arousal of fear. Alternate forms of the test were administered successively to a group of soldiers before they had learned they were to participate in atomic maneuvers, then after they had rehearsed for the explosion but 10 hours before it occurred, again immediately after it was safe to leave trenches 4,000 yards from the explosion, and finally 10 hours later. The appearance of fear-related imagery was greatest in the stories after the explosion and significantly greater in the last three administrations than during the initial control period.

Many other projective techniques can be devised. For example, to investigate changes in unconscious attitudes during a five-day group confinement study, Ruff, *et al.* (1959) used drawings of human figures, a sentence completion test, a modification of the Blacky test—where cartoons are used to assess psychosexual level—and an interpersonal projection test developed to measure changes in day-to-day feelings of crew members toward each other. Signs of regression and transient ego impairment were noted that were not reflected by the performance and physiological measures employed.

PSYCHOPHYSIOLOGICAL MEASURES

The term "psychophysiological measures" does not imply a particular class of variables, but rather a special application of these variables. Instead of using physiological measures to study particular subsystems of the individual, they are employed as indices of the state of excitation or arousal of the organism as a whole. This approach to stress is largely derived from three concepts. The first is Cannon's theory that fight or flight—emergency reactions of the organism are mediated by actions of the sympathetic nervous system. Subsequently, Ax (1953) demonstrated that physiological responses to fear and anger could be differentiated. Funkenstein, *et al.* (1957), Elmadjian, *et al.* (1957), and others later showed that stress responses involving fear are associated with secretion of adrenaline, while those involving anger are associated with secretion of noradrenaline. As a result, measures of activity in the sympathetic nervous system have commonly been used in stress research.

The second concept is that of Selye (1956), who has described a "General Adaptation Syndrome" mediated through the secretion of adrenocorticotrophic hormone (*ACTH*) by the pituitary, which stimulates the adrenal cortex to produce and discharge its steroid hormones. These hormones cause widespread changes throughout the body, including a decrease in lymphatic tissue and alterations in protein, carbohydrate, and fat metabolism. Selye found that the entire spectrum of these changes was elicited by such varied stressors as exposure to cold, infection, and emotional disturbance. He then defined stress by the appearance of this pattern. This work has led to the widespread use in stress research of measurements of adrenal hormones and their derivatives or of changes in circulating lymphocytes and other peripheral effects of these hormones.

The third concept underlying stress research is that of central nervous system arousal, based on the studies of Magoun (Lindsley, *et al.*, 1949; Moruzzi and Magoun, 1949) and others on the brain stem reticular system. According to this work, the reticular formation receives collaterals from sensory tracts and sends impulses to the cortex which presumably maintain arousal and alertness. Since it has been assumed that an organism subjected to a stressor responds with increased arousal, it has been measured in a variety of ways in stress studies during recent years.

Hebb's (1955) concept of arousal suggests that after arousal reaches an optimal level for effective performance, further increases lead to performance decrement and emotional disturbance. This has been substantiated by Silverman, *et al.* (1959), using acceleration as a stressor, tracking as a performance measure, and skin resistance as a measure of arousal.

These three concepts imply that an organism confronted with harmful stimuli undergoes a change in state. This change involves mobilization of reserves that attempt to restore the pre-stress state. Although certain compensatory mechanisms may be specific for particular stressors, there are presumably nonspecific changes that are found for all stressors. Stress can be defined and measured in terms of outputs affected by this hypothetical nonspecific internal state, such as activation, tension, arousal, or neuro-endocrine discharge. These outputs are usually physiological variables related to autonomic, adrenal, or reticular functioning, but can be psychological. Basowitz, *et al.* (1955), for example, have used anxiety as a nonspecific indicator of stress.

There may be advantages in postulating a nonspecific state of excitation or arousal that can be used to demonstrate stress. It must be remembered, however, that both the concept of arousal and the concept of stress are hypothetical constructs that may or may not represent something that exists in reality. In any case, efforts to define these concepts operationally have led to contradictory results. It is difficult to say at present whether this contradiction implies that they have too little basis in fact to be demonstrated or that techniques must be employed with care.

The nature of the stressor, the nature of the response, and the manner in which the response is expressed must always be considered. For example, Davis (1957) has pointed out that autonomic response patterns depend on the nature of the stimulus to which the subject is exposed. Funkenstein, *et al.* (1957), demonstrated that physiological reactions of subjects exposed to the same stimuli vary, depending on whether anger or anxiety were aroused and on whether anger was turned outward or in on the self. Lacey and Lacey (1958) demonstrated that subjects differ in their responsivity on different measures. They found that subjects respond to stress with a "hierarchy of activation." Each individual is relatively overactive in certain physiological measures, average in others, and underactive in still others. This pattern is idio-syncratic for a given subject and tends to be reproduced for a variety of stressors. Lacey and Lacey also point out that studies of relationships among autonomic variables indicate that no single physiological measure correlates well with others and that no single measure can indicate the total arousal of the organism.

Lacey (1959) has also called attention to two misleading assump-tions that could explain discrepancies between various psychophysio-logical studies of stress. The first is the idea that even a battery of variables can be used to measure the arousal value of a single aspect of the subject's environment. Since the autonomic nervous system always responds to the total situation, heart rate, for example, cannot be used as a measure of response to acceleration without defining the subject's anxiety and other factors which affect it. The second assumption involves the idea that autonomic measures indicate the activity of end organs. According to this, an increased level of an autonomic variable reflects increased autonomic activity and suggests increased central nervous system arousal. In fact, autonomic responses indicate the activity of feedback loops and may suggest either increased or decreased activity. An elevated heart rate, for example, may stimulate pressure receptors in the carotid sinus to exercise inhibitory control over cortical electrical activity.

It can be stated, therefore, that wherever psychophysiological vari-ables are to be employed in stress research, we must know (1) the effect of the total experimental situation on the variables we plan to use; (2) the nature of each individual's response to the situation or similar situations; and (3) his responsiveness for each variable we study. If a large number of subjects are used, physiological measures that seem most sensitive to a particular stress situation for a majority of the group can be chosen. Individual variations will then tend to cancel each other out. This approach, however, cannot be used to define the stress response of any individual within the group.

Rather than offer a complete review of psychophysiological measures, brief descriptions of those most commonly used will be presented.

Catechol Amines. Adrenaline and noradrenaline are secondary al-cohols produced by the adrenal medulla. Noradrenaline is also a chemical mediator released at sympathetic nerve endings. Although the concentra-tion in blood of these hormones has been measured in a few stress studies (Kety, 1961), the concentration in urine is better established. Urinary excretion can be most accurately determined through biological assay, but because of the expense of this technique, is usually measured bio-chemically.

Extensive psychophysiological studies of the catechol amines by Elmadjian and his collaborators (1957) and by Silverman, *et al.* (1961), have demonstrated that aggressive behavior is associated with noradrenaline, while fearful behavior is associated with adrenaline. Because of the complex relationship between these hormones and many bodily functions, however, the interpretation of their other roles is difficult. The urinary catechols represent only a few per cent of the quantity secreted in the body. Factors that affect the balance between production and destruction are poorly understood, as are the influences of muscular activity and the cardiovascular status of the subject. As a result, their general use at the present time is limited.

ACTH and Adrenal Steroids. Earlier stress studies relied on observations of tissue changes in organs influenced by adrenal cortical activity (Selye, 1950). While these changes provide an operational definition of stress, they appear too slowly to be useful in acute stress experiments. The introduction of a satisfactory method for measuring urinary 17-hydroxycorticoids, which are derived from cortisone, reduced the time scale. It was not, however, until Nelson and Samuels (1952) developed a method for the biochemical determination of plasma hydroxycortisone itself that adrenocortical activity could be effectively measured in experiments on stress. In an excellent example of this kind of study, Price, *et al.* (1957) found that in preoperative surgical patients the plasma 17-hydroxycorticosteroid concentration was positively correlated with the general emotional involvement of subjects in their situation.

More recently, Persky, *et al.* (1959), directly measured two forms of pituitary corticotrophic hormones and found that anxious psychiatric patients had strikingly higher levels than normal controls. Both the plasma hydrocortisone and urinary hydroxycorticoid levels were also significantly higher in the patients than in the controls. As Hamburg (1959) has pointed out, this finding illustrates the progress of stress research as it becomes closer and closer to the central nervous system. It seems reasonable that further steps will directly involve the hypothalamic mechanisms that influence the pituitary as well as functions of the limbic system which appear to mediate stress responses.

Thyroid. The relationship between stress and thyroid function has been apparent since Parry, in 1803, recorded the case of Elizabeth S., whose hyperthyroidism began after she was "thrown out of a wheel chair in coming fast downhill on April last" (Parry, 1825). Many years later, Brody (1949) found significant positive correlations between patients' self-reports of increased emotional tension and serum iodine concentrations. Board, *et al.* (1956) subsequently reported elevated serum protein-bound iodine levels in anxious psychiatric patients, but found that plasma hydrocortisone levels showed an even greater increase. While radioactive iodine uptake is a more sensitive measure of thyroid activity than the determination of protein-bound iodine, it cannot be determined repeatedly for research purposes. Thus, since thyroid activity seems associated with long-term stress, hydrocortisone determinations remain the method of choice for hormonal determinations in most stress studies.

Skin Resistance. While skin resistance has long been employed as a measure of autonomic activity, more recent evidence has suggested its use as an index of central nervous system arousal. Wang (1955) has offered evidence that the reticular activating system affects the galvanic skin response, while Greiner and Burch (1955) have described a direct association between spontaneous fluctuations in resistance and pharmacologic activation or depression of the reticular system. As a result, skin resistance is often used as a measure of state of consciousness or alertness. It appears to respond in a nonspecific manner to stimuli that increase the subject's responsiveness to his environment.

Skin resistance changes depend primarily upon alterations in permeability of the sweat gland cell membrane (Edelberg, *et al.*, 1960). Methods for measuring the electrical characteristics of this membrane fall into two categories. In the first, often referred to as the *endosomatic* method, electrodes are simply applied to the skin, and changes in potential are amplified and recorded. In the *exosomatic* method, current from an external source is applied across two points on the skin, and changes in resistance to passage of this current are recorded.

Skin resistance provides a good illustration of a general principle. Like other psychophysiological variables, it can be used to measure tension, lability, or nonspecific activity. Lacey (1959) has pointed out that these have different statistical properties, respond differently to different stimulus conditions, and may have different relationships to behavior. With skin resistance, therefore, we may express tension simply as the absolute level of resistance at a given time. This is usually called the basal resistance level. Lability is represented by the galvanic skin response (GSR or PGR), which is the magnitude of the resistance drop following a stimulus to the organism. Nonspecific activity is represented by the constant fluctuations in resistance level that may reflect spontaneous endogenous activity.

Heart Rate. In measurements concerning this variable, tension refers to the rate at a particular time, lability refers to the change in rate produced by a stressor or other situational change, and nonspecific activity refers to variations in the rate over time. These functions are usually indicated by a recorder, or cardiotachometer, which measures the interval either between successive pulse waves or between R-waves on the EKG and makes it possible to obtain a display of the rate at any given moment.

Heart rate has probably been the most widely used psychophysiologic measure. Since the experience of one's heart beating faster during emotional and other stress is widespread, it has been assumed that increased rate is an indication of stress. As pointed out above, however, the existence of feedback mechanisms complicates this picture. Lacey (1959) has shown that if a subject is required to note and detect what is going on in the environment, cardiac deceleration is the rule. Where he must concentrate on internal symbolic manipulations or is exposed to stimuli in which mechanisms to reduce environmental intake would be useful, cardiac acceleration is the rule. Lacey's recent data (personal communication) confirms his hypothesis that through action of the carotid sinus, heart rate changes are a kind of instrumental act of the organism, leading either to increased ease of "environmental intake" or to a form of "rejection of the environment."

Blood Pressure. Although direct pressure measurements using an arterial catheter are most accurate, they are often impractical in stress research. Indirect measurements, in which a cuff is inflated until the arterial pulse is blocked, are more frequently used. Through the use of automatic techniques for rapid, periodic inflation and deflation of the cuff, repeated pressure recordings can be obtained as often as every 15 seconds.

Blood pressure has been used less frequently than heart rate as a measure of change in arousal. To a great extent this results from the multitude of feedback mechanisms that regulate pressure changes within a relatively narrow range. Nevertheless, Malmo and Davis (1956), among others, have demonstrated that blood pressure is responsive to changes in arousal. Funkenstein, *et al.* (1957) found that systolic pressures were significantly different in subjects who responded to psychological stress by directing anger outward than in those who became anxious. As described above, their hypothesis that these responses were related to noradrenaline-adrenaline relationships was subsequently verified by other investigators.

Vascular Volume. The degree of constriction or dilation of peripheral arterioles is known to be a sensitive indicator of changes in the sympathetic nervous system. Many factors, however, in addition to external stimuli and internal emotional states affect vascular tone, which, since it is an important part of the heat regulatory mechanism, is particularly sensitive to temperature changes. As techniques for controlling the variables that affect this measure are improved, its use can be expected to become more common.

At present, methods of studying vascular tone depend on measuring the volume of a part of the body—usually the finger, toe, or pinna of the ear. Since volume changes are assumed to depend on changes in the amount of blood in the extremity under study, they yield an index of the degree of peripheral vasoconstriction. The technique first used in psychophysiological studies by Burch, *et al.* (1942), was the hydraulic plethysmograph, in which volume changes are indicated by displacement of water in a container fitted around the extremity under study. Subsequently, Whitney (1953) devised a strain gage in which volume changes are reflected by changes in resistance of a tube of mercury encircling the extremity. More recently, photocrystals have been employed to measure volume through changes in opacity of the extremity (Shmavonian, 1959). While all these methods have certain advantages and disadvantages, the hydraulic system is probably the most quantitative.

Like all psychophysiological variables, vascular changes reveal tension, lability, and nonspecific activity. Theron (1948), for example, has reported a factor-analytic study in which finger-volume changes were related to both emotional tension and stability. Burch, *et al.* (1942), have described nonspecific changes that appear closely related to personality variables.

Respiration. Psychophysiological studies have focused on the rate, volume, and rhythm of respiration, which have been recorded by collecting expired air in a spirometer, by placing a moisture-sensitive transducer near the mouth and nose, or by strain gages that measure expansion of the chest. Although results have varied, sensitivity to changes in arousal have been reported. Ax (1953), for example, found that the respiratory rate increase was significantly greater in fear than in anger.

The Electromyogram (EMG). Electromyography is a technique for recording the action potentials of skeletal muscles. These electrical impulses can be picked up by surface electrodes placed over the muscle, then amplified and displayed on an oscilloscope or inkwriter. No potentials are recorded from the normal muscle at rest in a relaxed subject. With increased tension, however, potentials appear even when no movement is apparent. The EMG has thus been used as an index of either tension or movement and has been found to increase as motivational conditions are varied from low to high levels (Stennett, 1957) or as individuals discuss emotionally significant topics (Shagass and Malmo, 1954).

The Electroencephalogram (EEG). This is a record, usually from the scalp, of the electrical activity of the brain. Although this technique produces a continuous record of cerebral activity, it yields too much information for most experimental purposes and consequently for most analytic methods. A recent trend, therefore, is the development of automatic analyzers that provide only the needed data. A good example is the period analyzer, developed by Burch and Childers (1961), which gives an index of the frequency and complexity of the EEG wave. Since a shift from relaxed to alert behavior is accompanied by a shift from lower to higher frequencies, this technique can be used as an index of behavioral arousal.

Summary

Stress can be defined in terms of inputs to a system or of outputs from a system. An input definition is possible where the environmental conditions are known to be consistently stressful and are well defined. With this type of definition, psychological variables are used to measure performance. An output definition is necessary where environmental conditions have diverse effects. The ability to maintain psychological variables within a certain range is then used to indicate the presence or degree of stress. Another type of output definition involves demonstration through psychological or psychophysiological variables that the system has mobilized compensatory mechanisms.

When input definitions are used, the choice of psychological measures depends on what aspect of performance must be studied. When output definitions are used, the choice depends on what tests can be administered under the conditions to be imposed, as well as on their sensitivity to effects of these conditions. When compensatory mechanisms are to be demonstrated, psychophysiological measures are usually used as indices of activation, tension, arousal, or neuroendocrine discharge.

The psychological measures discussed include tests of motor, perceptual, cognitive, and emotional responses. Usually objective tests are involved in the measurement of stress, while projective and other more subjective techniques are used to determine why the environment is stressful for a particular subject. Psychophysiological measures of the activity of the sympathetic nervous system, pituitary-adrenal function, and the activity of the cerebral cortex are discussed.

References

Ax, A. F. "The Physiological Differentiation between Fear and Anger in Humans," *Psychosom. Med.*, *15*:433, 1953.

Basowitz, H., Korchin, S. J., Oken, D., Goldstein, M. S., and Gussack, H. Anxiety and Performance Changes with a Minimal Does of Epinephrine, *A.M.A. Arch. Neurol. Psychiat.*, *76*:98, 1956.

————, Persky, H., Korchin, S. J., and Grinker, R. R. *Anxiety and Stress*. New York: McGraw-Hill, 1955.

Berman, M. L., and Pettitt, J. A. "The Effect of Stress and Anticipation to Stress of Urinary Levels of a Catecholamine Catabolite," *Aerospace Med.*, *31*:297, 1960.

Board, F., Persky, H., and Hamburg, D. A. "Psychological Stress and Endocrine Functions," *Psychosom. Med.*, *18*:324, 1956.

Brody, E. B. "Psychologic Tension and Serum Iodine Levels in Psychiatric Patients without Evidence of Thyroid Disease," *Psychosom. Med.*, *11*:70, 1949.

Brown, J. L., and Collins, C. C. "Air-to-Air Tracking During Closed Loop Centrifuge Operation." *J. Aviation Med.*, *29*:794, 1958.

Brozek, J., and Keys, A. "Changes in Flicker-Fusion Frequency Under Experimental Stress." *Fed. Proc.*, *3*:6, 1944.

Burch, G. E., Cohn, A. E., and Neumann, C. "A Study by Quantitative Methods of the Spontaneous Variations in Volume of the Finger Tip, Toe Tip, and Postero-Superior Portion of the Pinna of Resting Normal White Adults." *Amer. J. Physiol.*, *136*:433, 1942.

Burch, N. R., and Childers, H. E. "Physiological Data Acquisition," in B. E. Flaherty (ed.), *Psychophysiological Aspects of Space Flight*. New York: Columbia University Press, 1961.

Burns, N. M., and Gifford, E. C. "Effects of Long-Term Confinement on Performance. Environmental Requirements of Sealed Cabins for Space and Orbital Flights—A Second Study. Part 2," Naval Air Materiél Center Air Crew Equipment Laboratory, March, 1961 (Rep. TED NAM AE-1403).

———— and Ziegler, R. B. "Environmental Requirements of Sealed Cabins for Space and Orbital Flights—A Second Study. Part 3. Effects of Long-term Confinement on Personality and Perception," Naval Air Materiél Center, Air Crew Equipment Laboratory, July, 1960 (Rep. TED NAM AE-1403).

Buros, O. K. (ed.). *The Fifth Mental Measurements Yearbook*. Highland Park, N.J.: Gryphon Press, 1959.

Callaway, E., and Band, R. I. Some Psychopharmacological Effects of Atropine, *A.M.A. Arch. Neurol. Psychiat.*, *79*:91, 1958.

Cooperman, N. R., Mullin, F. J., and Kleitman, N. "Studies on the Physiology of Sleep: XI. Further Observations on the Effects of Prolonged Sleeplessness," *Amer. J. Physiol.*, *107*:589, 1934.

Davis, R. C. "Response Patterns," *Trans. N.Y. Acad. Sci.*, *19*:731, 1957.

Edelberg, R., Greiner, T., and Burch, N. R. "Some Membrane Properties of the Effector in the Galvanic Skin Response," *J. Appl. Physiol.*, *15*:691, 1960.

Elmadjian, F., Hope, J. M., and Lamson, E. T. "Excretion of Epinephrine and Norepinephrine in Various Emotional States," *J. Clin. Endocrinol.*, *17*:608, 1957.

English, Horace B. and Ava C. *A Comprehensive Dictionary of Psychological and Psychoanalytical Terms*. New York: Longmans, Green, 1958.

Forbes, W. H., Dill, D. B., DeSilva, H., and Van Deventer, F. M. "The Influence of Moderate Carbon Monoxide Poisoning upon the Ability to Drive Automobiles," *J. Indust. Hyg. Toxicol.*, *19*:598, 1937.

Forlano G., Bermack, J. E., and Conkley, J. D. "The Effect of Ambient and Body Temperatures upon Reaction Time," *Special Devices Center Rep.* No. 151-1-13, 1948.

French, J. W. (ed.). *Manual for Kit of Selected Tests for Reference Aptitude and Achievement Factors*, Princeton, N.J.: Educational Testing Service, 1954.

Funkenstein, D. H., King, S. H., and Drolette, M. E. *Mastery of Stress*, Cambridge, Mass.: Harvard University Press, 1957.

Goldberger, L., and Holt, R. R. "Experimental Interference with Reality Contact (Perceptual Isolation): Method and Group results," *J. Nerv. Ment. Dis.*, *127*:99, 1958.

Greiner, T. H., and Burch, N. R. "Response of the Human Galvanic Skin Reflex to Drugs That Influence Reticular Formation of the Brain Stem," *Fed. Proc.*, *14*:346, 1955.

Hamburg, D. A. "Some Issues on Human Behavior and Adrenocortical Function, *Psychosom. Med.*, *21*:387, 1959.

Hauty, G. T., and Payne, R. B. "Mitigation of Work Decrement," *J. Exp. Psychol.*, *49*:60, 1955.

Hebb, D. O. "Drives and the CNS (Conceptual Nervous System)," *Psychol. Rev.*, *62*:243, 1955.

Holtzman, W. H., and Bitterman, M. E. "Psychiatric Screening of Flying Personnel, VI, Anxiety and Reactions to Stress," *Project Report* No. 6, USAF School of Aviation Medicine, Randolph AFB, Texas.

Horvath, F. E. "Psychological Stress: A Review of Definitions and Experimental Research," *General Systems*, *4*:203, 1959.

Jerison, H. J. "Performance on a Simple Vigilance Task in Noise and Quiet," *J. Acoust. Soc. Amer.*, *29*:1163, 1957.

———, and Wing, S. "Effects of Noise and Fatigue on a Complex Vigilance Task," *USAF WADC Tech. Rep.*, No. 57-14, 1957.

Kety, S. S. "The Possible Relationships between the Catechol Amines and Emotional Stress," in A. Simon, C. C. Herbert, and R. Straus, *The Physiology of Emotions*, Springfield, Ill.: Charles C Thomas, 1961.

Korchin, S. J., and Basowitz, H. "Perceptual Adequacy in a Life Stress," *J. Psychol.*, *38*:495, 1954.

Krugman, H. E. Flicker Fusion Frequency as a Function of Anxiety Reaction: An Exploratory Study, *Psychosom. Med.*, *9*:269, 1947.

Lacey, J. I. "Psychophysiological Approaches to the Evaluation of Psychotherapeutic Process and Outcome," in *Research in Psychotherapy: Proceedings of a Conference,* Washington: American Psychological Association, 1959.

———, and Lacey, B. C. "Verification and Extension of the Principle of Autonomic Response Stereotypy," *Amer. J. Psychol.,* 71:50, 1958.

Lazarus, R. S., Deese, J., and Osler, S. F. "The Effects of Psychological Stress upon Performance," *Psychol. Bull.,* 49:292, 1952.

Lewinsohn, P. "Some Individual Differences in Physiological Reactivity to Stress," *J. Comp. Physiol. Psychol.,* 49:271, 1956.

Lindsley, D. B., Bowden, J., and Magoun, H. W. "Effect upon the EEG of Acute Injury to the Brain Stem Activating System," *EEG Clin. Neurophysiol.,* 1:475, 1949.

McFarland, R. "The Psychophysiological Effects of Reduced Oxygen Pressure," *Res. Publ. Ass. Res. Nerv. Ment. Dis.,* 19:112, 1939.

Mackworth, N. H. "Researches on the Measurement of Human Performance," *Med. Res. Council Rep.* No. 268, 1950.

Malmo, R. B., and Davis, J. F. "Physiological Gradients as Indicants of "Arousal" in Mirror Tracing," *Canad. J. Psychol.,* 10:231, 1956.

Mandler, G., and Sarason, S. "A Study of Anxiety and Learning," *J. Abnorm. Soc. Psychol.,* 47:166, 1952.

Miller, J. G. *Living Systems.* New York: Wiley, 1962.

Moruzzi, G., and Magoun, H. W. "Brain Stem Reticular Formation and Activation of the EEG," *EEG clin. Neurophysiol.,* 1:455, 1949.

Nelson, D. H., and Samuels, L. T. "A Method for the Determination of 17-Hydroxycorticosteroids in Blood: 17-Hydroxycorticosterone in the Peripheral Circulation," *J. Clin. Endocrinol.,* 12:519, 1952.

Parry, C. H. "Diseases of the Heart," *Elements of Pathology and Therapeutics,* 2:111, 1825.

Pepler, R. D. "Warmth and Lack of Sleep: Accuracy or Activity Reduced," APU 286, in *Human Perf. Rep.* No. 4, MRC Appl. Psychol. Res. Unit, 1958.

Persky, H., Maroc, J., Conrad, E., and Den Breeijen, A. "Blood Corticotropin and Adrenal Weight-Maintenance Factor Levels of Anxious Patients and Normal Subjects," *Psychosom. Med.,* 21:379, 1959.

Price, D. B., Thaler, M., and Mason, J. W. "Preoperative Emotional States and Adrenal Cortical Activity: Studies on Cardiac and Pulmonary Surgery Patients," *A.M.A. Arch. Neurol. Psychiat.,* 77:646, 1957.

Rapaport, D. *Diagnostic Psychological Testing,* Chicago: Year Book Publishers, 1946.

Rosen, A. C. "Changes in Perceptual Threshold as a Protective Function of the Organism," *J. Pers.,* 23:182, 1954.

Roos, B. M., Rupel, J. W., and Grand, D. A. "Effects of Personal, Impersonal, and Physical Stress upon Cognitive Behavior in a Card Sorting Problem, *J. Abnorm. Soc. Psychol.,* 47:546, 1952.

Ross, S., Hussman, T. A., and Andrews, T. G. "Effects of Fatigue and Anxiety on Certain Psychomotor and Visual Functions," *J. Appl. Psychol.,* 38:119, 1954.

Ruff, G. E., Levy, E. Z., and Thaler, V. H. "Studies of Isolation and Confinement," *Aerospace Med., 30*:599, 1959.

Selye, H. *The Physiology and Pathology of Exposure to Stress: A Treatise Based on the Concepts of the General-Adaptation Syndrome and the Diseases of Adaptation.* Montreal: Acta, 1950.

——. *The Stress of Life.* New York: McGraw-Hill, 1956.

Shagass, C., and Malmo, R. B. "Psychodynamic Themes and Localized Muscular Tension during Psychotherapy," *Psychosom. Med., 16*:295, 1954.

Shmavonian, B. "Methodological study of vasomotor conditioning in human subjects," *J. Comp. Physiol. Psychol., 52*:315, 1959.

Silverman, A. J., Cohen, S. I., and Shmavonian, B. M. "Investigation of Psychophysiologic Relationships with Skin Resistance Measures," *J. psychosom. Res., 4*:65, 1959.

——, ——, ——, and Kirshner, N. "Catecholamines in Psychophysiologic Studies," *Recent Advances in Biological Psychiatry*, Vol. III, New York: Grune & Stratton, 1961.

Silverman, R. E. "Anxiety and the Mode of Response," *J. Abnorm. Soc. Psychol., 49*:538, 1954.

——, and Blitz, B. "Learning and Two Kinds of Anxiety," *J. Abnorm. Soc. Psychol., 52*:301, 1956.

Smith, K. R. "Intermittent Loud Noise and Mental Performance," *Science, 114*:132, 1951.

Stennett, R. G. "The Relationship of Performance Level to Level of Arousal," *J. Exp. Psychol., 54*:54, 1957.

Stevens, S. S. *Handbook of Experimental Psychology*, New York: Wiley, 1951.

Taylor, J. A. "The Relationship of Anxiety to the Conditional Eyelid Response," *J. Exp. Psychol., 41*:81, 1951.

Teichner, W. H., and Wehrkamp, R. F. "Visual-Motor Performance as a Function of Short-Duration Ambient Temperature," *J. Exp. Psychol., 47*:447, 1954.

Theron, P. A. "Peripheral Reactions as Indices of Basic Emotional Tension and Lability," *Psychosom. Med., 10*:335, 1948.

Vernon, J. A., McGill, T. E., Gulick, W. L., and Candland, D. K. "Effect of Sensory Deprivation on Some Perceptual and Motor Skills," *Perceptual and Motor Skills, 9*:91, 1959.

Walker, E. L., and Atkinson, J. W. "The Expression of Fear-Related Motivation in Thematic Apperception as a Function of Proximity to an Atomic Explosion," in J. W. Atkinson, *Motives in Fantasy, Action, and Society.* Princeton, N.J.: Van Nostrand, 1958.

Wang, G. H. Brainstem Reticular System and Galvanic Skin Reflex," *Fed. Proc., 14*:346, 1955.

Whitney, R. J. "The Measurement of Volume Changes in Human Limbs," *J. Physiol., 121*:1, 1953.

Williams, M. "An Experimental Study of Intellectual Control under Stress and Associated Rorschach Factors," *J. Consult. Psychol., 11*:21, 1947.

Woodworth, R. S., and Schlosberg, H. *Experimental Psychology*, New York: Holt, 1954.

3

COMPUTER SIMULATION OF
MAN-MACHINE SYSTEMS

Arthur I. Siegel and J. J. Wolf

Applied Psychological Services
Wayne, Pennsylvania

In the past man has constructed physical models that imitate natural phenomena in order to demonstrate or investigate the characteristics of these phenomena. More recently, abstract mathematical models of events such as wars and baseball games have been built. These models are possible because of a concept called "computer simulation." In general computer simulation consists of constructing a mathematical model of some activity on the basis of known attributes of the activity. Then the computer is programmed (instructed) to repeat this activity a number of times under varying circumstances, to observe itself while it simulates the activity, and to produce a written summary of what has transpired.

It is the purpose of this chapter to describe a model, developed by Applied Psychological Services, that allows for the simulation of the human operator in a man-machine system even to the point of simulating operator stress and urgency conditions and the point beyond which the human operator would be expected to break down.

PURPOSES OF MODEL

The purpose of this model to give equipment designers quantitative answers, while equipment is in the early design stage, to question such as the following:

1. Given a selected machine design, can an average two-man team be expected to complete successfully all actions required for task performance within the time limits given for each operator?

2. How does task or system success probability change for slower or faster teams and longer or shorter periods of allotted time?

3. How great a relative stress is placed on each operator during his performance and in which portions of the task are the operators overloaded or underloaded?

4. What is the frequency distribution of each operator's failures as a function of various relative stress tolerances and team member speeds?

5. For how much time is each operator idle while waiting either for the other operator or for some outside event to occur?

Use of the model is based on the high-speed, general-purpose digital computer. The computer operates on source data concerning performance by average operators and on system parameters; using these it simulates each operator by calculating values for and keeping track of items such as his performance time, subtask and task success or failure, stress, and idle time.

The Applied Psychological Services' model is not based on transfer functions nor is it wholly dependent upon probability theory. It consists, rather, of a combination of techniques. The model provides quantitative results for the critical problems of task success probability and points of high stress and also yields the required interpretive data such as the following:

1. Peak and terminal stress levels and on which subtask they occurred.

The technique here described was developed under Contract Nonr 2279 (00). between Applied Psychological Services and the Office of Naval Research. We are indebted to Dr. Max Lund, Dr. Denzel Smith, and Dr. Paul Cheathan for their encouragement throughout the work. Permission to reproduce any part of this text for the purposes of the U.S. Government is granted.

2. Identification of non-critical subtasks skipped by an operator due to his high stress.

3. Identification of waiting or idle times.

ANALOG VERSUS DIGITAL SIMULATION

We note that the application of an analog computer to the feedback control loop model is logical, since this type of computer operation depends on establishing a system whose properties are electrically or mechanically analogous to the properties of the equations or the model under study. On the other hand, the digital computer is capable of much greater precision than the analog type. While the analog computer is applicable to a wide range of control and feedback problems, the digital computer is more directly suited to those models whose implementation is based on the calculation of discrete quantities rather than continuous variables. The digital calculators are particularly well suited to simulating the decision making required by operators; they are quickly adapted from problem to problem, are flexible, and readily available.

USE OF THE MODEL

Prior to the use of the model, an analysis is performed for the man-machine system under consideration. The performance of each operator is arranged into ordered, discrete actions called "subtasks"; and for each subtask certain specific required source data are compiled. These data, together with the selected parameter values (for example, the time allotted for performance), are prepared in punched card form and introduced into the digital computer, for which a computer program has been prepared. As directed by its program, the computer will sequentially simulate, according to the rules of the model, the performance of each operator in the team on each subtask. The simulation, consisting basically of stress, urgency, subtask execution time, and subtask success calculations, plus the proper bookkeeping, continues serially for each subtask performed by each operator. The normal sequence of subtasks, whether linear or nonlinear, may be modified with complete generality in the event that actions must be skipped or repeated because of operator failure on any subtask or as a result of operator decisions. A simulation is completed when the simulated operators run out of allotted time or successfully complete the task. During the course of the computer's "performance" of the task, results are recorded by the computer on magnetic tape; and these data are later printed to indicate the areas of operator

overload, failure, idle time, high stress, and so forth, for the given set
of selected parameters. Numerous repetitions of the task with different
parameter values yield additional records and printouts. Frequency distributions, and summarized and reduced data are provided automatically
by the computer, if desired. Performance graphs and charts are then
prepared from these data. If alternate designs are indicated as a result
of the analysis of the resulting data, the new designs are similarly prepared and analyzed in order to determine the extent of improvement
brought about by the modifications.

The basic flow chart for the model is presented as Figure 1. This
figure displays the logical computation sequence performed by the computer during the simulation. The subscript i is used to identify the subtasks that comprise the total task mission. The operators are denoted
by j and j', which may assume values of 1 or 2, where j denotes either
operator specifically and j' denotes the other operator. The simulation
is completed only after both operators complete the necessary sequences
of subtasks.

INPUT DATA, PARAMETERS, AND INITIAL CONDITIONS

Following the reading by the computer of its coded instructions, the
basic subtask input data are read and stored in the computer's memory.
As shown in Figure 1, twelve items of subtasks input data exist for each
subtask $(i = 1, 2, \ldots, n)$, and each operator $(j = 1, 2)$. These subtask
data may be derived from such procedures as task analysis, literature
search, and personal interviews. The required input data for each operator
are as follows:

1. Average subtask execution time, t_{ij}, the average time required by
the jth operator to perform subtask i. This average value represents the
case in which the operator is under no stress. Values applicable for most
subtasks have been derived and are presented in Table 1.

2. Average standard deviation, σ_{ij}, under the no stress condition
taken around the t_{ij}, for the average operator. Values for these data are
also presented in Table 1.

3. Average subtask probability, p_{ij}, that the average operator, j,
under no stress can perform subtask i successfully.

4. Indication of subtask essentiality, E_{ij}, an indicator specifying
whether or not the successful performance of subtask i by operator j is
essential to successful completion of the task. This datum, derived from
task analytic information, allows the computer to ignore nonessential subtasks during certain "highly urgent" conditions.

Table 1. Summary of Average Execution Times and Average Standard Deviations for Basic Operator-Control Actions

	Average Execution Time, t_{ij} (seconds)	Average Standard Deviation, σ_{ij} (seconds)
Set toggle switch	1.1	0.76
Set rotary control	8.6	3.00
Push button	4.2	1.02
Lever (throttle) setting	3.0	0.48
Joystick setting	3.8	0.48
Read instrument, N instruments	0.6N + 0.6	0.2N + 0.2
Trim	1.1	0.76
Communication, N words	0.66N + 0.6	0.34N + 0.4
Minimum value	0.75	—

5. Idle time requirement, I_{ij}, the point in time before which operator j is not permitted to begin subtask i.

6. Indication of whether subtask i is a decision subtask or a normal action subtask; the sign of I_{ij} is used as the indicator. A decision subtask is an artificial subtask used to enable the computer to simulate an operator's decision-making processes.

7. Subtask number, $(i, j)_f$, to be performed next by operator j in the event of failure of subtask i, or in the event the operator chooses the first of two alternate courses in a decision subtask.

8. Subtask number, d_{ij} (mnemonic delay), which must be successfully completed by the other operator (operator j') before operator j can begin subtask i. By proper selection of d_{ij} values, it is possible to cause either simulated operator to "wait" until his partner has completed a stipulated subtask successfully. Thus, "waiting" for one's partner is simulated differently from time spent "idling" until a fixed time event elapses as in 5 above.

9. Subtask number, $(i, j)_s$, to be performed next by operator j in the event he succeeds on subtask i or in the event he chooses the second alternate course in a decision subtask.

10. Indication of whether or not subtask i for operator j is a subtask in which the operators communicate with each other.

11. Time, T_{ij}^E, required to perform all remaining essential subtasks (including i) at average execution times, assuming no failures. With no branching or decisions,

$$T_{ij}^E = \sum_{k=i}^{n} \overline{t}_{kj}$$

12. Time, T_{ij}^N, required to perform all remaining nonessential subtasks (including i) at average execution times, assuming no failures.

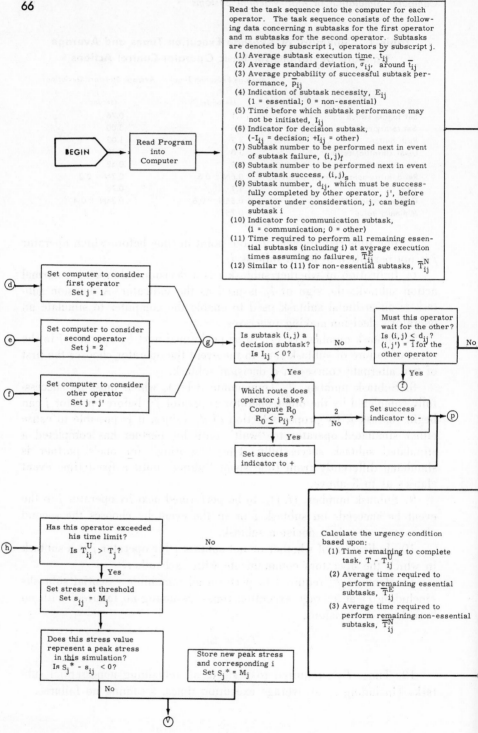

Read the task sequence into the computer for each operator. The task sequence consists of the following data concerning n subtasks for the first operator and m subtasks for the second operator. Subtasks are denoted by subscript i, operators by subscript j.
(1) Average subtask execution time, $\bar{t}_{ij}$
(2) Average standard deviation, $\bar{\sigma}_{ij}$, around $\bar{t}_{ij}$
(3) Average probability of successful subtask performance, $\bar{p}_{ij}$
(4) Indication of subtask necessity, E_{ij} (1 = essential; 0 = non-essential)
(5) Time before which subtask performance may not be initiated, I_{ij}
(6) Indicator for decision subtask, ($-I_{ij}$ = decision; $+I_{ij}$ = other)
(7) Subtask number to be performed next in event of subtask failure, $(i,j)_f$
(8) Subtask number to be performed next in event of subtask success, $(i,j)_s$
(9) Subtask number, d_{ij}, which must be successfully completed by other operator, j', before operator under consideration, j, can begin subtask i
(10) Indicator for communication subtask, (1 = communication; 0 = other)
(11) Time required to perform all remaining essential subtasks (including i) at average execution times assuming no failures, $\bar{T}_{ij}^{E}$
(12) Similar to (11) for non-essential subtasks, $\bar{T}_{ij}^{N}$

BEGIN

Read Program into Computer

(d) Set computer to consider first operator Set j = 1

(e) Set computer to consider second operator Set j = 2

(f) Set computer to consider other operator Set j = j'

(g) Is subtask (i,j) a decision subtask? Is $I_{ij} < 0$?

No → Must this operator wait for the other? Is $(i,j) \le d_{ij}$? $(i,j') = \bar{i}$ for the other operator → No

Yes ↓

Which route does operator j take? Compute R_0 $R_0 \le \bar{p}_{ij}$?

Yes → Set success indicator to +

No 2 → Set success indicator to - → (p)

Yes → (f)

(h) Has this operator exceeded his time limit? Is $T_{ij}^{U} > T_{j}$?

No →

Yes ↓

Set stress at threshold Set $s_{ij} = M_j$

Does this stress value represent a peak stress in this simulation? Is $S_j^* - s_{ij} < 0$?

No →

Store new peak stress and corresponding i Set $S_j^* = M_j$

Calculate the urgency condition based upon:
(1) Time remaining to complete task, $T - T_{ij}^{U}$
(2) Average time required to perform remaining essential subtasks, $\bar{T}_{ij}^{E}$
(3) Average time required to perform remaining non-essential subtasks, $\bar{T}_{ij}^{N}$

(v)

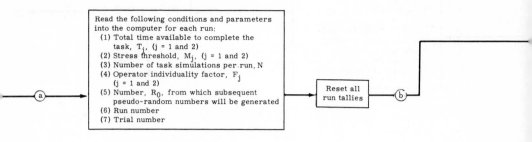

Read the following conditions and parameters into the computer for each run:
(1) Total time available to complete the task, T_j, (j = 1 and 2)
(2) Stress threshold, M_j, (j = 1 and 2)
(3) Number of task simulations per run, N
(4) Operator individuality factor, F_j (j = 1 and 2)
(5) Number, R_0, from which subsequent pseudo-random numbers will be generated
(6) Run number
(7) Trial number

Reset all run tallies

(a) (b)

Figure 1. Flow chart of the two-man machine model.

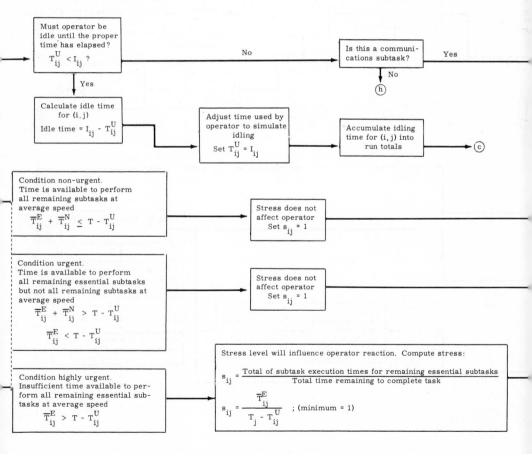

Must operator be idle until the proper time has elapsed?
$T_{ij}^U < I_{ij}$?

No

Is this a communications subtask? — Yes

No

(h)

Yes

Calculate idle time for (i, j)
Idle time = $I_{ij} - T_{ij}^U$

Adjust time used by operator to simulate idling
Set $T_{ij}^U = I_{ij}$

Accumulate idling time for (i, j) into run totals

(c)

Condition non-urgent. Time is available to perform all remaining subtasks at average speed
$\overline{T}_{ij}^E + \overline{T}_{ij}^N \leq T - T_{ij}^U$

Stress does not affect operator
Set $s_{ij} = 1$

Condition urgent. Time is available to perform all remaining essential subtasks but not all remaining subtasks at average speed
$\overline{T}_{ij}^E + \overline{T}_{ij}^N > T - T_{ij}^U$
$\overline{T}_{ij}^E < T - T_{ij}^U$

Stress does not affect operator
Set $s_{ij} = 1$

Stress level will influence operator reaction. Compute stress:
$s_{ij} = \dfrac{\text{Total of subtask execution times for remaining essential subtasks}}{\text{Total time remaining to complete task}}$

Condition highly urgent. Insufficient time available to perform all remaining essential subtasks at average speed
$\overline{T}_{ij}^E > T - T_{ij}^U$

$s_{ij} = \dfrac{\overline{T}_{ij}^E}{T_j - T_{ij}^U}$; (minimum = 1)

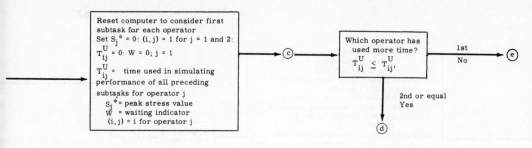

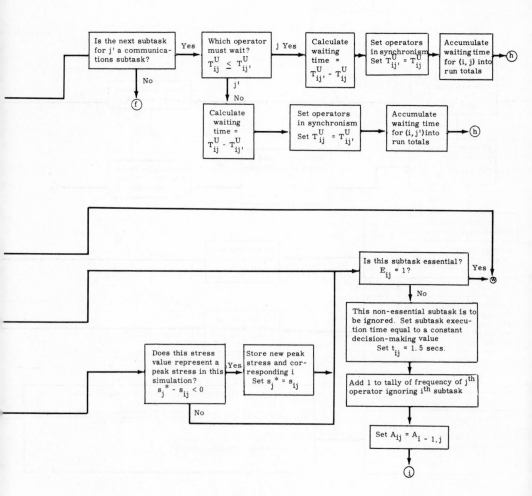

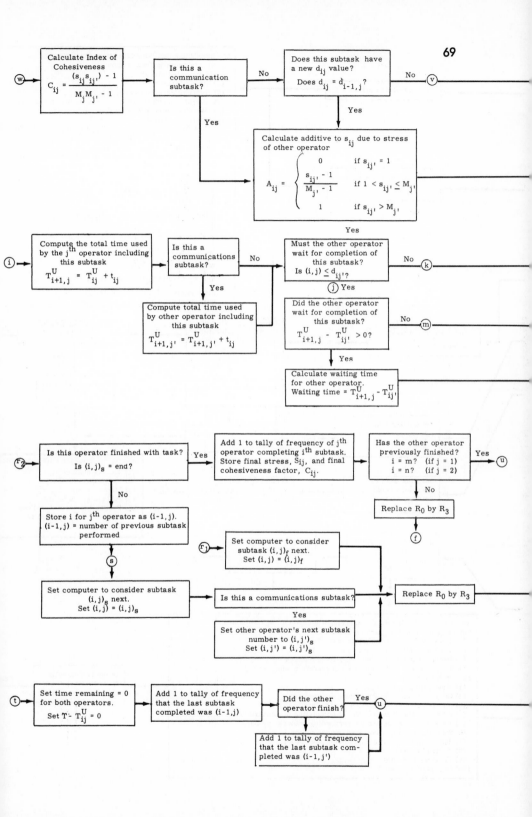

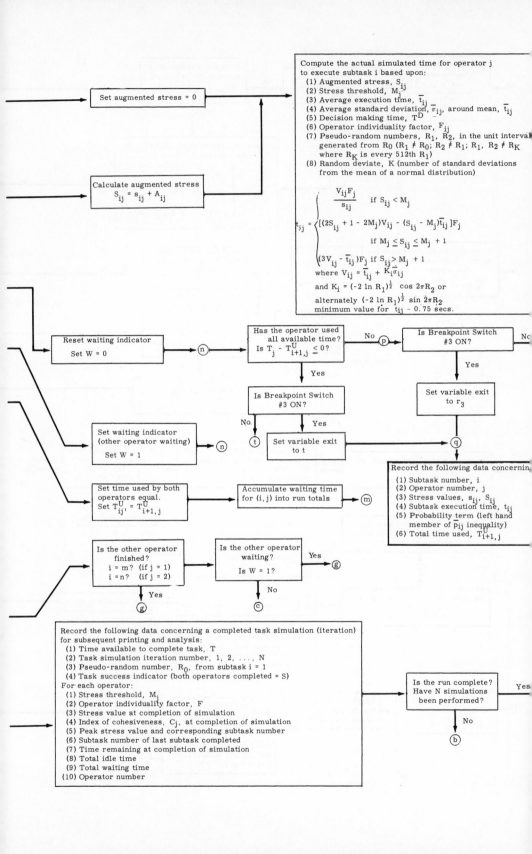

Set augmented stress = 0

Calculate augmented stress
$S_{ij} = s_{ij} + A_{ij}$

Compute the actual simulated time for operator j
to execute subtask i based upon:
(1) Augmented stress, S_{ij}
(2) Stress threshold, M_j
(3) Average execution time, $\bar{t}_{ij}$
(4) Average standard deviation, $\bar{\sigma}_{ij}$, around mean, $\bar{t}_{ij}$
(5) Decision making time, T^D
(6) Operator individuality factor, F_{ij}
(7) Pseudo-random numbers, R_1, R_2, in the unit interval
    generated from R_0 ($R_1 \neq R_0$; $R_2 \neq R_1$; R_1, $R_2 \neq R_K$
    where R_K is every 512th R_1)
(8) Random deviate, K (number of standard deviations
    from the mean of a normal distribution)

$$t_{ij} = \begin{cases} \dfrac{V_{ij}F_j}{s_{ij}} & \text{if } S_{ij} < M_j \\ [(2S_{ij} + 1 - 2M_j)V_{ij} - (S_{ij} - M_j)\bar{t}_{ij}]F_j \\ \qquad \text{if } M_j \le S_{ij} \le M_j + 1 \\ (3V_{ij} - \bar{t}_{ij})F_j \text{ if } S_{ij} > M_j + 1 \end{cases}$$

where $V_{ij} = \bar{t}_{ij} + K_i \bar{\sigma}_{ij}$
and $K_i = (-2 \ln R_1)^{\frac{1}{2}} \cos 2\pi R_2$ or
alternately $(-2 \ln R_1)^{\frac{1}{2}} \sin 2\pi R_2$.
minimum value for t_{ij} - 0.75 secs.

Reset waiting indicator
Set W = 0

(n)

Has the operator used
all available time?
Is $T_j - T^U_{i+1,j} \le 0$?

No — (p)

Is Breakpoint Switch
#3 ON?

No

Yes

Yes

Is Breakpoint Switch
#3 ON?

No

Yes

Set variable exit
to r_3

Set waiting indicator
(other operator waiting)
Set W = 1

(n)

(t)

Set variable exit
to t

(q)

Set time used by both
operators equal.
Set $T^U_{ij} = T^U_{i+1,j}$

Accumulate waiting time
for (i, j) into run totals

(m)

Record the following data concerning
(1) Subtask number, i
(2) Operator number, j
(3) Stress values, s_{ij}, S_{ij}
(4) Subtask execution time, t_{ij}
(5) Probability term (left hand
    member of $\bar{p}_{ij}$ inequality)
(6) Total time used, $T^U_{i+1,j}$

Is the other operator
finished?
i = m? (if j = 1)
i = n? (if j = 2)

Is the other operator
waiting?
Is W = 1?

Yes

(g)

No

Yes

(g)

(c)

Record the following data concerning a completed task simulation (iteration)
for subsequent printing and analysis:
(1) Time available to complete task, T
(2) Task simulation iteration number, 1, 2, ..., N
(3) Pseudo-random number, R_0, from subtask i = 1
(4) Task success indicator (both operators completed = S)
For each operator:
(1) Stress threshold, M_i
(2) Operator individuality factor, F
(3) Stress value at completion of simulation
(4) Index of cohesiveness, C_j, at completion of simulation
(5) Peak stress value and corresponding subtask number
(6) Subtask number of last subtask completed
(7) Time remaining at completion of simulation
(8) Total idle time
(9) Total waiting time
(10) Operator number

Is the run complete?
Have N simulations
been performed?

Yes

No

(b)

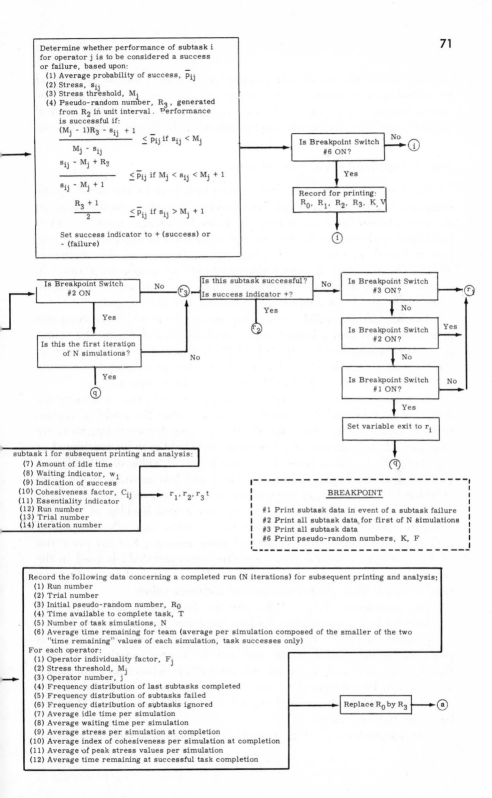

Determine whether performance of subtask i
for operator j is to be considered a success
or failure, based upon:
(1) Average probability of success, $\bar{p}_{ij}$
(2) Stress, s_{ij}
(3) Stress threshold, M_j
(4) Pseudo-random number, R_3, generated
from R_2 in unit interval. Performance
is successful if:

$$\frac{(M_j - 1)R_3 - s_{ij} + 1}{M_j - s_{ij}} \le \bar{p}_{ij} \text{ if } s_{ij} < M_j$$

$$\frac{s_{ij} - M_j + R_3}{s_{ij} - M_j + 1} \le \bar{p}_{ij} \text{ if } M_j < s_{ij} < M_j + 1$$

$$\frac{R_3 + 1}{2} \le \bar{p}_{ij} \text{ if } s_{ij} > M_j + 1$$

Set success indicator to + (success) or
- (failure)

Is Breakpoint Switch #6 ON?   No → (i)

Yes

Record for printing:
R_0, R_1, R_2, R_3, K, V

(i)

Is Breakpoint Switch #2 ON?   No → (r_3)

Yes

Is this the first iteration
of N simulations?   No

Yes

(q)

Is this subtask successful?
Is success indicator +?   No → Is Breakpoint Switch #3 ON? → (r_1)

Yes

(r_2)

No

Is Breakpoint Switch #2 ON?   Yes

No

Is Breakpoint Switch #1 ON?   No

Yes

Set variable exit to r_i

(q)

subtask i for subsequent printing and analysis:
(7) Amount of idle time
(8) Waiting indicator, w_1
(9) Indication of success
(10) Cohesiveness factor, C_{ij}
(11) Essentiality indicator
(12) Run number
(13) Trial number
(14) iteration number

$r_1, r_2, r_3 t$

BREAKPOINT

#1 Print subtask data in event of a subtask failure
#2 Print all subtask data for first of N simulations
#3 Print all subtask data
#6 Print pseudo-random numbers, K, F

Record the following data concerning a completed run (N iterations) for subsequent printing and analysis:
(1) Run number
(2) Trial number
(3) Initial pseudo-random number, R_0
(4) Time available to complete task, T
(5) Number of task simulations, N
(6) Average time remaining for team (average per simulation composed of the smaller of the two
"time remaining" values of each simulation, task successes only)
For each operator:
(1) Operator individuality factor, F_j
(2) Stress threshold, M_j
(3) Operator number, j
(4) Frequency distribution of last subtasks completed
(5) Frequency distribution of subtasks failed
(6) Frequency distribution of subtasks ignored
(7) Average idle time per simulation
(8) Average waiting time per simulation
(9) Average stress per simulation at completion
(10) Average index of cohesiveness per simulation at completion
(11) Average of peak stress values per simulation
(12) Average time remaining at successful task completion

Replace R_0 by R_3 → (a)

The other main set of data required by the computer in advance of the simulation consists of the parameters and initial conditions discussed below. These are inserted to permit the adjustment of critical variables and the consequent determination of the range of their effects.

INITIAL CONDITIONS AND PARAMETERS

The number of times, N, that a given task is to be simulated by the computer is the first initial condition inserted into the computer prior to the computation for a given task. In order to simulate intra and interindividual performance differences, the simulation of any individual subtask is based, in part, on a random effect. Because of this stochastic effect, it is necessary to repeat the simulation of a task many times in order to obtain sufficient performance data for each set of conditions. Thus, there are N simulations (or N iterations) per computer "run."

Another initial condition is R_0, the number from which the computer generates subsequent pseudo-random numbers needed during the course of the simulation. The R_0, selected for the first pseudo-random number in the first run is 123456789. Subsequently, the last pseudo-random number generated in one run is used as the first value in the next run.

Parameters are those initial conditions, selected prior to a computation, that may be varied in order to evaluate either the model or a manmachine system. The stress thresholds, M_j, one for each operator, are examples of such parameters. The stress threshold may be considered as the operator's breaking point. For example, an M_j value of 2.0 indicates that the operator begins to become slower and less accurate at the point at which he has more than twice as much to do (at average speed) as he has time available. Prior to this point, any added backlog of essential subtasks creates a mental inducement of stress that affects operator actions so that they become faster and more accurate. For any given run of N iterations or simulations, a specific stress threshold is used in the calculations. The effects of a change in M_j are studied by performing runs in which these parameters assume different values.

The parameters, $T_j (j = 1, 2)$, are the total times allotted to each operator for task performance. Various computer runs may be performed to determine the effect of a change of these parameters. This facility is provided because the T_j value may not be known exactly in systems that are proposed or designed but not yet built. In a two-man team model, the task can be considered to have been successfully completed if both operators complete all required subtasks within the time specified by the larger of the two values.

The parameters, F_j, that account for variance among individuals, are the individuality factors for the two operators. This parameter provides the ability to simulate an operator who usually performs faster or slower than the average operator. F_j possesses a value of unity for the average operator. The effect of faster, or more highly motivated, operators $(F_j < 1)$ and slower operators $(F_j > 1)$ in the performance of the task is examined by performing several computer runs with different values for these multiplicative factors.

A run number is used to identify runs and a trial number is inserted to identify later continuations of a particular run in which all parameters and initial conditions are identical except R_0. This enables replication on the same basic operators. The trial number and run number are retained for identification and subsequent analysis.

In summary, for a given run and trial, starting with R_0 as the first pseudo-random number, N simulations of a single task are performed by the computer with fixed values for each of the parameters M_j, T_j, and F_j.

The Simulation Sequence

The digital computer is a sequential device which performs individual operations at very high speeds. Having stored the program, parameters, and initial conditions, the computer begins processing these data in accordance with the logic presented as Figure 1.

For either operator and for any given subtask after the first, the computer determines which subtask to perform next in accordance with $(i, j)_s$ and $(i, j)_f$ input data. The computer's determination of which operator to simulate at any given time in the sequence depends upon the amount of time used by the operators. In Figure 1 (circled c), $T_{ij}{}^U$ indicates the total time used up by operator j while "performing" all subtasks from the start of the simulation through subtask $i - 1$. The operator having the smaller $T_{ij}{}^U$ value is selected, and his next subtask is simulated.

Having elected to simulate subtask i for operator j, the I_{ij} (decision) input is examined. If the sign of I_{ij} is negative, then the subtask is a decision subtask (discussed later). Otherwise, the computer proceeds to determine whether operator j must wait for his partner before performing subtask i. If waiting is required, the sequence recycles to the circled f on the flow chart; and the data for the other operator (j') are placed in proper storage for processing and the sequence continues. If waiting is not required, then a determination is made as to whether operator j must idle until I_{ij} simulated seconds have elapsed from the beginning of the simulation. If idling is required, the idle time $I_{ij} - T_{ij}^U$ is recorded, totals accumulated, T_{ij}^U set equal to I_{ij}, and the control returned to the circled c to determine which operator to simulate next. If no idling is required, a determination is made of whether or not subtask i is a communication subtask. If so, to synchronize the operators in time, the total time used by both operators is set equal to the larger value. This act may result in a wait for either operator and is treated as the wait described above. Following the synchronization of the operators, or in the event that the subtask was not a communication subtask, control is transferred to the circled h of Figure 1.

URGENCY AND STRESS

Next, one of three states of "urgency" is determined. Urgency is based upon the remaining time available to operator j for completing the task and the average time required to complete it.

1. The situation is nonurgent when (assuming average speed and no operator failures), on the average, sufficient time remains for an individual operator to complete all remaining subtasks. Thus, the nonurgent state exists during performance of subtask i when

$$\overline{T}_{ij}^E + \overline{T}_{ij}^N \leqq T_j - T_{ij}^U$$

2. The urgent state occurs for either operator whenever insufficient time is available for completing all remaining subtasks, provided that sufficient time is available to complete all remaining essential subtasks. That is, the situation is urgent if:

$$\overline{T}_{ij}^E + \overline{T}_{ij}^N \geqq T_j - T_{ij}^U \text{ and } T_{ij}^E \leqq \overline{T}_j - T_{ij}^U$$

These are based on estimated average operator execution times and the assumption that no operator failures will occur. In this situation the nonessential subtasks are ignored by the computer.

3. The situation is highly urgent if there is insufficient time available for completing even the remaining essential subtasks at average operator speeds, that is, when

$$\overline{T}_{ij}^E > T_j - T_{ij}^U$$

Similarly, in this urgency state nonessential subtasks are ignored by the computer.

Following the determination of the urgency condition, the stress condition is calculated for operator j in his simulated performance of subtask i.

The "certainty" in the operator's "mind" that there is insufficient time remaining to complete the essential subtasks (when performing at normal speed and efficiency) will impress a state of stress on the operator. The model defines stress, s_{ij}, as a state of mind of operator j just prior to his performance of subtask i. Current psychological theory suggests that emotion or stress up to a certain point acts as an organizing agent on behavior; beyond this point stress acts as a disorganizing agent. Accordingly, the model recognizes an organizing effect on operator performance as long as s_{ij} is less than M_j where M_j is a threshold value; if s_{ij} equals or exceeds M_j, the effect is disorganizing. During non-urgent and urgent conditions s_{ij} is defined to be equal to unity; when the situation is highly urgent, stress is defined as the ratio of the sum of the average remaining essential subtask execution times to the total time remaining:

$$s_{ij} = \frac{\overline{T}_{ij}^{E}}{T_j - T_{ij}^{U}}$$

Thus, basic stress is the ratio of how much is left to do, to the amount of time available in which to do it.

Table 2 summarizes the conditions for urgency and stress as incorporated into the model. Nonessential subtasks are ignored during urgent and highly urgent conditions.

TEAM COHESIVENESS

The team cohesiveness feature attempts to simulate the confidence of one operator in his partner. Team cohesiveness may also be reflective of disagreements in goals and/or their importance, methods, or locus of authority. An operator can often tell how well his partner is performing. When one operator "feels" that his partner is performing satisfactorily, it is assumed that the "peace of mind" this creates will enable him to perform normally; that is, his execution times will depend on his own stress value, stress threshold, and other factors as previously described. On the other hand, if a partner is performing poorly, it might be expected that the knowledge of this poor performance will cause the first operator to modify his actions. The model causes faster or slower than normal execution times by one operator if he knows his partner is in a high urgent situation. This is accomplished by causing the computer to add

Table 2. Summary of Urgency and Stress Conditions

Urgency	$\dfrac{\overline{T}_{ij}^{E} + T_{ij}^{N}}{T_j - T_{ij}^{U}}$	$\dfrac{\overline{T}_{ij}^{E}}{T_j - T_{ij}^{U}}$	Condition (assume average operator)	Result	Stress
Nonurgent	≤ 1	≤ 1	Time is available to perform all remaining subtasks	Perform this subtask	1
Urgent	> 1	≤ 1	Time is available to perform all remaining essential subtasks but not all remaining subtasks	Ignore this subtask if nonessential	1
Highly urgent	> 1	> 1	Time is not available to perform all remaining essential subtasks	Ignore this subtask if nonessential; compute stress	$\dfrac{\overline{T}_{ij}^{E}}{T_j - T_{ij}^{U}}$

to the stress value of operator j if operator j' has a stress value greater than unity. Specifically, an additive A is calculated as follows:

$$A = \begin{cases} 0 & \text{if } s_{ij'} = 1 \\ \dfrac{s_{ij'} - 1}{M_{j'} - 1} & \text{if } 1 < s_{ij'} \leq M_{j'} \\ 1 & \text{if } s_{ij'} > M_{j'} \end{cases}$$

The value of A is added to the individual stress value, s_{ij}, due to a single operator alone and the result, S_{ij}, is used in later calculations of subtask performance time, t_{ij}. In cases where direct visual contact between two operators is limited or absent, one operator may be correspondingly limited in his ability to discern the effectiveness of his partner's performance. With a further reduction in avenues of communication between operators (as, for example, where radio silence is maintained), a greater limitation is to be expected in the knowledge of one operator concerning the state of being of the other. Under such conditions, however, an operator can gain some knowledge of the efficiency of his partner's performance through subtasks that require waiting (simulated by d_{ij} values). Thus, if operator j cannot continue the execution of his required actions until operator j' has completed subtask i, and if operator j' is late in performing that subtask, operator j now has some basis for knowing (or assuming) that his partner is functioning poorly to some degree. This knowledge, in turn, will affect operator j's performance through the additive, A. Therefore, in certain two-man team tasks (and in the one here reported), the additive is computed only for those subtasks requiring waiting (either communication subtasks or those for which d_{ij} value differed from the previous value).

In addition, an index of cohesiveness, C_{ij}, is also calculated for each operator on each subtask as a measure of the joint stress condition of the team. It is the product of the stress levels of the two operators normalized by their respective stress threshold values:

$$C_{ij} = \frac{s_{ij}s_{ij'} - 1}{M_j M_{j'} - 1}$$

When neither operator is under stress, C_{ij} assumes a value of zero. Should both operators have a stress value equal to their thresholds, C_{ij} assumes a value of unity. Thus, increasing C_{ij} values indicate greater team discontinuity due to increased stress.

SUBTASK EXECUTION TIME

Next, the execution time of the subtask is computed. The average operator will require $\bar{t}_{ij}$ seconds to perform subtask i when s_{ij} equals unity. In this case, his average standard deviation will be $\bar{\sigma}_{ij}$. Of course, no two operators would be expected to perform any subtask in exactly the same time on each repetition, and no operator would be expected to perform the same task identically over two occasions except by chance. For each subtask, it is assumed that the actual subtask execution time, t_{ij}, for the specific subtask, i, is normally distributed with the mean dependent on $\bar{t}_{ij}$ and standard deviation dependent on $\bar{\sigma}_{ij}$. The computation of a reasonable and realistic specific value for the actual execution time, t_{ij}, for each subtask is made on the basis of a random selection from a normal distribution limited from below by a fixed minimum, selected as 0.75 sec. The computer accomplishes the selection of t_{ij} by a random, or Monte Carlo, technique. Pseudo-random numbers R_1 and R_2 uniformly distributed in the unit interval are sequentially generated from R_0 by the computer using the power residue method as described in an IBM manual (1959a) and summarized in a subsequent section of this chapter. By the use of these independent random numbers, corresponding values of an independent random variable are generated having a distribution function equivalent to that of the normal distribution (that is, normal deviates). This is done by the "direct" technique described by Box and Muller (1958) and evaluated by Muller (1959) and also discussed in a subsequent section of the present chapter.

Thus, if K_{ij} is the number of standard deviations from the mean corresponding to the random numbers generated in simulating subtask i for operator j, then the actual time of execution simulated by the computer, t_{ij}, is given by

$$t_{ij} = \begin{cases} \dfrac{\bar{t}_{ij}}{S_{ij}} + \dfrac{K_{ij}\bar{\sigma}_{ij}}{S_{ij}} \ F_j \\[2mm] [\bar{t}_{ij}(S_{ij} + 1 - M_j) + K_{ij}\bar{\sigma}_{ij}(2S_{ij} + 1 - 2M_j)] \ F_j \\[2mm] [2\bar{t}_{ij} + 3K_{ij}\bar{\sigma}_{ij}] \ F_j \end{cases}$$

$$\text{if} \quad S_{ij} < M_j$$

$$\text{if} \quad M_j \leqq S_{ij} \leqq M_j + 1$$

$$\text{if} \quad S_j > M_j + 1$$

where F_j is the individuality factor described previously in this chapter. To effect these calculations from a computed value of K_{ij}, a linear change of variables is made through the calculation of $V_{ij} = \bar{t}_{ij} + K_{ij}\bar{\sigma}_{ij}$, which is normally distributed. The above expressions may then be put in the form

$$t_{ij} = \begin{cases} \dfrac{V_{ij}F_j}{S_{ij}} & \text{if } S_{ij} < M_j \\[2mm] [(2S_{ij} + 1 - 2M_j)\, V_{ij} - (S_{ij} - M)\, \bar{t}_{ij}]\, F_j & \text{if } M_j \leq S_{ij} \leq M_j + 1 \\[2mm] [3V_{ij} - \bar{t}_{ij}]\, F_j & \text{if } S_{ij} > M_j + 1 \end{cases}$$

The effect of the above is to provide a $\bar{t}_{ij}$ value, as shown in Figure 2, in which the values of $\bar{t}_{ij}$ and $\bar{\sigma}_{ij}$ are

1. Used unchanged when stress equals unity.
2. Decreased with increasing stress until stress assumes the threshold value.
3. Used unchanged when stress equals the threshold value.
4. Increased linearly with increasing stress beyond M until, when stress equals $M > 1$, the contributions of $\bar{t}_{ij}$ and $\bar{\sigma}_{ij}$ remain constant at $2\bar{t}_{ij}$ and $3\bar{\sigma}_{ij}$, respectively.

SUBTASK SUCCESS AND FAILURE

An average probability of successful performance for subtask i, $\bar{p}_{ij}$, is given as an input for each subtask. In the model, it is assumed that the actual probability of successful performance of a given subtask, p_{ij}, is a function of $\bar{p}_{ij}$, s_{ij}, and the threshold, M_j, as follows:

$$p_{ij} = \begin{cases} \bar{p}_{ij} + \dfrac{(1 - \bar{p}_{ij})\,(s_{ij} - 1)}{M_j - 1} & \text{if } s_{ij} < M_j \\[2mm] \bar{p}_{ij}(s_{ij} + 1 - M_j) + (M_j - s_{ij}) & \text{if } M_j \leq s_{ij} \leq M_j + 1 \\[2mm] 2\bar{p}_{ij} - 1 & \text{if } s_{ij} > M_j + 1 \end{cases}$$

A review of Figure 3, which displays this function, indicates that the probability of success increases linearly with stress until the stress threshold is reached. At this point, the probability assumes the average value, $\bar{p}_{ij}$, after which it decreases linearly until, when stress has a value

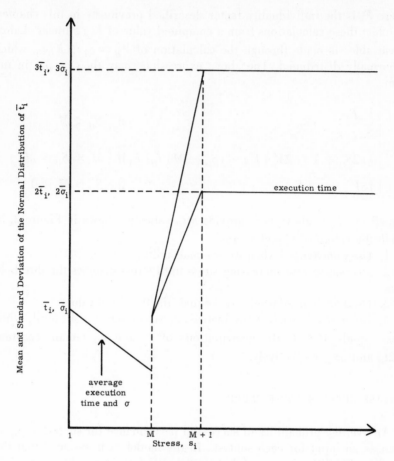

Figure 2. Average execution time and its standard deviation as functions
of stress.

equal to $M_j + 1$, it levels off at a value that is decreased from $\bar{p}_{ij}$ by an
amount equal to $1 - \bar{p}_{ij}$. In order to determine actual success or failure
for any subtask, the computer generates a pseudo-random number, R_3,
from R_2 according to the method described later in this chapter. The
value of R_3 is thus uniformly distributed over the unit interval. The
subtask is considered to have been performed successfully if R_3 is less
than p_{ij}; otherwise, it is assumed that the operator failed to perform the
subtask properly. This implementation indicates a failure with probability, p_{ij}, in the long run. To facilitate the calculation, these expressions
can be rearranged to indicate success if

$$\frac{(M_j - 1)\, R_3 - s_{ij} + 1}{M_j - s_{ij}} \qquad < \bar{p}_{ij} \qquad \text{when } s_{ij} < M_j$$

$$\frac{s_{ij} - M_j + R_3}{s_{ij} - M_j + 1} \qquad < \bar{p}_{ij} \qquad \text{when } M \leq s_{ij} \leq M + 1$$

$$\frac{R_3 + 1}{2} \qquad < \bar{p}_{ij} \qquad \text{when } s_{ij} > M + 1$$

The computed left-hand member of these inequalities is called the probability term and is made available as a printed result. In event of either success or failure, input information indicates the subtask which is performed next.

DECISION SUBTASKS

If the test for I_{ij} indicated a negative result, then the subtask is a decision subtask, that is, a subtask in which the operator makes a

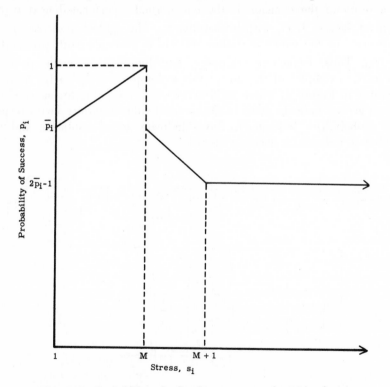

Figure 3. Probability of subtask success as a function of stress.

decision. The purpose of this type of subtask is to simulate the real world by providing for possible task execution in other than a straight, linear sequence. For example, an operator may find it desirable to skip one or more subtasks with a certain probability; or, having reached a critical point, he may find it desirable to select one of several alternate action pathways. Such a branching in the sequence may also be imposed by external conditions; the operator then takes one of several paths depending on these conditions. Such a subtask has the effect of causing the computer to select the next subtask (that is, branch) without "consuming operator time." (No operator time is consumed in the model for decision subtasks, since the time to shift attention between subtasks is included in the time for each subtask).

Decision subtasks may be appropriately placed anywhere in the sequence of subtasks. In this case, the values of $\bar{t}_{ij}$, $\bar{\sigma}_{ij}$, and essentiality have no meaning. The t_{ij} calculation is bypassed and the last pseudo-random number, R_3, from the previous subtask is compared with the p_{ij} of the decision subtask. Therefore, the next subtask to be performed as a result of the decision is the one normally performed next in the event of success $(i,j)_s$ with probability $\bar{p}_{ij}$. The subtask indicated to be performed in the event of failure $(i, j)_f$ is executed with probability $1 - \bar{p}_{ij}$. Thus, branching, skipping, and looping are made possible. Schematic examples of the use of this technique are shown for a single operator in Figure 4, where solid arrows indicate paths for success and dotted arrows indicate paths in the event of subtask failure (with respective probabilities indicated). Boxes indicate action subtasks, and the symbol # indicates a decision subtask.

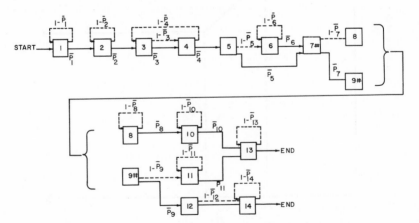

Figure 4. Schematic examples of progress between subtasks.

OTHER COMPUTER OPERATIONS

The remainder of the computer operations (starting at the circled i in Figure 1) are concerned with bookkeeping, updating memory values, and recording results. In general, the model is organized so that at the completion of calculations for one run, any combination of the following sets of recorded results may be produced:

1. Detailed results   Pertaining to individual subtasks
2. Pseudo-random numbers   Pertaining to individual subtasks
3. Intermediate results   Summary for one (out of N) simulations
                                     or iterations
4. Final results   Summary for all N iterations of a run

TASK SUCCESS

Task success occurs when the operators complete the required sequence of subtasks within the allotted time. Since each operator has an individual time limit on his performance and a task failure occurs only when the larger of these limits is exceeded, it is possible for the simulation to continue with one operator (arbitrarily selected as operator 1) having exceeded his limit. Should this be the case, the stress condition of this operator is set equal to his threshold value, M_j, for the duration of the task simulation.

CALCULATION OF PSEUDO-RANDOM NUMBERS

The use of the model requires the sequential generation of pseudo-random numbers, uniformly distributed in the unit interval 0–1. The method selected for generation of these numbers is the power residue method described by IBM (1959a). This general method as applied to the model 705 computer may be summarized as follows:

1. Select any starting value of nine digits, R_0.
2. Form the product $10003R_0$.
3. The least significant nine digits of the product is R_1.
4. Each successive pseudo-random number, R_{m+1}, is obtained from the nine low-order digits of the product $10003R_m$.

By this method, a given pseudo-random number is dependent upon the preceding one; and the process is acceptable only because the quantity of numbers generated by the computer before repetition is large. The method produces approximately 50 million nine-digit pseudo-random numbers before repetition. Employment of this method permits the exact repetition of any simulated task or subtask if the initial random number for that task or subtask is known. The exact repetition of a random process is thus facilitated by the recording of initial R_0 values for each iteration and enables detailed review of any selected simulated task.

CALCULATION OF RANDOM DEVIATES

In the calculation of t_{ij}, it is necessary to generate values of a random variable with a frequency function equivalent to that of the normal distribution (that is, a random deviate). This is done by the direct method discussed by Box and Muller (1958) and by Muller (1959). This method gives higher accuracy than previous methods and also compares favorably with other methods in computation speed. The technique is based on the availability of two random numbers in the unit interval, R_m and R_{m+1}, taken from the same rectangular density function. Then X_1 and X_2 are

$$X_1 = (-2 \ln R_m)^{1/2} \cos 2\pi R_{m+1}$$
$$X_2 = (-2 \ln R_m)^{1/2} \sin 2\pi R_{m+1}$$

are a pair of independent random variables from the same normal distribution with a mean of zero and unit variance. This method is reported to produce normal deviates with a precision of approximately 5×10^{-7} except for probabilities less than 4×10^{-8}.

ASSUMPTIONS

It is assumed in the use of the model that the operators remember and execute the correct sequence of subtasks. It should be noted, however, that the possibility of one or both operators neglecting a subtask or of rearranging the performance of a sequence of subtasks may be studied by additional runs using these different sequences, that is, assuming new subtasks or subtask sequences.

Similarly, a change in the predetermined sequence of subtasks by either or both operators is conceivable in the event of emergency. Such a dangerous situation may result from operator action or an external event during the task. In either case, it may be assumed that the operators, upon noticing the danger, will abandon their normal tasks and take up the emergency sequence of subtasks associated with the problem of survival, and the sequence of operations will change. Thus, the simulation of dangerous conditions need not be especially provided for as an integral part of the model, since the danger condition may itself be studied using the model. This is done by establishing special danger sequences to be simulated. Therefore, this situation does not limit the model.

It must also be assumed that $\bar{p}_{ij}$, $\bar{t}_{ij}$, and $\bar{\sigma}_{ij}$ are independent of whether the subtask is being performed for the first time or is being repeated because of a previous subtask failure. It is noted, however, that upon repetition, less time will remain for the operator, possibly affecting the stress and consequently affecting p_{ij}, t_{ij}, and σ_{ij}.

RESULTS OF FOUR APPLICATIONS OF THE MODEL

The digital simulation technique here described was first developed for application to uni-operator man-machine systems. Then it was expanded to allow for the simulation of two operator systems. Although model changes have been made throughout, the same basic logic has been involved over four tasks: carrier landing, in-flight missile launching, in-flight refueling, and in-flight intercept. For all four tasks reasonable concordance was found between the predictions from the model and outside criteria of success on the task involved.

Those F_j and M values over which agreement with outside criteria data was found for the four tasks are presented in Figure 5. It was stated as a result of the first effort of this series (Siegel and Wolf, 1959a) that reasonable concordance between the results from the model and outside criteria data could be anticipated when M_j ranged between 1.95 and 2.8. If we allow a variation of ± 0.1 in F_j value, then it can be seen (shaded area in Figure 5) that this anticipation was met in each of the later applications of the model. Our best estimate of the range of F_j and M_j values, which should yield moderate concordance with reality, is shown by the dashed line in Figure 5.

Evaluation of the ability of the model to predict system effectiveness is continuing. At present it appears that for systems similar to those tested, reasonable predictive efficiency may be anticipated from the model.

References

Box, G., and Muller, A. "Note on the Generation of Normal Deviates," *Annals of Math. Stat.*, 28:610–611, 1958.

Muller, M. "A Comparison of Methods for Generating Normal Deviates in Digital Computers," *J. Assoc. for Computing Machinery*, 6:376, 1959.

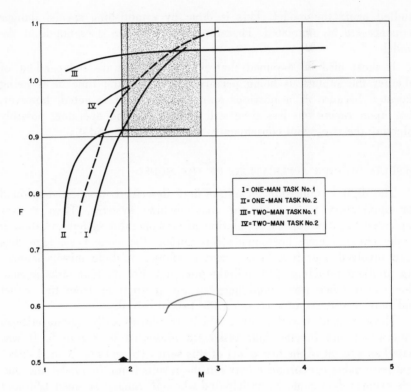

Figure 5. Parameter values that yield agreement with outside criteria data.

Reference Manual, 705 Data Processing System A22–6506–0. New York: International Business Machines, 1959a.

Reference Manual, Random Number Generation and Testing. New York: International Business Machines, 1959b.

Siegel, A., and Wolf, J. *Techniques for Evaluating Operator Loading in Man-Machine Systems. A Description of a Model and the Results of Its First Application.* Wayne: Applied Psychological Services, 1959a.

———— and ————. *Techniques for Evaluating Operator Loading in Man-Machine Systems. Application of a Previously Derived Model to the Launching of an Air-to-Air Missile.* Wayne: Applied Psychological Services, 1959b.

4

PSYCHOLOGICAL PROBLEMS OF PROLONGED MARINE SUBMERGENCE

Benjamin B. Weybrew

U.S. Naval Medical Research Laboratory
New London, Connecticut

THE modern atomic submarine is an example of a closed ecological system in a certain sense. As oxygen is not necessary for the nuclear propulsion system, all of the ecological factors are contained within the confines of its (400-ft steel) hull. In contrast to maximum submerged periods of 72 hours possible with World War II submarines, modern nuclear submarines such as the Nautilus and Triton have remained submerged for 60 days or more while transiting beneath the Arctic ice cap and circumnavigating the globe. In fact, the duration of submergence is limited only by the amount of food, oxygen, and other vital essentials that the submarine is able to transport or manufacture. Even though the size of the modern submarine has increased by about one-third and the size of the crew by approximately the same proportion, the space per man has in fact decreased as a result of the introduction of additional instrumentation necessary to propel and navigate the vehicle and to fire its weapons.

Modern submarine psychology is concerned with problems of selection and training, with the effects of a spatially restricted environment, with the effects of living in a circumscribed psychosocial situation, and with the noxious (and quite possibly toxic) effects of continuously breathing a completely self-contained, regenerated atmosphere.

Since the emergence of the submarine as a potent weapon during World War I, a considerable amount of literature pertaining to the problems of human adjustment to the conditions of prolonged submergence has accumulated (Hoff and Greenbaum, 1954; Nall, 1959; Committee on Undersea Warfare, 1954). As might be expected, however, the major portion of the submarine habitability literature, as it has come to be called, pertains to the problems of atmospheric control, toxicology, air revitalization, filtration, and, more recently, radiation control and monitoring. Apart for the sizable body of anecdotal literature that has accumulated (for example, Duff, 1947; Roscoe, 1958), there is a comparatively small amount of technical literature concerned directly with the problems of human adjustment to the conditions of prolonged submergence.

This chapter, therefore, is not intended as an exhaustive review of the literature of submarine psychology. Rather, the purpose of this chapter is to identify and, where possible, to delineate the most important areas of submarine psychology that have emerged largely since the *Nautilus,* the first atomic submarine, was commissioned in 1954. Hopefully, in the course of this review there will emerge the outlines of a theoretical model from which will emanate a "family" of hypotheses to be used as guide lines for future research in this rapidly developing area of applied psychology.

The Concept of Stress as It Applies to the Closed Ecology of the Submarine

If frequency of usage of a word is an acceptable criterion for the significance of a concept, the use of the term *stress* in the chapters of

---

The opinions or assertions where they appear in this chapter are those of the author and are not to be construed as the official views of the Navy Medical Department.

this text and elsewhere in the literature of the biological sciences argues for its importance. Borrowed from physics, "stress" as applied to submarine psychology has the connotation of two or more forces in opposition. One of these forces is motivational,* resulting in goal-directed activity, and the other an immediately perceived or anticipated barrier to this activity (Weybrew, 1957b). The degree of stress imposed upon a submariner at a given time, therefore, is a complex function of the number and impenetrability of the barriers or stressors (real or imaginary) impeding progress toward the attainment of the goals or satisfiers appropriate for his prepotent needs.

The responses to stress that lead to submariner adjustment are classified here as emotions. If the environmental resistance to strong motives is maximum, negative emotions such as fear, anger, and depression appear. On the other hand, if resistance to motives is minimum, positive emotions such as joy and elation predominate. These emotional processes, overt and covert, are the "responses to stress" of concern in understanding the dynamics of submariner adjustment. Accordingly, the evaluation of behavior in stressful conditions such as a submerged submarine or a space capsule implies, within this oversimplified conceptual schema, that knowledge exists or can be obtained regarding the prepotent needs (and their consequent motives) operating in the situation over a given time. Moreover, the environmental "blockages" (stressors) accounting for the emotional responses under surveillance must be identifiable. Individual differences in the quality of adjustment to submerged conditions, therefore, are related to the degree to which personal and group motives (and the needs underpinning them) are blocked or satisfied by the goal opportunities provided within the limits of the submarine.

The reason for this brief excursion into the fringes of theoretical psychology is to give some order to the current submariner research program and, at the same time, to systematize the literature that has accumulated in the past two decades. Three major questions for which answers are sought in this chapter stem from this conceptual approach. First, what are the environmental stressors peculiar to the submarine environment? Second, how do the stresses of submergence affect motivational, emotional, perceptual, and other behavioral processes? And third, what classes of behavior are relevant for the assessment of the adjustment potential of men for prolonged periods of submerged duty?

---

* The term *motive* is equated with behavior directionality, according to Muenzinger (1942).

The Submarine Environment

PHYSICAL ASPECTS

AMBIENT ATMOSPHERE

The nuclear fission process by which the propulsion system of an atomic submarine operates is completely anaerobic, thus providing a virtually unlimited energy source completely separated from the earth's atmosphere. This "sealed-off" condition results in unprecedented toxicological problems that, although only of tangential importance for submarine psychology, are none the less important to note. Thus, carbon dioxide produced at the rate of 20 cu ft per man per day must be "scrubbed out" so as to be maintained at a tolerable concentration. Carbon monoxide and aerosols largely derived from the combustion of smoking tobacco, from hydrocarbons in paints and lubricants, and from acrolein in cooking fats are known to be toxic at high concentrations for the most part and must also be removed (Hoff and Greenbaum, 1954).

The technology of submarine atmospheric revitalization and decontamination has been and still is rapidly advancing (Ebersole, 1960). As a result of these advances, the atmosphere aboard the nuclear submarine submerged for 60 to 90 days is presumably maintained in a toxicological "safe" condition (Ebersole, 1958).

There are two aspects of the atmospheric problem of importance for the psychologist. First, there is the possibility of some systemic physiological effects, which in turn contribute to generalized fatigue or headaches or otherwise reduce the adjustment potential of the personnel. Secondly, there are the beliefs and attitudes of the crew members concerning the possibility of harmful effects resulting from prolonged exposure to these atmospheric conditions. Headaches of varying degrees of severity have been reported by 15 to 40 per cent of the crew on any one day during protracted submergence (Weybrew, 1957b; Weybrew, 1961c). In the past, these symptoms have often been attributed to atmospheric conditions (Duff, 1947). Essen (1948) has suggested a sympatheticotonia, and Schaefer (1959) a vagotonia with concomitant changes in the general excitation level of the nervous system as being possible consequences of prolonged exposure to the level of carbon dioxide characteristically found in a submerged submarine.

The first systematic study designed to evaluate the psychological and physiological effects of breathing atmosphere containing well above normal concentrations of carbon dioxide and other substances involved the confinement of 22 men within a sealed submarine for 60 days (Faucett and Newman, 1953). Based upon changes in pulse rate, blood pressure, blood cell counts, and the presence of urinary excretory products (urinary 17-ketosteroid production, for example), it was reported that some adaptation phenomena had occurred. It was also concluded, however, that no physiological effects of a debilitating nature had occurred as a result of the long exposure to these atmospheric conditions. Based upon additional data from the same study, psychomotor efficiency as measured by manual dexterity declined, whereas hand tremor increased slightly after the first week of the six-week experiment. Mechanical abilities as measured by paper-and-pencil tests also declined slightly after two weeks. Findings obtained from biweekly self-ratings of the 22 men were as follows: motivation declined gradually; tension increased somewhat; anxiety moderated but was high throughout; the quality of sleep declined until the third week of the study then subsequently improved; over-all alertness of the group declined.

In the absence of any evidence to the contrary, it has been assumed that most, if not all, submariners are quite confident that the submarine atmosphere maintained during prolonged cruises is not harmful. However, the distribution of responses to the question, "Do you think the submarine atmosphere is dangerous to your health?" of one shore-based submarine crew was compared with the same distribution for a matched crew that had been submerged for 60 days (Molish, *et al.*, 1961). The data in Table 1 indicate the differences in the attitudes toward the sub-

Table 1. Percentage of a Submerged and a Shore-Based Crew Choosing Each Category of Response to the Question, "Do You Think the Submarine Atmosphere Is Dangerous to Your Health?"

Response Category	Submerged Crew (N = 106)	Shore-based Crew (N = 106)
Positively and probably	28	13
Undecided	17	7
Probably not and certainly not	55	80

With df = 2, p of $\chi^2 < 0.001$

marine atmosphere of the submerged group as compared with the shore-based control group.

Changes in response to the same questionnaire item were examined by administering it to a submarine crew before submerging and again just before surfacing approximately two months later (Molish, *et al.*,

1961). A matched shore-based crew responded to the item twice separated by the same time interval. Table 2 indicates that the attitudes of the submerged crew tended to change toward perceiving more potential danger from the atmosphere than did those of the shore-based crew.

Table 2. Percentage of Submerged and Shore-Based Crews Changing Their Response to the Question, "Do You Think the Submarine Atmosphere Is Dangerous to Your Health?"

	Change Toward "Less Danger"	No Change	Change Toward "More Danger"
Submerged crew ($N = 101$)	7	38	55
Shore-based crew ($N = 101$)	16	54	30

With df $= 2$, p of $\chi^2 < 0.01$

The probability of harmful effects of radiation exposure during prolonged submergence on the nuclear submarines is indeed remote (Ebersole, 1960). However, 35 per cent (11 men) of a random sample of 31 enlisted men from the crew of the *Nautilus* expressed concern about the possibility of injury due to radiation (Weybrew, 1957b). Significantly more enlisted volunteers (15 per cent, $N = 256$) than officer volunteers (5 per cent, $N = 185$) for the submarine service indicated their belief that "the dangers of radiation exposure aboard nuclear submarines is serious" (Weybrew and Molish, 1959).

In short, techniques of atmospheric revitalization during prolonged submergence are now highly efficient and are continually improving. No acutely harmful effects of specific atmospheric contaminants have been reported, yet it cannot be gainsaid that there may be some noxious (if not toxic) consequences of breathing higher than normal concentrations of carbon dioxide, carbon monoxide, and other contaminants for a period of from 60 to 90 days. At present, the most relevant problem with respect to the psychological effects of atmospheric conditions appears to be an attitudinal one to which some considerable research effort may be profitably directed.

SPATIAL LIMITATIONS

It has been estimated that there are about 5 cu yd of space provided for each crew member of a nuclear submarine. Propulsion, navigation, fire control, and data analysis equipment as well as hotel facilities for 100 to 170 men are indeed space-consuming. What, if any, psychological problems are related to this restricted spatial environment?

Although the majority of submariners adapt remarkably well to the closeness, one study reported that 20 per cent of 331 men indicated that "confinement" was the most frequently mentioned aspect of submarine life disliked, while "general living conditions" was the second most frequently mentioned aspect disliked (King, 1957). Similarly, commanding officers from a sizable number of submarines indicated that 7 per cent of a group of 186 submariners were disqualified after six months of submarine duty because of "extreme dislike for crowded conditions" (Kinsey and Weybrew, 1953). Research probably is not needed to show that the day-to-day inconveniences resulting from the somewhat crowded conditions account in part for these attitudes.

Perhaps contrary to popular opinion, rarely, except in an occasional case history (Kinsey and Weybrew, 1953) does the submarine literature contain references to claustrophobic reactions as such. In fact, Kinsey and Murphree (1955) suggest that the term may be a misnomer as applied to the submarine service. Perhaps with some justification, it is assumed by some submarine medical officers that claustrophobic-prone persons are eliminated by virtue of the training in the recompression chamber prior to their acceptance for the service (Duffner, 1954; Alvis, 1957).

The effects of the restricted viewing distances in a submarine are problematical. One study (Faucett and Newman, 1953) provided data that indicated that the lateral phorias (near and far) tended progressively to become esophoric during a 60-day confinement period. This tendency toward esophoria was reported in a later study together with a decrease in near-vision acuity. The authors state, "It is suspected that the confining structure of submarines is the cause of these changes in visual function" (Schwartz and Sandberg, 1954, p. 7). Instances indicating the direct effect of visual impairment upon performance aboard submarines are reported only in the anecdotal literature (Duff, 1947).

SENSORY AND PERCEPTUAL ASPECTS

LEVEL OF EXTEROCEPTIVE INPUT

Recently there has accumulated a voluminous literature pertaining to the various effects of reduced or deprived sensory input (Weybrew and Parker, 1960). Except during depth charging, the submarine environment can in no way be categorized as sensory-deprived or even sensory-reduced. In fact, in many of the engineering spaces the sound level reaches 60 to 100 or more decibels at mixed frequencies (Harris, 1957).

Hi-fi recordings, ample opportunities to chat, illumination levels varying from "rig for red" to 20 foot-candles in the dining and recreational areas—all contribute to the maintenance of a rather high stimulation level. The submarine would seem then to be characterized, under ordinary operating conditions, more as a stimulus-invariable rather than as a stimulus-reduced environment.

The level of stimulation is of course reduced while "running silent" during depth charging. The anecdotal literature (Duff, 1947) contains a number of accounts of neurotic and even psychotic-like behavior under the conditions of depth charging. It is impossible in these reports, however, to separate the effects of stimulus reduction from the stresses of unbearable heat and the threat to life and limb. Except in rare instances in which prepsychotic symptoms were reported (Duff, 1947), there is no evidence of the bizarre hallucinatory behavior reported during laboratory studies involving experimentally-induced sensory deprivation (Heron, 1961).

Behavioral effects of prolonged exposure to a relatively high level of background noise have not been investigated systematically under operating conditions aboard a submarine. Focusing upon the noise problem in submarines, Berrien (1949) points out that in addition to the possibility of some degree of deafness occurring in some of the personnel occupying certain areas of the submarine, exposure to these noise levels for prolonged durations might be expected to increase the physiological cost of survival in this type of environment. As to the first point, the ear-defender program now in effect in the submarine service affords considerable protection against hearing loss. As for the second point, it may be said that in the absence of any reliable evidence that submariners exposed to these high noise levels show excessive fatigue, performance decrements, or other adverse effects, Berrien's notion stands as an hypothesis perhaps warranting some concentrated research.

Research is perhaps not needed to show that the over-all level of olfactory stimulation aboard a submarine sealed off from the outside atmosphere is indeed elevated (Bureau of Medicine and Surgery, Navy Department, 1956). The odoriferousness of clothing and other material removed from the submarine into fresh air attests to this fact. Cooking odors, odors from hot lubricants, compressed air, and tobacco smoke, as well as body odor—all contribute to this problem. Perhaps the most objectional odor stems from the sanitary tanks, the contents of which must be "blown" outboard by means of compressed air and vented inboard, at least while the vessel is submerged. Whereas the vent filtration systems have been greatly improved in recent years, there are still objectionable odors that are quite noxious at times.

While somewhat sparse, there is evidence that olfactory thresholds increase with time in the "sealed-boat" condition (Weybrew, 1961c). Apparently the processes of olfactory adaptation are remarkably efficient. The effects, however, of prolonged exposure to this relatively high odor level upon appetite, digestion, and sleep habits would seem to pose an interesting research problem. The fact that approximately 5 lb of food were consumed per day per man during the 83-day world circumnavigation by the *Triton* would seem to argue against any serious appetite loss resulting from odor level or from any other causes.

TIME PERCEPTION

One final area that may be loosely classed as perceptual refers to the phenomenon of time estimation, that is, how long 10 minutes or an hour "seems." With the exception of scattered anecdotal information referring to monotony and the slow passage of time during extended war patrols (Willmon and Ritch, 1948), there have been no published reports of systematic research pertaining to this phenomenon in connection with prolonged submergence.

The relationship between time perspective and group morale first pointed out by Lewin (1942) suggests that this may be a fruitful area of research. That the perceived passage of time seems to be symptomatic of morale level during prolonged submergence is attested to by an observation recorded on the seventy-seventh-day of submergence during the world circumnavigation of the *Triton*. Found on the combat center plotting board was the following: "Time remaining on cruise, 10,260 minutes, 171 hours, 7.13 days, 0.23 months, 0.0195 years, and 0.000195 centuries" (Weybrew, 1961c).

The elimination of night-day cycles during continuous submergence may distort time perspective. For example, a number of incidents were reported in which a person observing that his watch indicated 8 o'clock, for example, was unable to determine whether it was 8 A.M. or 8 P.M. (Weybrew, 1961c). The importance of research aimed at ascertaining the physiological and psychological effects of the removal of day-night cues appears already to have been recognized (Schaefer, 1959).

Several suggestions for future research in time perception in connection with prolonged submergence can be found in the experimental literature. For example, void intervals of an hour or more tend to be overestimated, while task-filled intervals tend to be underestimated (Gulliksen, 1927). One study (Weybrew, 1956) involving the *Zeigarnik* technique, showed that when problem-solving tasks (addition problems) were interrupted, the time interval elapsed during the task was characteristically overestimated. Conversely, in the control group, who were allowed to complete the problem-solving tasks, the time necessary to complete the test was characteristically underestimated.

These findings suggest that a regimen in which successive tasks, each of which could be completed within a reasonable length of time (hour-long casualty drills, for example), may be conducive to negative time errors, that is, underestimation of passage of time. Presumably, though there is little factual evidence to support this hypothesis, the morale of the group may be enhanced and maintained by such a procedure. Finally, in anticipation of the discussion of submariner assessment later on in the chapter, it seems possible that individual differences in characteristic time perspective may be predictive of criteria of adjustment to submergence. The specific hypothesis raised here is that the forward-looking (anteverted as opposed to retroverted) submariner will adjust most adequately.

SOCIAL ASPECTS

French (1949) has integrated the literature of social psychology in terms of its applicability to the circumscribed social environment of the submarine. It is interesting to note that this comprehensive literature survey consisting of 99 references contained only one entry parts of which pertained to the social psychology of the submariner (Duff, 1947). More recently, however, the significance of the social psychological problems appears to have been recognized. For example, Levine (1958b) points out the importance of group cohesiveness for the maintenance of the resilient mental health of the crew members of Fleet Ballistic Missile (FBM) submarines.

Upon analysis, the most relevant areas for the social psychology of submariners would seem to be (1) the significance of social motives, (2) the relevance of conformity motivation, (3) the significance of role behavior in relation to group structure, and (4) the importance of leadership.

SOCIAL MOTIVATION

It is apparently an accepted fact that men volunteer and later on re-enlist in the submarine service largely because of the personal satisfaction of belonging to a closely-knit high-status group and because of the privilege of wearing the highly coveted dolphins (Duffner, 1954).

Other comments in the literature indicate that a considerable amount of the behavior of submariners is directed toward satisfying strong needs for status, affiliation, and prestige (French, 1949).

There is only a small amount of evidence bearing on this point. Focusing upon the motives involved in volunteering for the service, Youniss (1956) reported that 80 per cent ($N = 221$) of enlisted men volunteer to identify with a glamorous group, to be with "good fellows," or to be with a "better class of men." Another study, in which 1,125 enlisted submarine candidates indicated the traits "submariners have," demonstrated "a slight tendency for submarine candidates to emphasize social factors of the good shipmate, such as *good pals* and *good mixers,* more than did either of the other naval groups [receiving station personnel and recruits]" (Crissy and Pashalian, 1952, p. 35). Of a sample of officers 97 per cent ($N = 185$) and of a sample of enlisted men 81 per cent ($N = 256$) (difference significant at the 1 per cent level) indicated that the "main reason for volunteering is to be a member of a group of very high-caliber fighting men" (Weybrew and Molish, 1959, p. 46). Finally, 41 per cent of qualified submariners ($N = 186$) indicated that the aspects of submarine life they liked most pertained to the "close, interpersonal relations and the high-caliber personnel" (King, 1957, p. 11).

Though somewhat disjoined and sparse, the available evidence suggests rather clearly the relevance of social motives both in the decision to volunteer for the service and quite possibly in the decision to become a career submariner.

CONFORMITY MOTIVATION

In order to be an accepted member of any military organization, it would seem a fair assumption that a person must conform to "rules and regulations"—within certain unprescribed limits. When asked, 94 per cent of both officers and enlisted men ($N = 185$ and 256 in that order) stated that "taking orders from superiors never bothers me" (Weybrew and Molish, 1959, p. 47). At the same time, "dislike of authority" is given as the commanding officer's reason for 5 per cent ($N = 186$) of those who become disqualified (Kinsey and Weybrew, 1953). Tending to support this finding were the self-reported data indicating that 15 per cent ($N = 162$) of disqualified men as compared with 8 per cent ($N = 169$) of the qualified group indicated that the least liked aspect of submarine life pertained to "authority figures and regulations" (p of $\chi^2 < 0.05$, df $= 1$) (King, 1957). Literature pertaining to the classes of regulations that evoke resistance and the conditions under which authority is resented by some crew members is completely lacking. A researchable problem area may be suggested by these findings.

ROLE BEHAVIOR AND GROUP STRUCTURE

Perhaps nowhere in the military services are there found so many small, clearly delineated, almost impermeable subgroupings as are found among the 80 to 170 men making up the crew of a submarine. For the most part, localized with respect to rating specialties such as electronic technicians, sonarmen, enginemen, cooks, and, with the advent of FBM, missilemen, these subgroups may become cliques, depending upon the significance of the group's specialty for the survival of the crew or the success of the mission (Ninow, 1961). Rohrer (1959) has pointed out the tendency for status leveling within the subgroupings. Yet the dependence between the subgroups upon the technology identified with these groupings would appear to result in considerable status maintenance by virtue of group membership alone.

There appears to be a repertoire of role behavior peculiar to each of the subgroups. For example, one frequently hears, "He acts like an ET (electronics technician)," "He always carries tools with him like an auxiliaryman," or "He is an accomplished acey-deucey player like a cook" (Weybrew, 1961c). Perhaps research is not needed to show that the group's cohesiveness is a function of the uniqueness of the role behavior ascribed to the group. Laboratory findings obtained from a nonsubmariner population, however, suggest that individual members of groups such as those found within submarine crews may have an unclear perception of their role in the group (and in the crew for that matter), and as a result group productivity may be reduced (Smith, 1957). Bearing on this point, evidence is now available showing that missilemen, whose roles are sharply delineated, maintain more favorable attitudes during submergence than nonmissilemen personnel, some of whom tend to have less definitive roles ascribed to them (Molish, *et al.*, 1961).

The discrepancy between self-perceived roles and the role ascribed by the ship's organization chart as a correlate of group morale and leadership has been examined (Scott, 1952). Analysis of data collected by means of interviews, sociometry, and questionnaires from 686 officers and enlisted men from 10 submarines provided the basis for two major conclusions:

1. Crews that tend to have low discrepancy between self-perceived roles and roles ascribed by the organization charts tend to be rated higher in morale than those with high discrepancy scores.

2. In general, "The results of this study have implications for administrative practice, since the morale, if not the effectiveness of an organization, may be dependent upon each member having a clear conception of his responsibilities and relationships to his fellow members" (Scott, 1952, p. 3).

The conflict of roles between these subgroupings with intergroup hostility as a possible resultant has been suggested (Rohrer, 1959). Most of the available information pertaining to this problem is recorded in World War II patrol reports written largely by the commanding officers of the submarines (Duff, 1947). There is reason to believe, however, that the captain of a submarine, or of a surface ship for that matter, occupies a particular position in the group structure whereby it is difficult for him to observe indices of crew atmosphere. Coser (1961), a sociologist, describes this difficulty quite aptly: "An instructive illustration comes from the U.S. Navy, where the captain of a ship is not expected to show up unannounced with the men or even in the officers' mess, and tends by design to isolate himself" (p. 35). However, the efficacy of obtaining indices of crew atmosphere from remote informants (three squadron yeomen) was demonstrated quite well by a study involving the enlisted crews from 10 submarines (Campbell, 1955).

LEADERSHIP

At present, there is more or less agreement among social psychologists generally that the quality of leadership behavior is in some dynamic way related to the traits that the leader possesses, to the structure of the follower group, and to the environmental situation in which the leader is functioning (Fiedler, 1961). References to the importance of leadership during war patrols is found in numerous places in the anecdotal literature (Duff, 1947; Roscoe, 1958). The high quality of leadership has been given as the most important factor contributing to the maintenance of morale during the subpolar transit of the *Nautilus* (Kinsey, 1959).

There is little systematic information concerning submariner leadership available. Campbell (1953) presented a comprehensive correlational study of sociometric and other rating data collected from the crews of 10 submarines ($N = 600$ enlisted men and 68 officers). The most significant predictors of the leadership criteria reported in this study were the ability to delegate authority and the number of personal contacts with the other officers and men. The positive relationship of these leadership criteria to crew morale was also indicated. A recent factor analysis involving extensive trait ratings of 150 officers suggested that successful submarine officers were characterized by factors related to drive, aptitude for the submarine service, and stable career orientation (Parker, 1961). In passing, it is interesting to note that Tagiuri (1958), using a number of submariners as subjects in the early development of his "relational analysis" approach, presented evidence that the leader's preference for members of the group is especially transparent to the group members themselves. This finding suggests the importance of each individual's perception of the officer's position within the socio-metric matrix making up the submarine crew.

HUMAN ENGINEERING ASPECTS

A considerable body of literature pertaining to control accessibility and simplification, dial visibility, lighting, and so on has accumulated. Considerable progress has been made since Channell and Tolcott (1947) reviewed the literature of World War II submarines. For example, detailed recommendations concerning the most important human factors problems peculiar to FBM submarines are now available (Bureau of Naval Weapons, 1960). Problems that may be considered as being on the fringes of human engineering were suggested from self-reported data obtained from the crew of the *Nautilus* (Weybrew, 1957b). These suggestions were of two general classes, namely, (1) those pertaining to modification of berthing and leisure-time facilities so as to provide more opportunities for privacy and (2) those pertaining to design of equipment for ease of maintenance. The last mentioned human engineering problem appears to have become acute with the advent of the missile-firing submarine.

Nonspecific Behavioral Changes During Prolonged Submergence

Although overlapping the contents of the preceding section in certain respects, the present material consists of a review of the literature in which rather gross behavioral changes during submergence are reported without any systematic attempt to delineate the specific environmental factors causing them. For the purpose of this chapter these data are classified as studies of changes in vigilance, in psychomotor performance, in autonomic nervous system function, and in certain subjective indices of adjustment.

VIGILANCE

It would seem to be a fair assumption that accuracy of radar and sonar target detection and the ability to read the dials and manipulate the controls necessary to operate a nuclear submarine are effected by the "readiness" of the men to respond to signals of various kinds. In the context of an outline of the major problem areas anticipated in the FBM program, Levine (1958b, p. 1) states, "Even if the atmosphere is such that men can live in a submerged submarine for periods of 60 days or so, the subtle and more psychological antialertness factors would still be present."

Observations made during a 30-day simulated war patrol indicated a tendency toward reduced alertness, inability to concentrate, and a general reduction in excitation level as the cruise progressed (Ritch, 1948). Self-reported data collected daily during the first prolonged (11 days) submerged cruise of the *Nautilus* suggested the possibility that reduced alertness was symptomatic of the majority of the 30 men included in the sample (Weybrew, 1957b). However, daily measures of critical flicker frequency thresholds indicated no significant changes in visual sensitivity during the same submerged period. Similarly, plots of means of perceptual spans for numbers and letters measured biweekly during eight weeks' incarceration in an evacuated submarine showed no decrement (Faucett and Newman, 1953).

In one publication surveying the literature of psychophysiology as it applies to the stress of submergence reference is made to the relationship of palmar sweating to vigilance: ". . . GSR is probably our best expressive indicator for alertness and changes in attention" (Darrow and Henry, 1949, p. 430). A brief pilot study might be mentioned in this context (Weybrew, 1961b). To test the hypothesis that monotony was coincident with reduced excitation level and consequently lowered vigilance, six submariner candidates one at a time pressed a key each time a pointer on a 12-in dial passed the 9, 12, 3, and 6 o'clock positions. With the pointer turning at the rate of one revolution per minute, the subject must of necessity press the key while the pointer moves thru 3 degrees of central angle or within a time span of ½ sec if a "hit" or correct response was to be recorded. During the experimental (monotony) session, none of the subjects received feedback as to the correctness of their responses. On the other hand, during the control (nonmonotony) session six weeks later, each of the same six men had a conspicuous counter placed immediately in front of them, so that continuous monitoring of their own responses was possible. Measurement

of palmar resistance as well as number of "hits" was recorded continuously during both 60-min sessions.

The results suggest that feedback as to the correctness of their responses (and presumably reduced monotony) received during the control session resulted in the maintenance of a higher excitation level as
measured by palmar conductance. Interestingly enough, however, the
alertness in terms of percentage "hits" was significantly higher in the
"nonmonotony" session only during the first 10 min of the experimental
period. Responses to an adjective checklist, however, indicated that the
group did report more fatigue symptoms during the "monotony" session.
Although based upon a very small subject sample, the results of this
study may have implications for maintaining the excitation level of men
during prolonged sonar and radar watches and during long countdowns.

PSYCHOMOTOR PERFORMANCE

Most of the studies in this area of submarine psychology have been
designed to determine grossly whether performance efficiency is, in fact,
maintained during prolonged periods of submergence. One study involved the confinement of 22 men to a submarine for 60 days (Faucett
and Newman, 1953). The performance measures were the Minnesota
Manual Dexterity Test, a two-hand tapping task, a letter-cancellation task,
and the seven subtests of the MacQuarrie Test for Mechanical Ability.
Plots of means for each test or subtest score showed some significant
changes between sessions but no definite trends over the period of confinement. Where performance did decline between sessions, self-reported
motivation coincidentally also declined, suggesting that the observed
decrements may have been due to deteriorating motivation rather than
to any direct effect of the experimental conditions upon psychomotor
processes. This finding points up the very serious limitation to this kind
of experimentation, namely, the difficulty in determining the difference
between capacity and performance, that is, what the person "will do" as
compared with what he "can do."

The anecdotal literature (Duff, 1947) is replete with instances of
increased muscular tension observed during prolonged submerged cruises.
Estimated by means of scores obtained from a standard stylus-in-hole
apparatus, the level of muscular tension of 22 subjects during a 60-day
simulated submergence decreased sporadically at the outset then maintained the approximate level of the control period throughout the remainder of the experiment (Faucett and Newman, 1953). Similarly the
mean hand-steadiness scores obtained from 30 men from the crew of the

Nautilus were plotted by day during an 11-day submerged cruise (Wey-brew, 1957b). These data indicated a trend toward increased muscular tension as measured from the fifth day submerged until the end of the cruise. In short, the level of muscular tension does change during submergence. The literature fails to indicate, however, whether the change in tension is related to performance efficiency as the submergence progresses.

PROCESSES RELATED TO AUTONOMIC FUNCTION

The frame of reference presented in the introductory section of this chapter equated the effects of stress with the emotional responses resulting from environmental blockage (or threat thereof) of goal-directed (motivated) activity. Elsewhere it has been argued that indices of autonomic nervous system function are usefully valid indicants of the effect of stress (Weybrew and Alves, 1959).

Although in various places in the submarine literature mention is made of the probable changes in autonomic function resulting from submergence (for example, Essen, 1948), very little experimental data are available. In so far as autonomic reactivity can be inferred from the function of the adrenal system, significant drops in eosinophile counts were reported during eight weeks of simulated submergence (Faucett and Newman, 1953). Moreover, a significant fall in blood pressure during submerged exposure to an atmosphere containing from 2 to 4 per cent carbon dioxide was reported by Schaefer (1959). A decline in mean ($N = 30$) radial pulse the first five days and a rise in the same measure during the remaining five days of the submerged cruise aboard the *Nautilus* were also reported (Weybrew, 1957b).

However, measures of blood pressure and pulse rate changes and recoverability obtained by means of the U.S. Navy "step-up" procedure (Behnke, *et al.*, 1943) were collected from 28 men during a 30-day snorkel cruise (Willmon and Ritch, 1948) and again from 22 men during a 60-day simulated submergence (Faucett and Newman, 1953). There were no significant fluctuations in these variables reported in either study.

SUBJECTIVE INDICES

Most of the studies aimed at evaluating behavioral changes during prolonged submergence have relied heavily on self-reported material.

What has this kind of data contributed in terms of information pertaining to the behavioral effects of prolonged submergence?

Although presumably not severely handicapping for most of the crew members, symptom trends have been reported during a 12-day "sealed-ship" cruise of the *Nautilus* (Weybrew, 1957b). During this cruise, there appeared to be a trend toward increase in subjective tension, toward more difficulty in sleeping, and toward increased interpersonal irritability. Self-reported data from another study suggested a rather strong trend toward an increase in the frequency and severity of headaches as the submergence proceeded (Weybrew, 1961b).

The most recent data of this kind were collected as a means of evaluating changes in the quality of adjustment to submerged conditions during the *Triton* world circumnavigation (Weybrew, 1961a; Weybrew, 1961b). Since the duration of the submergence was approximately three months, a duration similar to that planned for the FBM submarines, the circumnavigation provided a unique opportunity to observe changes in the psychological status of the man, changes that may be applicable to the FBM situation.

A list of adjectives or behavioral statements designed to tap moods, self-perceived efficiency, interpersonal attitudes, and the like were compiled for use in the *Triton* study. Examples of these items are: tense, happy, irritable, can't concentrate, energetic, difficult to breathe, tired out, etc.—50 items in all. Each man of a sample of approximately 40 men from the crew of the *Triton* indicated daily the degree to which each of these items described himself at that time. The multiple-category response format used by the men to indicate the relative significance of each item on each day of the cruise is presented in Figure 1.

The methodology employed in analyzing these data is perhaps as important as the content. A mean for each of the 50 adjectival expressions was computed for each of the 79 days on which data were collected. Pearson correlation coefficients were computed between the means for the 50 variables over the arrays of 79 days. To investigate the possibility that atmospheric variables would covary with the subjective indicators provided by the checklist, the correlation coefficients of the average daily level of oxygen, hydrogen, freon-12, carbon dioxide, carbon monoxide, as well as the average daily barometric pressure were also included in the matrix with the 50 adjectival items.

Removal of three centroid factors exhausted the 56×56 correlation matrix. The first factor, loaded by virtually all of the variables including one of the six atmospheric variables (barometric pressure) was without question a general factor accounting for a large portion of the communalities. The loadings for the most significant variables identifying the

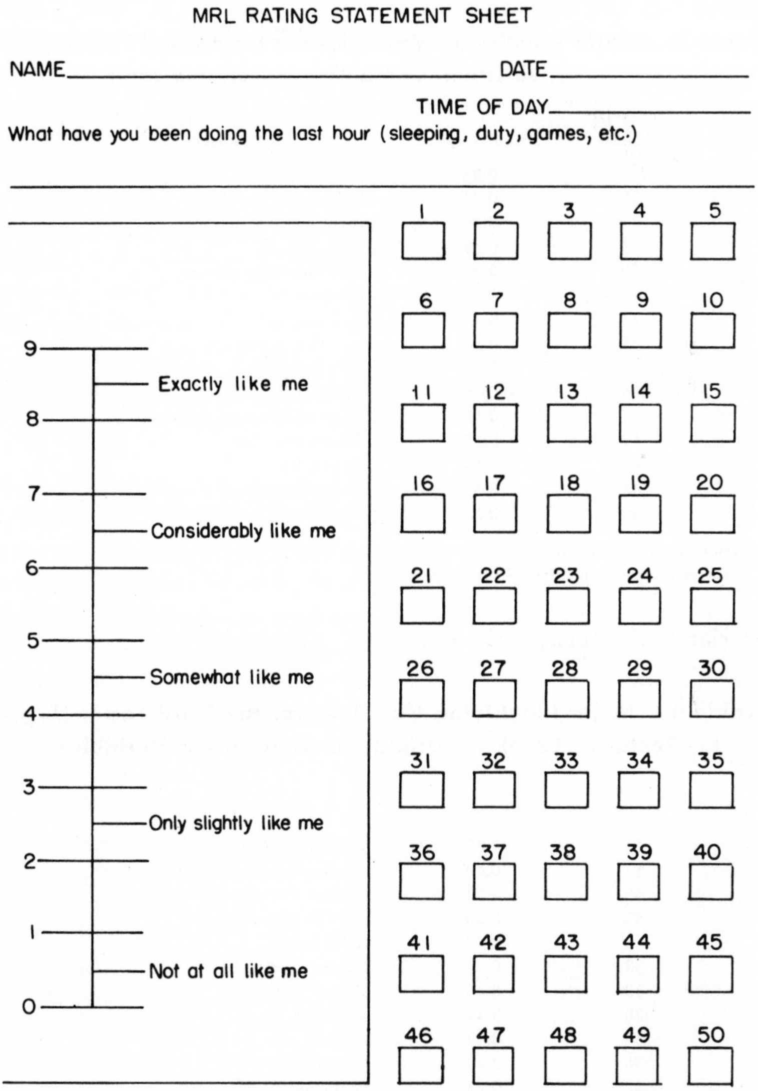
MRL RATING STATEMENT SHEET

NAME__________ DATE__________

TIME OF DAY__________

What have you been doing the last hour (sleeping, duty, games, etc.)

____

9
Exactly like me
8
7
Considerably like me
6
5
Somewhat like me
4
3
Only slightly like me
2
1
Not at all like me
0

1 2 3 4 5
6 7 8 9 10
11 12 13 14 15
16 17 18 19 20
21 22 23 24 25
26 27 28 29 30
31 32 33 34 35
36 37 38 39 40
41 42 43 44 45
46 47 48 49 50

Figure 1. Multiple category scale used with adjectives or behavioral statements during the *Triton* circumnavigation.

remaining two factors are presented in Table 3 and Table 4. The second factor (F_{T_2}) was tentatively labeled a "Composite Morale Indicator" (Table 3), whereas the third factor (F_{T_3}) received the tentative label

Table 3.   Major Identifying Variables for the Second Factor (F_{T_2}).
F_{T_2} Tentative Label: Composite Morale Indicator.

Variable Number	Loading[a]	Content[b]
7	0.88	Morale low
22	0.76	Fed up
10	0.70	Irritable
37	0.68	Homesick
15	0.65	Don't feel like talking
13	0.64	Annoyed
24	0.64	Disinterested
41	0.64	Feel like giving up
11	0.63	Mouth dry
4	0.59	Bored stiff
5	0.58	Don't feel like doing anything
19	0.58	Daydream a lot
40	0.58	Headachy
43	0.58	Uncomfortable
50	0.56	Frustrated

a. Factor has been reflected.
b. Takes into account the sign of the loading.

"Covariants of Atmospheric Variables" (Table 4).

Table 4.   Major Identifying Variables for the Third Factor (F_{T_3}).
F_{T_3} Tentative Label: Covariants of Atmospheric Variables.

Variable Number	Loading	Content[a]
56	1.00	Hydrogen (0/0)
51	0.60	Barometric pressure (mm)
45	0.53	Difficult to sleep
53	0.50	Carbon dioxide (0/0)
6	0.47	Inefficient
52	0.46	Oxygen (0/0)
30	0.45	Jittery
28	0.44	Anxious
34	0.43	Excited
36	0.43	Clutched up
42	0.43	Feel closed in
14	0.42	Joints and limbs tired
43	0.41	Uncomfortable
44	0.41	Don't feel like eating
25	0.40	Tight or hot feelings in stomach

a. Takes into account the sign of the loading.

Scores for each of the 79 days for the two factors delineated in Table 3 and Table 4 were estimated* and plotted (Figure 2) in order to shed some light on the question: What environmental conditions were coincident with (or perhaps causal for) the factor fluctuation from day to day?

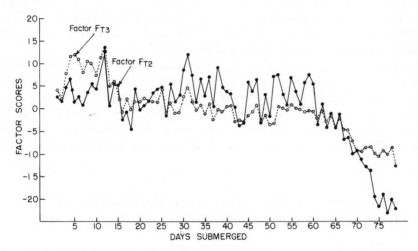

Figure 2. Factor scores for F_{T2} and F_{T3} plotted by day during the submerged circumnavigation of the world by the *Triton*.

Before some environmental conditions are suggested that may have affected the level of the factor scores in Figure 2, it should be pointed out that a high positive score in F_{T_2} (Table 3) indicates reduced morale and presumably less favorable adjustment. Similarly, high scores on F_{T_3} (Table 4) also appear to be indicative of less favorable adjustment. In addition, the structure of F_{T_3} (Table 4) suggests the possibility that atmospheric conditions at least tend to covary with (and could be causally related to) the subjective indices used in this study.*

Several general findings emerge from an inspection of the curves in Figure 2. First, adjustment adequacy as indicated by troughs in both curves are found wherever a landfall is approached. Accordingly, troughs are seen on the tenth day, St. Peter's and Paul's Rocks; on the

---

* Factor scores were estimated for each day summing the daily means (converted to standard score form) for the highest loading variables, each mean being weighted by its loading on the factor.

* Nothing as to the typical gaseous concentrations maintained during submergence either is implied or can be inferred from the factor loadings in Table 4.

twentieth day, Cape Horn; on the twenty-sixth day, Easter Island, and so on (Beach, 1960a). Second, adjustment is most favorable on Sundays (days 13, 20, etc.) and least favorable on the weekly field days (complete clean-up of ship), as indicated by peaks in the factor curves, for example, days 11, 18, 25, 32, etc. (Beach, 1960b). Third, the subjective effects of a smoking curfew may have been reflected by the peak in the F_{T_2} curve coinciding with the fifty-nineth day (Beach, 1960b). Finally, the well known "end effect" appeared to have set in approximately two weeks before the end of the cruise.

These findings suggest certain environmental conditions that appear to affect the morale and the general adjustment status of the submerged personnel. Perhaps equally important is the fact that the study demonstrates the methodological possibilities of this type of factor analysis for identifying trend or fluctuation factors from covariance patterns measured successively over a period of time in a stressful environment.

Assessment of the Adjustment Potentiality of Volunteers for Extended Submerged Duty

The selection of men for hazardous duty during aerial or submarine war patrols or space flight involves a dilemma alluded to in a list of recommendations submitted by the officers of the submarine *Puffer* (No. 1), after having been exposed to 203 depth charges (Duff, 1947, p. 80).

> Be careful and slow to form an estimate of a man's value until he has been observed under stress. To a great extent the men who were on their feet, working to save themselves and the ship, when the long dive was over, were not the normal leaders of the crew. The people who lasted out were those of a more phlegmatic disposition who didn't bother too much when things were running smoothly. The worriers and the hurriers had all crapped out, leaving the plodders to bring home the ship.

As pointed out in this quotation, the difficulty lies in the fact that the ultimate criterion with respect to which the assessment measures are to be evaluated can be obtained only from data obtained in the stress situation itself.

The history of submariner psychological selection began in 1943, at which time a psychiatrist was assigned to interview submariner personnel with questionable behavioral backgrounds (Shilling and Kohl, 1947). Then, as now, the prime selective device operating was the fact that each man entering the submarine service was a "volunteer."

Figure 3 presents in diagrammatic form the various stages of the process of training enlisted submariner volunteers and at the same time indicates the ranges of attrition at the various levels of training.

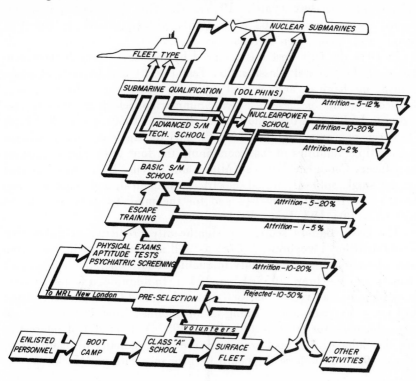

Figure 3. Schematic drawing showing the attrition rate of enlisted submariner volunteers at the various levels of training.

As may be inferred from Figure 3, systematic screening for both the 350 officers and 3,500 enlisted volunteers received at New London annually ends when the candidate enters Submarine School. From that time until the men are qualified and awarded the dolphins, the only selectors operating are the performance criteria in effect at the different levels of training.

ASSESSMENT OF ABILITIES

In 1943 the Otis Self-Administering Test was applied to the problem of enlisted submariner selection. A product-moment correlation of 0.47 ($N = 145$) was reported with respect to Submarine School grades

(Bartlett, 1950). The same test, however, correlated 0.19 ($N = 145$) with the pass-fail criterion in Submarine School, while it correlated only 0.05 ($N = 796$) with the commanding officers' ratings of men after considerable sea duty (Satter, 1945). The Otis Test scores, however, showed a correlation of 0.63 ($N = 1940$) with psychiatric judgment of "good" and "poor" men (Graham, *et al.*, 1943).

In 1944 the Otis Test was replaced by the Navy Basic Battery consisting of the General Classification Test (GCT) and by tests of arithmetical, mechanical, and clerical aptitudes (Bond and Miller, 1947). Raw correlations of these tests with Submarine School grades were reported to be between 0.35 and 0.49 by Bartlett (1950) and by Weybrew (1954) as approximately 0.33 ($N = 1,320$) for single predictive validity and multiple validities of 0.42 combining the four tests. The validity of the Officers Candidate Battery (Miller and Owens, 1947) was reported for the single subtests, verbal, electrical-mechanical, and relative movement, to be from 0.38 to 0.44 and for the predictor composite to be 0.50 ($N = 90$) (Weybrew, 1954).

The Basic Battery scores are significantly predictive of Submarine School attrition (Weybrew, 1957c) as well as usefully predictive of the more ultimate criterion of ability to qualify aboard operating submarines (Kinsey and Weybrew, 1953; King, 1957). In addition, a factor analytic study identified a "verbal" factor (centered around GCT) that correlated 0.75 ($N = 23$) with a trait rating factor obtained from 22 men confined to a submarine for 60 days (Weybrew, 1957a). It is also of interest to note the Submarine School grades are usefully predictive of qualification (King, 1957) as well as shipboard performance ratings (Mackie, *et al.*, 1954).

There is very little literature pertaining to the relationship of psychomotor abilities to submariner performance. Scores obtained from the Heinrich Two-Hand Coordination Test showed low but nonchance correlation with Submarine School criteria (Bartlett, 1950) with escape training-tank performance and with psychiatric ratings (Graham, *et al.*, 1943). However, a "psychomotor" factor, loaded heavily by the Heinrich score, was not correlated with rating criteria during 60 days of confinement (Weybrew, 1957a).

In summary, it appears that the absolute size of the validity statistics reported for the ability measures is indeed rather low. It has been shown, however, that selection of men in the upper 25 per cent of the Basic Battery distributions would yield a probability of success in the submarine service of from three to five times as great as would be found for those candidates who fall below the lowest quartile (Weybrew, 1954; Weybrew, 1957c).

ASSESSMENT OF PERSONALITY TRAIT PATTERNS

OBJECTIVE TESTS

There are two rather comprehensive summaries of the literature of personality assessment pertaining to submariner selection (Bartlett, 1950; Hoff and Greenbaum, 1954). The NRC-Neurotic Inventory, the New London Inventory, the Shipley Personnel Inventory, the NDRC Cornell Selectee Index, and the Personal Inventory (Form 2) were at one time or another used in the assessment program from 1943 to 1945. These questionnaires were designed to tap neurotic symptoms, attitudes, interests, and biographical information obtained either by self-rating or forced-choice techniques. The majority of these scores showed low but nonchance correlations with Submarine School attrition, with training tank performance, and with officers' shipboard ratings (Graham, *et al.*, 1943). However, a factor analysis of the Minnesota Multiphasic Personality Inventory (MMPI), together with aptitudinal and other measures showed no relationship of the six factors extracted to any of the criteria included (Cook and Wherry, 1950a). All in all, it appears that total scores as well as item responses from this type of test instrument have been in the main used as "probes" indicating the area of personality that should be investigated further by personal interviews or other means.

PROJECTIVE TESTS

There have been a number of projective tests used experimentally in the submariner assessment program. Scores obtained from the Harrower-Erickson Modification of the Rorschach Test have been examined as to their predictive validity with respect to the training criteria (Bartlett, 1943). The results were essentially negative (Bartlett, 1950). Predictive indices, however, obtained by means of the scoring techniques developed by Eron and Auld (1954), as applied to the group of the Thematic Apperception Test (TAT) developed by Briggs (1954), were shown to have useful validity with respect to criteria of achievement in Submarine School (King, 1958). Finally, scores obtained from the same TAT form did not identify submariners with a history of claustrophobia (Kinsey and Murphree, 1955).

In short, although it is believed that information obtained from projective tests such as the group TAT may be a useful adjunct to interview data (Duffner, 1954), the quantitative scores used to date appear to be of only marginal value in the submariner assessment program.

Interview data have been used in one way or another since the inception of the submariner assessment program. This literature has been comprehensively surveyed (Pashalian, *et al.*, 1952). Reliability based upon the consistency of the content areas sampled and evaluated by pairs of interviewers during 1,159 interviews was judged satisfactory (Pashalian and Crissy, 1953). In another study the validity of 1,000 interviews with respect to Submarine School criteria was found to be usefully high but showed no margin over the predictive validity of the Basic Battery Scores (Weybrew, 1954). More recently, a study using enlisted FBM submariners as subjects has shown the comparatively high validity of impressions obtained from a standardized psychiatric interview for predicting the intensity of motivation for the submarine service (Ninow, 1960). Unfortunately, this literature survey did not show any systematic studies of the validity of standardized interview information from which the confounding effects of aptitude and other test data had been removed.

SUBMARINER ASSESSMENT IN THE NUCLEAR AGE

With the advent of the nuclear submarine, new adjustment demands have been made upon the submariner, virtually unlimited periods of submergence apart from air and sunlight, need to assimilate advanced nuclear technology and others. More recently, with the advent of the FBM program, the role of the submarine as a weapon of war has changed. The mission of the FBM submarine is largely a deterrent one —a 60-to-90-day submerged mission is successful if the missiles *are not* fired. Ability to withstand boredom and monotony, at least the sameness of things, may be a necessary characteristic of the person who remains maximally effective during these prolonged submerged periods.

In general, since 1955, submariner assessment research has been focused in four somewhat overlapping areas, namely, aptitude measurement, measures of the over-all adjustment status of the candidates, motivational measurement, and, finally, the psychophysiological characteristics related to the ability to adjust optimally to the conditions of long submergence.

The basic aptitudes discussed earlier are still usefully predictive of the training criteria. For example, the multiple correlation of the Basic Test Battery scores correlated 0.48 with grades in Nuclear Power School

(Kipnis and Glickman, 1961). The Navy Bureau of Personnel are now field-testing two new test batteries, an aptitude battery and a battery of noncognitive tests using Nuclear Power School performance as the criterion. The results look promising (La Gaipa, 1959; Kipnis and Glickman, 1961).

ASSESSMENT OF MOTIVATION

Speaking of submariner selection, Dyson and Shilling (1955, p. 1025) state, "Perhaps the problem all hinges on motivation. A great deal of investigating needs to be done." Moreover, Levine (1958a) appears to agree that motivational maintenance may be the most crucial psychological problem associated with the *Polaris* submarine program.

Youniss (1956) reported the reasons for volunteering for the submarine service (in decreasing order of frequency with which they were mentioned by a large group of enlisted men) to be pay, good food, and opportunities to learn interesting skills. Based largely upon the results of this study, the Self-Reported Motivational Questionnaire (SMQ), was constructed. This questionnaire consists of 52 items pertaining to reasons for volunteering, attitudes toward the Navy in general and the submarine service in particular, and relative significance of the available goals (status, a submarine engineering career, affiliation with submariners, and so on) (Weybrew and Molish, 1959). The respondents indicate the significance of each item by means of the multicategory response scale contained in Figure 4. Examples of the item are "My ultimate goal in volunteering is to get into nuclear submarines" and "I believe that submariners are the most highly respected men in the Navy." Summed scores significantly predicted both officer (Weybrew and Molish, 1959) and enlisted attrition in Submarine School (Rubin and Parker, 1961). The SMQ scores have also been shown to be significantly related to performance ratings of FBM crews (Ninow, 1960).

ASSESSMENT OF OVER-ALL ADJUSTMENT STATUS

Since only 56 psychiatric casualties were reported from 126,160 man-patrols during World War II (Duff and Shilling, 1947), the question might be raised as to whether the psychiatric screening techniques (largely interviews) being used at that time can be improved. World War II adjustment criteria would, however, seem to be inappropriate for the modern submariner exposed to somewhat different stresses during submergence in a nuclear submarine.

The general adjustment status of candidates is presently being evaluated by means of a questionnaire still in its experimental stages, the Personal Inventory Barometer (PIB) (Weybrew and Youniss, 1957). Again employing the multiple-response format (Figure 4) applied to neurotic symptom items, this inventory yields a score that significantly predicts Submarine School attrition of enlisted men (Weybrew and Youniss, 1957; Weybrew, 1957c). In addition, those submariner candidates who fail the recompression chamber training also obtain significantly higher PIB scores (high scores indicative of less adequate adjustment) than do those who pass the training (Weybrew and Youniss, 1960).

The interaction of the PIB, as a measure of psychiatric status, the SMQ as a measure of motivation for the submarine service, and the GCT as a measure of verbal intelligence (Table 5) shows, in an actuarial sense, the efficacy of these measures in terms of predicting attrition in enlisted Submarine School (Rubin and Parker, 1961). The same sort of interrelationships have been shown for officers (Weybrew and Molish, 1959). All in all, the data in Table 5 indicate that the least desirable combination of scores; that is, high PIB, low SMQ, and low GCT scores as compared with the reverse pattern of scores are significantly predictive of Submarine School attrition (p of $\chi^2 < 0.001$).

PSYCHOPHYSIOLOGICAL ASSESSMENT

The discussion earlier in this chapter pertaining to the interrelationship of motivation, emotion, and the concept of stress suggests a general working hypothesis pertaining to submariner selection. Stated briefly, this hypothesis holds that when strong motives are "blocked" by the limitations of the submarine environment, energy is mobilized to overcome these barriers. Furthermore, the individual differences in the modes of channeling this energy has relevance for predicting differences in the quality of adjustment to prolonged submergence. An additional working hypothesis is that peripheral indices of autonomic nervous system changes in response to stress are the most useful indicators of modes of energy mobilization and direction of discharge (Weybrew and Alves, 1959).

Only a start has been made to explore these hypotheses. It has been shown that urinary 17-ketosteroid increases significantly during the training-tank experience; and, as a result, this index has been suggested as a measure of stress tolerance (Cook and Wherry, 1950b). One factor-analytic study resulted in several meaningful factors loaded by observer ratings and patterns of autonomic nervous system changes during a

Table 5.   The Interaction Effect of Measures of Psychiatric Status, Motivation, and Aptitude upon Attrition in Enlisted Submarine School (N = 1,249).

Variable	UNFAVORABLE PSYCHIATRIC STATUS[a]	FAVORABLE PSYCHIATRIC STATUS
	Attrition (Per Cent of Frequency in Each Cell)	
High[a] Motivation	12.8	4.1
	(N = 109)[b]	(N = 195)
High[a] Aptitude		
Low Motivation	10.4	3.3
	(N = 192)	(N = 121)
High Motivation	16.7	10.3
	(N = 132)	(N = 184)
Low Aptitude		
Low Motivation	22.3	15.4
	(N = 193)	(N = 123)

Note: Abstracted from Table 6, Rubin and Parker (1961).
a. All dichotomies are at the approximate median of the test score distributions.
b. Total frequency in each cell.

situational stress test (Weybrew, 1959a). Another correlational study indicated that palmar resistance changes and that the degree of recoverability to basal level following hyperventilation and breath holding were significantly correlated with trait ratings related to excitability and emotional stability (Weybrew and Alves, 1959). Finally, a recent correlational study showed that the ratio of external energy mobilization (increase in muscular tension) to internal energy mobilization (palmar resistance drop) observed during induced pacing stress was inversely correlated with peer nominations as to emotional stability and over-all potentiality of volunteers for the submarine service (Weybrew, 1962).

From these studies there has emerged an additional working hypothesis that for lack of a better term we have called the "stair-stepping" hypothesis (Weybrew and Alves, 1959). Figure 4 presents this hypothesis diagrammatically. A statement of the hypothesis or class of hypotheses depicted in Figure 4 is that certain individuals when exposed to successive stressors fail to recover the autonomic nervous system (ANS) displacement to one stressor (S_1 in Figure 4) before a subsequent stressor (S_2) is imposed. The result may be chronic ANS disequilibrium. In order to obtain factual support for this hypothesis, it will be necessary to categorize a sample of submariners according to the degree to which they exhibit this "stair-stepping" response sequence in an experimentally induced stress situation and then to search for differences between these "types" with respect to adjustment criteria obtained during a prolonged submerged period.

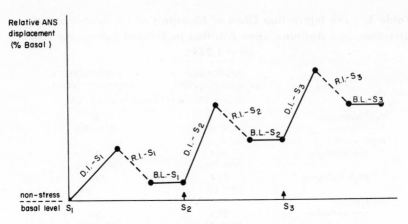

Figure 4. Schematic representation of the "stair-stepping" hypothesis, showing incomplete recovery following displacement to successive stress situations (S_1, S_2, S_3, . . . , etc.). D.I. $-S_1$, R.I. $-S_1$, and B.L. $-S_1$ stand for Displacement Index, Recovery Index, and Re-established Basal Level, respectively, resulting from S_1, and so on, for S_2, S_3, . . . , etc. The slope of the graph is equal to the ratio of ANS-displacement to time and is a complex function of the stress conditions S_1, S_2, S_3, . . . , etc.

ASSESSMENT METHODOLOGY

It would seem to be a tenable proposition that the most serious limitation in submariner assessment research has been the lack of appropriate methods of collecting, classifying, analyzing, and interpreting data of this kind. Cronbach (1949) has reviewed the methodology of submariner selection. Multivariate approaches appear to be necessary both in predictor and criterion research, since it seems unlikely, for some time at least, that any unifactorial predictors or criteria with high interrelationships will be identified. One over-all approach that has been explored in the work with submariners is to factor-analyze both predictor and criterion variables included in the same correlation matrix, thus abstracting compounded predictor-criterion factors (Weybrew, 1955). The recently developed analytical method of evaluating predictors singly with respect to one or more criteria would seem to offer a more refined approach to the same type of problem (Horst and MacEwan, 1960).

Several methodological approaches to the development of adjustment criteria have been tried in the submariner assessment program. Behavioral statements abstracted from "critical incidents" were Q-sorted and factor analyzed in order to identify clusters of traits describing an effective submariner (Weybrew, 1953). In a subsequent study these criterion types (persons identified by Q technique) were exposed to 60 days of confinement to a submarine. Ten measures were obtained successively from each of two persons (Q types) over 22 equally spaced testing sessions. The resultant matrixes were each submitted to a type of factor analysis called "P technique" by Cattell (1952) in order to identify the intraperson trend of fluctuation factors describing the differences between the two subjects' adjustment to confinement (Weybrew, 1955).

Other applications of factor analysis to certain aspects of the problem of criterion construction have been explored. For example, the existence of different subgroupings within the submariner population and the efficacy of computing separate prediction formulas for these groupings were demonstrated by a recent Q-technique study (Weybrew, 1959b). In addition, the methodological possibilities of the application of factor-analytical techniques to self-rating data obtained repetitively over time in a stressful environment have been demonstrated (Weybrew, *et al.*, 1961). In this study a mean for each of a group of 100 men wintering over in the Antarctic was computed over 10 successive monthly ratings with respect to 33 trait dimensions (moods, tensions, quality of sleep, and the like). Correlation coefficients were computed between the means of the 33 traits and the resulting matrix factor analyzed. Estimated factor scores for each of the four factors extracted were used as adjustment criteria with some degree of success as judged by the relationship of these scores to observer rating criteria also included in the study. All in all, the methodological possibilities of multivariate techniques as applied to the problems of submariner assessment seem far from being exhausted at this time.

Next Steps in Research in Submarine Psychology

The contents of this chapter have quite probably raised as many questions as have been answered; several research focuses may, however, have been suggested by this somewhat cursory coverage of the whole area of submarine psychology. These are as follows:

1. Selection methodology that emphasizes the positive factors contributing to resilient psychological health as well as those negative factors related to behavioral disorders. For example, intense, appropriately

directed motivation for the submarine service may compensate for, or at least reduce the handicapping effect of, the presence of neurotic symptomatology.

2. Development of new multivariate techniques of collecting predictor data. The reduction of computational labor resulting from the use of electronic computer techniques makes feasible a rather simple assessment method given here as an example. Suppose a catalog of 200 or perhaps 1,000 or more traits, both those desired and undesired in submariners, could be compiled. Furthermore, suppose these traits could be measured and coded in a binary fashion, that is, either the submariner candidate has each trait to a strong degree or does not have it at all. The margin of assets over liabilities very quickly determined by the computer may provide highly useful predictors of submariner success.

3. Assessment of initial motivation for the submarine service and perhaps equally important, the problem of maintaining optimal motivation during extended submerged cruises. Perhaps what is needed is a carefully conceived theoretical model from which our research hypotheses systematically emanate. It seems a fair assumption that certain aspects of both goal-directed as well as drive reduction or homeostatic maintenance theories are appropriate. For both types of theories an approach in terms of energy would seem to be the most heuristic. In the vectorial language used in the first section of this chapter, motivation is conceptualized as behavioral directionality and motivational intensity as being proportional to the amount of energy mobilized and channeled in the direction of the goal(s). Blockage of motives results in energy demobilization or redirection. Operational indices of the energy disequilibrium resulting from motivational blockage, if quantifiable, should be a useful measure of motivational intensity.

Some of the classes of variables, hypothetically at least, affecting motivation maintenance are depicted in the following proportionality statement:

$$M_{is} = K_{is}(G_p)(G_{exp})(\text{sym-sat})$$

$$(B_{per})(B_{ant})$$

where M_{is} = over-all maintenance of motivation of individual i in situation s

K_{is} = proportionality constant for individual i in situation s

G_p = goal proximity

G_{exp} = goal expectancy

sym-sat = symbols of need satisfaction

B_{per} = perceived barriers to goal attainment

B_{ant} = anticipated barriers to goal attainment

Attitude change during submergence appears to be an important area of submarine psychology (Table 2). A proposition stated in the language of energetics may suggest the mechanism of positive and negative attitude formation. The person (an open system) seeks out in the closed ecology of the submerged submarine those energy sources (stimuli) that result in states of energy disequilibrium for which he has a specific reduction mechanism ready. Conversely, the person avoids these energy-displacing aspects of the environment for which he has no reduction mechanisms.

4. The development of operational criteria reliably indicating individual differences in the changes in the quality of adjustment as a function of time in the submerged conditions. The methodological possibilities of several "hybrid" techniques of factor analysis have been indicated. In one way or another these methods have argued for the development of adjustment criteria that involve repetitive (rather than static) behavioral observations over *time*. A specification equation (Cattell, 1952) can be written for each variable and each day submerged (for each point on the curves in Figure 5 for example), indicating the significance of a given variable as an adjustment criterion at a given time (occasion).

This equation is

$$S_{om} = S_{o1} F_{m1} + S_{o2} F_{m2} + S_{o3} F_{m3} + \ldots + S_{or} F_{mr} + \ldots$$

where S_{om} = standard score indicating the relative significance of variable m for occasion o

$S_{o1}, S_{o2}, S_{o3}, \ldots, S_{or}$ = factor scores (in standard form) for occasion o on factor 1, 2, 3, ... up to and including the rth factor

$F_{m1}, F_{m2}, F_{m3}, \ldots, F_{mr}$ = factor loadings of variable m in factors 1, 2, 3, ..., r

Hopefully, identification of the psychobiological processes by which men adapt to the conditions of marine submergence will contribute at least a modicum to the understanding of the processes of adjustment to more natural environmental conditions, and, at the same time, will provide some insight into those maladjustive processes contributing to, or diathetic for, debilitative psychopathology.

References

Alvis, H. J. "Submarine Medicine—an Occupational Specialty," *New Engl. J. Med.,* 256:21–25, 1957.

Bartlett, N. R. "Investigation of the Harrower-Erickson Modification of the

Rorschach Test." *U.S.N. Med. Res. Lab. Rep.*, New London, October, 1943, 2 (15, Whole No. 28).

————. "Review of Research and Development in Examination for Aptitude for Sumarine Training 1942–1945," *ibid.*, May, 1950, 9 (2, Whole No. 153), pp. 11–53.

Beach, E. L. *Log of* Triton *Circumnavigation*. No. D201.2: T 73. Washington: Government Printing Office, 1960a.

————. "*Triton* Follows Magellan's Wake," *National Geographic Magazine, 118*: 585–615, 1960b.

Behnke, A. R., Welham, W. C., White, W. A., Jr., and Pace, N. "The Step-up Test to Evaluate Fitness for Physical Exertion in Healthy Men," *U.S.N. Med. Res. Inst.*, December, 1943, Rep. No. 2.

Berrien, F. K. "Relation of Noise to the Habitability of ·Submarines," *A Survey Report on Human Factors in Undersea Warfare*, Washington, D.C.: National Research Council, 1949, pp. 345–355.

Bond, G. L., and Miller, J. "Basic Tests for Enlisted Personnel," in D. B. Stuit (ed.), *Personnel Research and Test Development*, Princeton, N.J.: Princeton University Press, 1947, pp. 53–83.

Briggs, D. L. A. "A Modification of the Thematic Apperception Test for Naval Enlisted Personnel (N-TAT)," *J. Psychol., 37*:233–241, 1954.

Bureau of Medicine and Surgery, Navy Department. *Submarine Medicine Practice*, Washington: U.S. Government Printing Office, 1956.

Campbell, D. T. "A Study of Leadership Among Submarine Officers," *Off. Naval Res.*, N60ri-17 T.O. III NR 171 123, Columbus, Ohio: Ohio State University Research Foundation, 1953.

————. "The Informant in Quantitative Research," *Amer. J. Sociol., 60*:339–342, 1955.

Cattell, R. B. *Factor Analysis*, New York: Harper, 1952.

Chambers, A. N., and Preusser, P. B. (eds.). *Human Factors Design Standards for the Fleet Ballistic Missile Weapon System*, Vol. 1; Bureau of Naval Weapons, Navy Department, Special Projects Office; OD 18413, Contract NORD 18100, Stamford, Conn.: Dunlap, 1960.

Channell, R. C., and Tolcott, M. A. "The Human Factor in the Design and Layout of Submarine Equipment: Analysis of War Patrol Reports and Interviews," *Off. Naval Res., SDC*, September, 1947, Rep. 151-1-4.

Committee on Undersea Warfare. *Bibliography of the Submarine, 1557 to 1953*, National Academy of Sciences, Publication No. 307, Washington, D.C.: National Research Council, 1954.

Cook, E. B., and Wherry, R. J. "A Factor Analysis of M.M.P.I. and Aptitude Test Data," *J. Appl. Psychol., 34*:260–266, 1950a.

————, and ————. "The Urinary 17-Ketosteroid output of Naval Enlisted Candidates during Two Stressful Situations," *Hum. Biol., 22*:104–124, 1950b.

Coser, Rose L. "Insulation from Observability and Types of Social Conformity," *Amer. Soc. Rev., 26*:28–39, 1961.

Crissy, W. J. E., and Pashalian, Siroon. "The Interview, III. Aids to the Interview—the Submariner Stereotype," *U.S.N. Med. Res. Lab. Rep.*, New London, October, 1952, 11 (31, Whole No. 214), 63 pp.

Cronbach, L. J. "Selection and Training," in Committee on Undersea Warfare, *A Survey Report on Human Factors in Undersea Warfare*, Washington, D.C.: National Research Council, 1949, pp. 491–513.

Darrow, C. W., and Henry C. E. "Psychophysiology of Stress," *ibid.*, pp. 417–439.

Duff, I. F. "Medical Study of the Experiences of Sumbariners as Recorded in 1,471 Submarine Patrol Reports in World War II," *U.S.N. BuMed*, 1947, ix, 259 pp.

———, and Shillings, C. W. "Psychiatric Casualties in Submarine Warfare," *Amer. J. Psychiat.*, 103:607–613, 1947.

Duffner, G. J. "Crew Selection for Submarine Duty," *U.S. Armed Forces Med. J.*, 5:1192–1198, 1954.

Dyson, G. W., and Shilling, C. W. "Military Application of Research in Psychological Science," *U.S. Nav. Inst. Proc.*, 81:1023–1029, 1955.

Ebersole, J. H. "Submarine Medicine on USS *Nautilus* and USS *Seawolf*," *Proc. Royal Society Med.*, 51:63–74, 1958.

———. "The New Dimensions of Submarine Medicine," *New Engl. J. Med.*, 262:599–610, 1960.

Eron, L. D., and Auld, F., Jr. "A Study of the Thematic Apperception Test Stories and Sentence Completions of Subjects in Operation Hideout," *U.S.N. Med. Res. Lab. Rep.*, New London, February, 1954, 13 (4, Whole No. 243, iii, 64 pp.

Essen, K. W. "The Nervous Syndrome of Submariners. Clinical Findings, Pathogenesis, Attempt at Therapy," *Monograph on Submarine Medicine*, Folio VII, Germany, U.S. Zone: Office of Naval Advisor, 1948, pp. D IV-1–D IV-40.

Faucett, R. E., and Newman, P. P. "Operation Hideout: Preliminary Report," *U.S.N. Med. Res. Lab. Rep.*, New London, July, 1953, 12 (13, Whole No. 228), iii, 79 pp.

Fiedler, F. E., "Leadership and Leadership Effectiveness Traits: A Reconceptualization of the Leadership Trait Problem," in L. Petrullo and B. M. Bass (eds.), *Leadership and Interpersonal Behavior*, New York: Holt, Rinehart and Winston, 1961, pp. 179–186.

French, R. L. "Morale and Leadership," in Committee on Undersea Warfare, *A Survey Report on Human Factors in Undersea Warfare*, Washington, D.C.: National Research Council, 1949, pp. 463–488.

Graham, C. H., Riggs, L. A., Bartlett, N. R., Berry, R. N., Verplanck, W. S., Solomon, R. L., and Mueller, C. G. "A Report of Research on Selection Tests at the U.S. Submarine Base, New London," National Defense Research Committee, Office of Scientific Research and Development, Project 44, Division 7, OSRD Rep. No. 1770, Contract No. OEMsr-570, Brown University, 1943.

Gulliksen, H. "The Influence of Occupation upon the Perception Time," *J. Exp. Psychol.*, 10:52–59, 1927.

Harris, J. D. "Survey and Analysis of Engine Room Noise in Representative Submarines and Associated Vessels," *U.S.N. Med. Res. Lab. Rep.*, New London, January, 1957, 16 (4, Whole No. 282), iii, 8 pp.

Heron, W. "Cognitive and Physiological Effects of Perceptual Isolation," in P. Solomon, P. E. Kubzansky, P. H. Leiderman, J. H. Mendelson, R. Trumbull, and D. Wexler (eds.), *Sensory Deprivation*, Cambridge, Mass.: Harvard University Press, 1961, pp. 6–33.

Hoff, E. C., and Greenbaum, L. J., Jr. *A Bibliographical Sourcebook of Compressed Air, Diving and Submarine Medicine*, Vol. 2, Washington, D.C.: Office of Naval Research and U.S.N. Bureau of Medicine and Surgery, 1954.

Horst, P., and MacEwan, Charlotte. "Predictor Elimination Techniques for Determining Multiple Prediction Batteries," *Psychol. Reps.*, Monograph Supplement 1-V7, 7:19–50, 1960.

King, B. T. "Some Correlates of Disqualification in the Submarine Service," *U.S.N. Med. Res. Lab.*, New London, August, 1957, 16 (13, Whole No. 291), iii, 23 pp.

———. "Relationships between Submarine School Performance and Scores on the Navy Thematic Apperception Test," *ibid.*, October, 1958, 17 (8, Whole No. 301), ii, 15 pp.

Kinsey, J. L. "Psychologic Aspects of the *Nautilus* Transpolar Cruise," *U.S. Armed Forces Med. J.*, 10:451–462, 1959.

———. and Murphree, H. B. "Claustrophobic Reactions to Some Stresses of the Submarine Service," *U.S.N. Med. Res. Lab. Rep.*, New London, April, 1955, 19 (2, Whole No. 262), v, 39 pp.

———. and Weybrew, B. B. "Etiological Factors in the Disqualification of Submarine Personnel," *ibid.*, June, 1953, 12 (11, Whole No. 226), iv, 40 pp.

Kipnis, D., and Glickman, A. S. "Development of a Noncognitive Battery: Prediction of Performance aboard Nuclear Powered Submarines," *U.S.N. BuPers, Technical Bull.* 61-5, February, 1961.

La Gaipa, J. J. "The Development and Validation of the Advanced Technicians Test," *ibid.*, 59-15, U.S. Naval Personnel Research Field Activity, July, 1959.

Levine, A. S. "Habitability and Motivation as Related to the *Polaris* Submarine," *U.S.N. BuPers, Personnel Res. Div.*, Rep. FBM-11, December, 1958a.

———. "Major Problem Areas in Personnel Management," *ibid.*, Rep. FBM-1, February, 1958b.

Lewin, K. "Time Perspective and Morale," in C. Watson (ed.), *Civilian Morale*, Boston: Houghton Mifflin, 1942, pp. 48–70.

Mackie, R. R., Wilson, C. L., and Buckner, D. N. "Interrelationships between Aptitude Test Scores, Performance in Submarine School as Determined by Ratings and Tests," *Mgmt and Marketing Res. Corp.*, Tech. Rep. V, 1954.

Miller, J., and Owens, W. A. "Basic Tests for Officer Personnel," in D. B. Stuit (ed.), *Personnel Research and Test Development*, Princeton, N.J.: Princeton University Press, 1947, pp. 84–111.

Molish, H. B., Weybrew, B. B., and Ninow, E. H. "Attitude Changes during and Recoverability Following Prolonged Periods of Marine Submergence," *U.S.N. Med. Res. Lab. Rep.*, New London, Report 369, December, 1961.

Muenzinger, K. *Psychology: The Science of Behavior*, New York: Harper, 1942.

Nall, M. L. *Submarine Habitability: A Literature Survey (1951–1959)*; *A. Atmospheric Control; B. Performance under stress;* Contract No. NONR-2718(00), M-MIC 1228, Washington, D.C.: Documentation, Inc., 1959.

Ninow, E. H. "The Use of a Standard Psychiatric Interview to Predict Motivation of Enlisted Men for the Submarine Service," *U.S.N. Med. Res. Lab. Rep.*, New London, November, 1960, 19 (19, Whole No. 344), iv, 26 pp.

———. "Significance of Preventative Psychiatry in the Submarine Service," paper read at Medical Education for National Defense Annual Meeting, New London, Conn., April, 1961.

Parker, J. "A Factor Analysis of the Submarine Officer Selection Battery," paper read at Eastern Psychological Association, Philadelphia, April, 1961.

Pashalian, Siroon, and Crissy, W. J. E. "The Interview: IV. The Reliability and Validity of the Assessment Interview as a Screening and Selection Technique in the Submarine Service," *U.S.N. Med. Res. Lab. Rep.*, New London, January, 1953, 12 (1, Whole No. 216), v. 67 pp.

———, Crissy, W. J. E., Siegel, A. I., and Buckley, E. P. "The Interview: I. A. Selectively Abstracted Bibliography," *ibid.*, June, 1952, 11 (28, Whole No. 202), 57 pp.

Ritch, T. G. "Report on the Effects of Prolonged Snorkelling on the Health of the Officers and Men and on the General Habitability of the Guppy-Snorkel Submarine USS *Trumpetfish* (SS425)," *ibid.*, April, 1948, Rep. No. 132. 9 pp.

Rohrer, J. H. "Studies of Human Adjustment to Submarine Isolation and Implications of These Studies in Fallout Shelters," working paper, Disaster Research Group, 1959.

Roscoe, T. *United States Submarine Operations in World War II*, Annapolis, Md.: U.S. Naval Institute, 1958.

Rubin, Barbara, and Parker, J. W. "The Self-Reported Motivational Questionnaire (SMQ) as a Predictor of Success in Enlisted Submarine School," *U.S.N. Med. Res. Lab. Rep.*, New London, February, 1961, 20 (2, Whole No. 348).

Satter, G. A. "An Evaluation of the Personal Inventory and Certain Other Measures in the Prediction of Submarine Officers' Evaluations of Enlisted Men," Office of Science Research and Development, Rep. No. 5557, 1945, 16 pp.

Schaefer, K. E. "Experiences with Submarine Atmospheres," *J. Aviation Med.*, *30*:350–359, 1959.

Schwartz, I., and Sandberg, N. Elaine, "The Effect of Time in Submarine Service on Vision," *U.S.N. Med. Res. Lab. Rep.*, New London, August, 1954, 13 (14, Whole No. 253), iii, 9 pp.

Scott, E. L. *Perceptions of Organization and Leadership Behavior: A Study of Perceptions of Organization Structure and Their Social Correlates in a*

Submarine Squadron of the U.S. Navy, NOR Contract N6ori-17 T.O. III N.R. 171 123, Columbus, Ohio: Ohio State University, Personnel Research Board, 1952.

Shilling, C. W., and Kohl, Jessie W. "History of Submarine Medicine in World War II," *U.S.N. Med. Res. Lab. Rep.,* New London, May, 1947, 9 (3. Whole No. 112), 213 pp.

Smith, E. E. "The Effects of Clear and Unclear Role Expectations on Group Productivity and Defensiveness," *J. Abnorm. Soc. Psychol.,* 1957, 55, 213–217.

Tagiuri, R. "Social Preference and Its Perception," in R. Tagiuri and L. Petrullo (eds.), *Person Perception and Interpersonal Behavior,* Stanford, Calif.: Stanford University Press, 1958, pp. 316–336.

Weybrew, B. B. "Q-methodology in Criterion Research," *U.S.N. Med. Res. Lab. Rep.,* New London, October, 1953, 12 (24, Whole No. 239), iii, 28 pp.

———. "Predicting Success in Submarine School," *ibid.,* November, 1954, 13 (20, Whole No. 259), v, 37 pp.

———. "Predicting Adjustment to Long Periods of Confinement: A Study in Factor Analytic Methodology," unpublished doctoral dissertation, University of Colorado, 1955.

———. "Some Factors Affecting Errors in Time Perception," paper read at the Connecticut State Psychological Society, Yale University, New Haven, May, 1956.

———. "An Exploratory Study Designed to Suggest Clusters of Traits and Assessment Tests Related to Submariner Adjustment," *U.S.N. Med. Res. Lab. Rep.,* New London, January, 1957a, 16 (1, Whole No. 279), iii, 14 pp.

———. "Psychological and Psychophysiological Effects of Long Periods of Submergence. I. Analysis of Data Collected during a 265-Hour, Completely Submerged, Habitability Cruise Made by the USS *Nautilus* (SSN571)," *ibid.,* February, 1957b, 16 (3, Whole No. 281), iv, 43 pp.

———. "Some Trends in the Submariner Selection Data for 1956–1957," *ibid.,* October, 1957c, Memo Rep. No. 57-6, iii, 12 pp.

———. "Patterns of Reaction to Stress as Revealed by a Factor Analysis of Autonomic-Change Measures and Behavioral Observations," *J. Gen. Psychol.,* 60:253–264, 1959a.

———. "The Personal Inventory Barometer (PIB): II. Obverse Factor Analysis with PIB Items as a Validation Technique with Submarine School Criteria," *U.S.N. Med. Res. Lab. Rep.,* New London, May, 1959b, 18 (4, Whole No. 309), iv, 13 pp.

———. "Factor Analysis of Ratings from Two Populations: Wintering-over Antartic Personnel and the Crew of the USS *Triton* during the World Circumnavigation," paper read at the Invitational Conference on Research Relevant to Behavioral Problems of Small Military Groups under Isolation and Stress, Texas Christian University, Fort Worth, March, 1961a.

———. "Impact of Isolation upon Personnel," *J. Occup. Med.,* 3:290–294, 1961b.

———. "Psychological Effects of Long Periods of Marine Submergence: Preliminary Results of an Experiment Conducted during the World Circumnavigation by *Triton*," paper read at Medical Education for National Defense Annual Meeting, New London, April, 1961c.

———. "Behavioral Energetics: I. A. Factorial Study of Individual Differences in Modes of Energy Discharge Resulting from Experimentally-Induced Frustration," *U.S.N. Med. Res. Lab. Rep.*, New London, Report No. 378, March, 1962.

——— and Alves, D. "An Exploratory Study of the Relationship of Autonomic Resiliency to Manifest Anxiety and Selected Personality Traits," *ibid.*, March, 1959, 18 (2, Whole No. 307), iii, 14 pp.

——— and Molish, H. B. "Approaches to the Study of Motivation of Officer Candidates for the Submarine Service," *ibid.*, October, 1959, 18 (16, Whole No. 321), iv, 47 pp.

———, and Molish, H. B., and Youniss, R. P. "Predicting Adjustment to the Antarctic," *ibid.*, April, 1961 20 (4, Whole No. 350).

———, and Parker, J. W. "Bibliography of Sensory Deprivation, Isolation, and Confinement," *U.S. Armed Forces Med. J.*, *11*:903–911, 1960.

———, and Youniss, R. P. "The Personal Inventory Barometer (PIB): I. Development of the Questionnaire," *U.S.N. Med. Res. Lab. Rep.*, New London, August, 1957, 16 (12, Whole No. 290), iii, 25 pp.

——— and ———. "The Relationship of Breathholding Ability, Manifest Anxiety, and Past Aquatic Experience to Performance in the Pressure Chamber and Escape Training Tank," *ibid.*, January, 1960, 19 (4, Whole No. 329), iv. 15 pp.

Willmon, T. L., and Ritch, T. G. "Report on the General Health and Morale of The Officers and Crew During a 30-Day Simulated War Patrol Aboard a Snorkel Submarine," *ibid.*, November, 1948, Rep. No. 140a, 7 pp.

Youniss, R. P. "An Investigation of Motivation for Submarine Duty and its Relation to Submarine School Success," *ibid.*, November, 1956, 15 (7, Whole No. 278), iv, 13 pp.

5

PSYCHOPHYSIOLOGY OF HIGH-ALTITUDE EXPERIENCE

**David G. Simons,
Don E. Flinn,
and Bryce Hartman**

USAF School of Aerospace Medicine
Brooks Air Force Base, Texas

I. Introduction

THE term psychophysiology is employed to describe the relationship between psychological performance and measurable physiological changes. High-altitude stress experience is divided into three general categories: *acute psychophysiological stress* of a few hours' duration, *acute fatigue stress* in excess of 24 hours of continuous duty, and *task-commitment stress* involving many days.

Acute psychophysiological stress may occur in response to anticipated and real hazards of flight, for example, in experimental high-performance aircraft and in space flight. It may occur in the acute physiological form as hypoxia, G stress, hyperthermia, and the like.

Acute fatigue stress (as distinguished from chronic fatigue) describes

---

The views and the opinions expressed in this chapter in no way constitute a statement of official Air Force policy.

the stress experienced by an initially well-rested individual required to perform continuous duty longer than approximately 24 hours. We are concerned here when this occurs under real or simulated hazardous flight conditions. Acute fatigue stress includes 24-to-48-hour one-man "out and home again" space flights that require constant vigilance and performance on the part of the astronaut.

Task-commitment stress describes the experience of an individual committed to a highly prescribed activity regime in a restricted environment for a prolonged period of time. Examples are multiday space-chamber experiments and multiday space flights.

This chapter consists of four sections. The three sections following the introduction consider examples of each of the above three categories of high-altitude stress experience in turn. The final section relates these experiences in terms of psychophysiological concepts and suggests directions for future research in this area.

II. Acute Psychophysiological Stress

Von Beckh (1959) was one of the first to record the kind of physiological data that can be correlated with reactions of the psyche in acutely stressful aircraft flight. In order to study the reactions of human subjects to alternation between weightlessness and 3 G acceleration, he recorded their electrocardiogram and skin resistance, took serial photographs of their heads and shoulders, and recorded radio voice communications. ECG and skin resistance were recorded on a galvanometer oscillograph on board an F-94C aircraft.

Figure 1 illustrates a typical record obtained with this instrumentation. Von Beckh (1959) calls attention to the increased arousal of the subject at 0.5 minute when he was warned of the imminent sustained 3 G maneuver preceding weightlessness. The series of undulations in the skin resistance record immediately following announcement of the plan to initiate a spiral (between 0.50 and 1 minute in Figure 7) present the typical picture of a series of galvanic skin reflex responses characteristic of increased central nervous system (CNS) arousal. The abrupt 2:1 drop in skin resistance concomitant with the transition from 3 G to weightlessness presents the characteristic picture of a strong startle reaction. This could well be the strong arousal of the individual anticipating the crucial weightlessness test, the point of the flight; that is, the GSR changes are probably psychological in origin. The author did not analyze the changes in heart rate. Measurement of the published data, however (Figure 1), shows that between minutes 2.1 and 2.2 at the

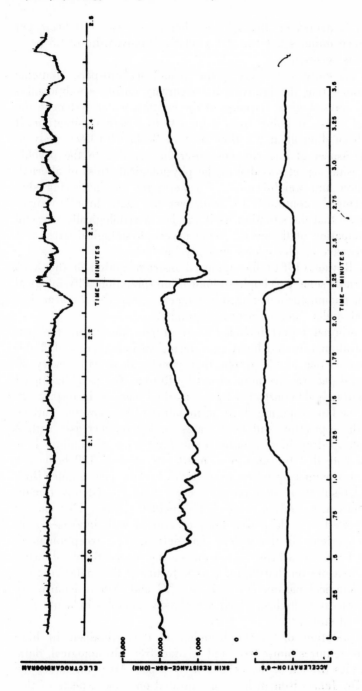

Figure 1. Pre-through postweightlessness records of ECG, skin resistance, and acceleration in F-94C flight. (By permission *Journal of Aerospace Medicine.*)

end of the 3 G maneuver, the subject's heart rate was 110 beats per minute. Between minutes 2.3 and 2.4 a relative bradycardia of 83 beats per minute was recorded.

Research currently under way at the School of Aerospace Medicine has demonstrated that the bradycardia occurring during weightlessness is a primarily physiological response of the cardiovascular system to the environmental stress of going from a high G to a zero G situation. It would have been difficult at the time of Von Beckh's (1959) study to identify what aspect of any changes observed was due to the psychic stimulus and what aspect was due to the physiological stress of alternating acceleration and weightlessness. Furthermore, the increasing skin resistance during the continued 3 G maneuver and again through weightlessness suggests that the situation itself was less psychologically stressful than the anticipation of the event. Acute psychophysiological stress is a complex interweave of physiologic and psychic factors.

Recently, Rowen (1961) has reported instrumentation of the X-15 pilots that permits some psychophysiological interpretation. Physiological data included pneumotachometry, skin temperature of the forearm, leg, abdomen, and axilla, and electrocardiography.

Rowen's original report includes eight graphs illustrating the patterns of respiration rate and heart rate during various phases of flight. Figure 2 presents one of his graphs that samples these rates every 30 seconds. Several patterns are pointed out by Rowen. The psychic impact of launch is strongly demonstrated by the marked increase in respiratory rate through the launch period. With termination of the powered portion of flight, both respiration and heart rates tended to decrease, with a particularly sharp drop in respiration upon completion of landing. It is of interest to note that the maximum heart rate exceeds 180 beats per minute and maximum respiration exceeds 37 breaths per minute. Both the pulse and respiration rates on the second flight consistently remain lower than the corresponding rates on the maiden voyage. This change can be interpreted as a decreased level of arousal with increased confidence and experience in the system. The only marked exception is an excess of heart rate for a brief period during the second flight following a premature flameout on that flight. It is unfortunate that data from additional physiological parameters such as EEG and skin resistance are not available on these flights, which are classic examples of acute psychophysiological stress.

The interpretation of psychophysiological data obtained in high altitude flight requires noise-free and artifact-free physiological data. The Biodynamics Branch of the School of Aerospace Medicine under the direction of Dr. James Roman has concentrated on some aspects of this problem. His group (1961) reported that, by concentrating on refine-

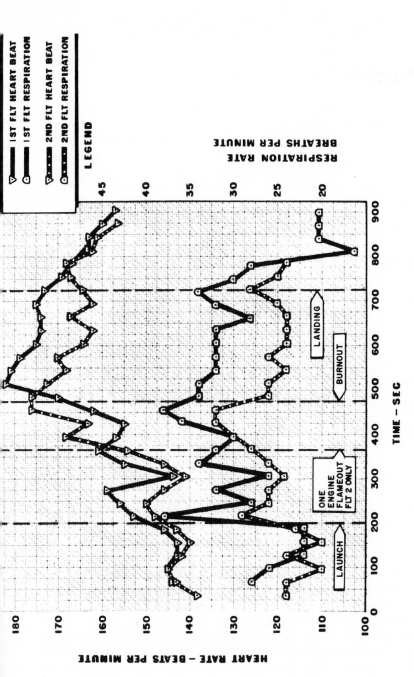

Figure 2. X-15 in-flight pulse rates and respiratory rates comparing the first and second flights of two pilots. (By permission from Rowen, AFFTC, Edwards AFB.)

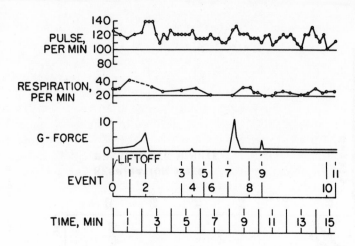

Figure 3. Pulse rate, respiration rate, and acceleration in Astronaut Shephard's MR-3 Redstone ballistic trajectory flight. (From Burch and Greiner, 1960.)

EVENTS

1. Maximum dynamic pressure
2. Launch-vehicle engine cutoff: Spacecraft separation: Turn-around
3. Retroattitude
4. Retrofire
5. Retrojet
6. Reentry attitude
7. 0.05 g
8. Drogue chute deployment
9. Main chute deployment
10. Impact
11. Loss of signal

ment of electrode technique and refinement of lead placement, they have been able to obtain laboratory quality ECG records (nonstandard leads) from the pilot during F-100 flights. To measure respiration, they use a heated thermo-couple sensor fitted within the quick-disconnect fitting of the pilot's oxygen line, developed for and used by the X-15 program. Based on their F-100 studies, they concluded that heart rates between 120 and 150 beats per minute are normal during critical phases of high performance aircraft flight.

In addition, Ware (personal communication) has developed a means of automatically continuously monitoring systolic and diastolic blood pressure during flight. This procedure, too, is said to provide laboratory quality records during flight. A major part of this group's effort concerns the development of a seat pack that permits the physiological data to be recorded by an on-board oscillograph or telemetered directly to the ground from the aircraft. No detailed flight data using this instrumentation have been published to date.

At 9:34 A.M. on May 5, 1961, Astronaut Shepard piloted the MR-3 Redstone Ballistic Space Flight. Augerson and Laughlin (1961) reported Shepard's physiological responses during this flight as illustrated in Figure 3. Instrumentation included two channels of nonstandard ECG with the electrodes placed in axillary and sternal positions during flight. Pulse rates were determined at 15-sec intervals through a 10-sec period. Rectal body temperature was sensed with a thermistor and computed at 30-sec intervals through a 30-sec period. In addition, pictures of the astronaut's face were taken at six frames per second and his voice transmissions recorded "of quality sufficient to convey a suggestion of mental state."

Until 1 minute before launch, the heart rate remained close to 80 beats per minute. Between lift-off and the end of the flight, it varied between 100 and 138 beats per minute. This change was interpreted as reflecting the pilot's increased level of arousal at launch, his high level of activity during the 5½ minutes of weightlessness and his close attention to the critical re-entry phase (Augerson and Laughlin, 1961).

The respiratory rate remained close to 20 breaths per minute before launch. During launch, the respiratory rate peaked at 40 breaths per minute, but returned to the previous initial level of 20 during weightlessness, fluctuating between 20 and 25 during descent and entry into the atmosphere. Body temperature increased $\frac{2}{10}$°F during the flight. The authors draw no psychophysiological inferences from this analysis of the physiological data.

In each of these examples of acute psychophysiological stress, the problem of obtaining interpretable physiological data eclipsed considerations of more refined methods of analysis and psychophysiological interpretation. The problem to date has been to obtain any data at all. Refinements have had to wait.

III. *Acute Fatigue Stress*

This section considers high-altitude experiences involving approximately 24 hours of continuous duty. The data from these acute fatigue stress situations are selected and discussed from a psychophysiological point of view.

The first high-altitude experience of sufficient duration to fall under this category that also included an attempt to gather psychophysiological data was the 32-hour MANHIGH II balloon flight. The instrumentation (Simons, 1959) included the telemetry of respiration rate and heart rate 4 minutes out of every 5. In addition to this physiological information, the pilot was required to render two subjective reports regularly in conjunction with his hourly reports to the ground. One required an estimate of his personal condition (Operational efficiency and judgment) based on a scale from 0 to 100 per cent. The second required a report of his thermal comfort based on the following five-point scale:

> Too hot
> Hot
> Comfortable
> Cold
> Too cold

Following launch at 9:22 A.M. the telemetry system operated continuously for 13 hours but functioned intermittently thereafter. The ground personnel were depending largely on an improvised tape recorder to record the physiological data. Since it failed, only sporadically recorded values are available. Based on these records, the heart rate ranged between 78 and 132 beats per minute and the respiration rate ranged between 19 and 44 breaths per minute during the flight. The high heart rate was observed during the night and early morning, the high respiration rate around noon of the second day.

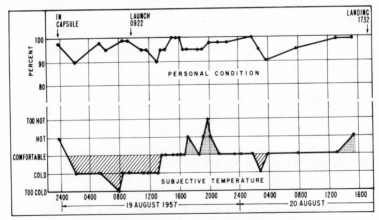

Figure 4. Subjective ratings by MANHIGH II pilot during a 32-hour high-altitude solo balloon flight, August, 1957.

Figure 4 presents the pilot's subjective assessment of how well he was performing his tasks during the flight. Toward the end of the flight, between 4:00 A.M. and 5:32 P.M., the consistently high ratings above 90 per cent are clearly contrary to the actual level of performance that the pilot exhibited in his state of acute fatigue. By the end of the flight, he had been incapsulated and continuously "on duty" for 42 hours, relieved only by occasional naps of 10 to 20 minutes' duration (Simons, 1960). Additional subjective observations and comments are available (Simons, 1958). It is now recognized (McFarland, 1953) that subjective evaluations of performance are poorly correlated with actual levels of performance in the absence of feedback information.

Reliable objective measures of performance in operational situations are difficult to find, particularly measures that do not interfere with, or add additional burdens to, the primary task. One of the prime objectives of the MANHIGH II flight was to take maximum advantage of the opportunity to record as many observations as possible of subjective experiences and physical phenomena during the flight. A miniature tape recorder was reserved just for this purpose. No mandatory comment or scheduled reports were required on it. Thus, any time spent dictating to this recorder represented a form of initiative or spontaneous activity. Figure 5 is a bar graph in which the percentage of time spent dictating to this recorder is averaged over arbitrary periods selected partly when the time was identified on the tape.

The first major recording activity peak occurred between 8:30 and 10:00 A.M. during the prelaunch and launch period; the second peak, between 12:00 noon and 1:00 P.M., represented the pilot's first opportunity to make observations from an altitude of 100,000 ft. The pilot's initiative, as indicated by this graph, dropped off through the afternoon, exhibiting a relatively low and short-lived peak of activity around sunset, at 9:00 P.M. The next surge of spontaneity, between 5:00 and 6:00 A.M., represents the second time the pilot had an opportunity to observe the sun crossing the horizon, sunrise. It is noteworthy that during sunrise a longer period of time and a significantly higher percentage of time was spent dictating to the recorder than at sunset, even though it was the pilot's second opportunity to see this phenomenon. Possibly the numerous short periods of sleep, totaling 2½ hours during the night, plus circadian periodicity, permitted a much higher level of arousal and increase in the pilot's spontaneous activity in the morning. The remainder of the flight until 3:32 P.M. is marked by sporadic bursts of activity interrupting extremely low levels of initiative. This intermittent loss of alertness is characteristic of advanced acute fatigue (McFarland, 1953).

The senior author had an opportunity to participate in a 30-hour SAM one-man space-cabin simulator run that was similar in many ways to the 32-hour MANHIGH flight. He was required to be in the chamber 7 hours before the run, as compared with 12 hours within the capsule before the MANHIGH flight. The physical space available, 50 cu ft, was comparable in each case. The atmospheric environment was similar. The busy MANHIGH flight was filled with all of the challenges of detecting new phenomena and responsibilities of conducting the flight. On the other hand, the chamber experiment involved an operator system that demanded constant attention but very little activity. Two other individuals not assigned primary duty as Air Force pilots completed a similar run in this phase of the program. One additional run aborted.

Upon completion of each experiment, the subject was asked when he thought he had performed most efficiently during the 30-hour period. In each case, the subject felt that he had rated his highest scores during the final hours of the run. The results showed that each operator maintained a high level of vigilance throughout the first 20 to 24 hours. All operators showed intermittent periods of seriously deteriorated vigilance during the final hours. The fact that they were unaware of this deteriorated performance and were even in fact, congratulating themselves on their superior performance may have ominous implications for space flights involving acute fatigue stress.

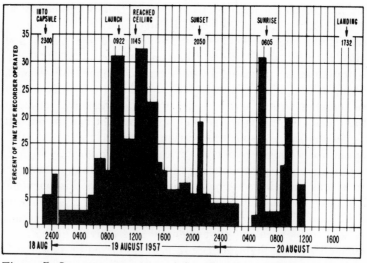

Figure 5. Spontaneous activity of the pilot of the MANHIGH II flight as measured by the per cent of time spent dictating to the on-board tape recorder.

Technically, the fact that the MANHIGH III flight (scheduled a year after MANHIGH II) ended as a 12-hour rather than a 24-hour flight as planned places it in the acute psychophysiological stress rather than the acute fatigue stress category in terms of our definition. Since, however, the instrumentation and tests were designed to measure psychophysiological phenomena on a longer flight, it is presented here.

A number of lessons were applied to the MANHIGH III flight (Simons, *et al.*, 1961) from the MANHIGH II experience (Simons, 1959):

1. An effort was made to provide continuous physiological data on individual telemetry channels.

2. Continuous tape recordings of all transmitted data were obtained.

3. The physiological data themselves were written out in real time to permit immediate assessment and to minimize the danger of losing data due to undetected difficulties.

4. The psychological performance rating scales were modified in an attempt to increase their scope and sensitivity. The scales employed included:

a. *Subjective Temperature.* This pilot report item was renamed "comfort." The same criteria were used as before.

b. *Personal Condition.* This report item was renamed "efficiency" to clarify its meaning. The pilot was thoroughly briefed that this represented a subjective assessment of his performance, that is, the effectiveness with which he was doing things. The original scale of 0 to 100 per cent was retained, but the pilot was repeatedly admonished to center the reports around 50 per cent.

c. *Alertness.* This is the first of three items that were added to gain further insight into the loss of thinking ability. Alertness was reported on a five-point scale:

> Acutely alert
> Alert
> Normal
> Tired
> Desperately sleepy

d. *Drive.* This item, too, was reported on a five-point scale. It concerned the innate desire to do things and served to distinguish between a feeling of spontaneous enthusiastic pleasure in doing things *versus* the feeling of having to force oneself to drag through a chore. It was reported as follows:

> Very eager
> Enjoy activity
> Don't care
> Requires effort
> Requires extreme effort

e. *Tension.* This five-point scale gave the pilot an opportunity to indicate the tension level at which he was operating. It had no reference to any specific source of tension, but represented the pilot's assessment of the total load of anxiety he felt, either from specific identifiable problems or the nonspecific background situation in which he found himself. This was reported as follows:

> Completely relaxed
> Calm
> Ready
> Uneasy
> Panicky

A similar subjective rating scale, more refined from a psychological methodology point of view, has been carefully formulated and validated (Pearson and Byars, 1956).

The MANHIGH III flight carried a three-channel FM telemetry transmitter that transmitted physiological data to the ground recording station. The subject was wired into this transmitter through an umbilical-cord-type wiring harness. The physiological parameters included one channel of respiration, one channel of ECG primarily for heart rate, and one channel subcommutated to include three ½-minute samples of basal skin resistance every 5 minutes.

In addition to the telemetry, the subject was automatically photographed by an infrared flash (invisible to him) recording his face and shoulders. A four-point body-temperature null-balance potentiometer scale permitted voice reports of three skin and one rectal temperature.

The details of the MANHIGH III flight have been reported (Simons, *et al.*, 1961). The subjective pilot ratings obtained during the flight are presented in Figure 6. Several points should be kept in mind concerning these pilot reports. The pilot was repeatedly impressed with the importance of centering his efficiency ratings around 50 per cent. Readings were not made after 5 hours because the hyperthermia emergency and voice communication failure interrupted this report schedule. This report is remarkable for the lack of awareness by the pilot that he was becoming

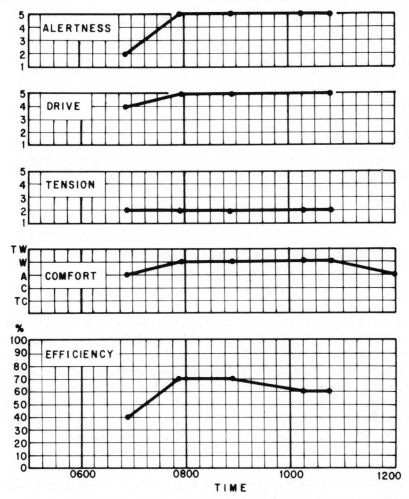

Figure 6. Subjective pilot ratings by the pilot of the MANHIGH III
high-altitude balloon flight, October, 1958.

too warm. It again emphasizes *unreliability* of subjective evaluations,
which may be aggravated in a tension-breeding operational situation.

The physiological data obtained during the flight (Figure 7) are
presented against the background of the flight time-altitude curve. Although the physiological measures were selected for their psychophysiological importance, they served as valuable indices of thermal physiological stress. The fact that heart rate began to increase at noon aroused
concern as to the reason. Investigation revealed that the near-normal

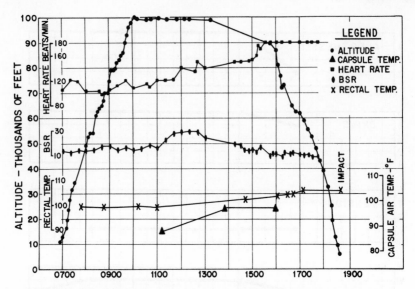

Figure 7. Physiological data related to flight altitude observed during the MANHIGH III high-altitude balloon flight.

telemetered temperature values were in error. In fact, the capsule was intolerably hot. At 1:50 P.M. it was firmly established that the temperature was 96°F at head level. This situation demanded immediate descent to provide relief from the heat. Later in the afternoon, during descent, Lt. McClure's heart rate reached a plateau of 180 beats per minute while his basal skin resistance steadily declined. Although his internal body temperature reached a final value in excess of 106°F when he landed at 5:30 P.M., he accomplished the delicate procedure safely.

Although on this flight psychophysiological effects were masked by the severe physiological stress, the course of events emphasized the importance of complete physiological monitoring of pilots undertaking hazardous exploratory space missions.

IV. Stress Arising from Prolonged Commitment to the Task

This third category of high-altitude stress is available only in the simulated form. This section considers the psychophysiological aspects of multiday simulated high-altitude experiences.

The altitude chamber has played a significant role in space-flight research. Fitted out with living facilities and life-support systems, it has been used as a test bed for concepts in space capsule design and life-support subsystems and as a tool for studying a variety of psychological and physiological problems of prolonged manned space flight. Most studies involving prolonged commitment to the task have been carried out in these modified altitude chambers. The number of such facilities is limited, and for the most part only government laboratories or aircraft industries have been able to support this kind of space cabin simulator. The Air Force School of Aerospace Medicine developed the first such simulator. The Aeromedical Laboratory at Wright-Patterson Air Force Base, Lockheed Aircraft Corporation at Marietta, Georgia, the Air Crew Equipment Laboratory, Philadelphia, and, more recently, North American Aviation at Los Angeles, also have space cabin simulators built around modified chambers.

Psychological problems in chamber programs have been given major emphasis at the School of Aerospace Medicine and the Lockheed facility. Hauty, performed a number of experiments using the SAM One-Man Space Cabin Simulator and also supervised the psychological and other aspects of the development of the SAM Two-Man Space Cabin Simulator (Hauty, 1958, 1960). In the one-man cabin program, Hauty made explicit the concept of operator reliability, using it as a more operational statement of the problem of the maintenance of proficiency at a level acceptable for over-all systems function in space flight. It is obvious that operator reliability has special significance for space flight, because of the extended commitment of the astronaut to the task and because of the fact that support or relief is feasible only to a minimal degree.

The one-man simulator was a small altitude chamber just large enough for one occupant, his life-support equipment, and a psychomotor test apparatus. During "flights," the front part of the chamber was completely filled with the operator task apparatus and a television tube upon which part of the task was presented. Cabin pressure was maintained at ½ atmosphere with a twice normal percentage of oxygen. The subject was monitored at all times by closed circuit television. During work periods he was presented with tasks involving the functions of spatial discrimination, perceptual judgment, vigilance, and problem solving. The situation provided many elements of isolation and monotony of sensory input. The subject had no visual contact with anything outside the chamber and was required to attend intensively to a small field of work for a prolonged period. The occurrence of perceptual aberrations in such a situation has been demonstrated previously.

Flight schedules were of two types: a 30-hour mission during which continuous performance was required and a 7-day mission. During the latter, two different work-rest schedules were followed: some of the subjects were on a 4-hours-on-4-hours-off duty schedule, while the remainder were on a 5-hours-on-3-hours-off duty schedule. The performance data on all of these flights have been reported by Hauty. (1958, 1960).

Seven subjects have made the 7-day flight (Steinkamp, *et al.*, 1959). Six of these were experienced pilots. They maintained performance at consistently high levels. Another subject, similar to the others in intelligence and education, but without flying training or experience, showed a significant performance decrement. His performance dropped off within each work period, and very low levels of proficiency occurred during the third work period (1:00 to 5:00 A.M.). This latter decrement is what would be predicted from the literature on diurnal cycles. It is interesting that the other, more sophisticated, subjects showed no diurnal effects.

Of equal interest was the observation that the over-all behavior of the trained pilots was generally purposeful, relevant, and well organized. In contrast, the behavior of the inexperienced subject was undisciplined and poorly organized. In addition, he showed increasing irritability and emotional lability during the later days of the flight. None of the seven subjects experienced any hallucinations or other perceptual aberrations.

The 30-hour flight schedules were undertaken by eight subjects. During these missions, continuous performance was required. After about 18 hours, under the combined conditions of fatigue and a marked restriction of the perceptual field, a variety of visual, auditory, and proprioceptive aberrations were experienced by more than half the subjects. Several reported that the dials on the task panel sometimes looked like faces or other figures. Other subjects heard music or voices, had the sensation that their arms and legs were enlarged, felt that someone else was sitting beside them in the chamber, or believed that a large hole had opened up in the floor of the chamber. Usually these illusions were momentary, although in the last-mentioned case, the subject reached down and felt the floor to convince himself it was still intact.

In one case, the aberration was less benign. It centered on the television tube on which part of the operator task was displayed. This subject at the twenty-first hour of the flight suddenly developed the hallucination that the tube was on fire and about to explode. He thought the inside of the tube had turned black and believed that he felt the heat and smelled the smoke. He could not be convinced that the tube was functioning perfectly, and the flight had to be terminated because of the subject's mounting anxiety.

Perceptual aberrations such as these are quite similar to those reported in experimental studies of severely restricted sensory input in sensory deprivation studies. In these chamber experiments, fatigue was undoubtedly an important additional factor. For the most part, the subjects recognized their illusions as unreal, but the last case illustrates the critical importance of misperceptions with a plausible content. Such illusions during a space flight, especially if they involved some mechanical aspect of the flight system, might provoke inappropriate responses that would seriously jeopardize the mission. Only one other 30-hour flight had to be prematurely terminated. The subject, who was not a pilot, developed severe anxiety at being confined and asked to be removed after 2 hours.

These flights also provided some provocative results concerning the influence of diurnal variation. Four of the eight subjects were experienced pilots. In the 7-day runs, these subjects showed no diurnal effects. In three 30-hour runs, the subjects maintained acceptable levels of proficiency during the first 18 hours of the flight. At that point, two of the subjects show a decrement that persisted for 4 to 6 hours. This decrement occurred during the early morning from 2:00 to 6:00. The other two subjects started the flight 8 hours earlier in the 24-hour period. They showed a comparable decrement, but it did not appear until 24 hours after the beginning of the flight. Because of the difference in starting times, however, this decrement also occurred during the early morning, from 2:00 to 6:00. Hauty concluded that short space flights involving *continuous* work by the astronaut should be initiated *at a point in the day where diurnal effects will be minimized.*

In the one-man cabin studies, then, both fatigue and diurnal cycles were significant variables under certain circumstances. Fatigue appeared to be the more important of the two. Continuous performance was the key condition under which fatigue is an important problem. The diurnal cycle seemed to be less of a problem, except under conditions of continuous performance for extended periods of time.

Research in the two-man cabin has indicated that in orbital flights of more than one or two days' duration, a minimum of two crew members will be required. While this situation can be expected to mitigate the effects of solitude, new problems related to personal interactions are introduced. Although the primary purpose of the two-man simulator is the study of life-support, logistic, and metabolic characteristics of a closed ecological system, it offers a unique opportunity to observe the effects of prolonged confinement on a two-man crew.

The simulator requires the subjects to manage three broad categories: logistics of the mission, such as waste disposal, food preparation, and recycling of fluids; cabin pressure, oxygen concentration, CO_2 level, humidity, and other such internal environmental conditions; and an operator task, or psychomotor test apparatus, by means of which the proficiency of the subjects is assessed. The operator task incorporates measures of vigilance, perceptual judgment, problem solving, and decision-making, like the apparatus in the one-man cabin but at a more complex level and with greater demands on the subjects.

In order to give the subjects motivation and a frame of reference for operating the system, the tasks were given descriptive names and functions simulating those a man in space might be expected to perform, such as Navigation and Orbital Flight Computer System, Airborne Radar and Doppler Position System, and Data Telemetry System. An operating manual was written that elaborated on these functions and instructed the subjects how the tasks were to be performed. It appeared to have high acceptability to the subjects and contributed to their motivation.

The work schedule required the operator task to be manned a total of 22 hours each day with two 1-hour periods of ground control. The subjects manned the system on alternate shifts, with work periods ranging from 2 to 5 hours.

Half of the flights had the long work periods at night to permit the subjects to sleep as much as 6 or 7 hours at a single stretch each day. Since only one subject manned the operator system at a time, it might appear that there was a considerable amount of free time. This was not the case. In addition to the required sleep periods, there were a variety of other duties to be performed including fixing meals, operating the waste disposal and water recycling units, and checking and calibrating the environmental controls.

The over-all behavior and interaction of the subjects was studied through pre-flight and post-flight psychiatric and psychological evaluations and in flight observations by means of closed-circuit television and concealed microphones.

To date, seven flights have been completed. The first flight of 14 days' duration at a simulated altitude of 18,000 feet was a check-out of the chamber itself, and the operator task was not activated. A second full-scale flight, at the same altitude, was of 30 days' duration. A third flight, of 17 days' duration, at an altitude of 33,000 feet with a 100 per cent oxygen atmosphere, was recently completed. The fourth flight was of 30 days' duration, and the remaining three have lasted 17 days. The subjects on all but the first flight were rated pilots. The results on psychological elements of the early flights have been reported by McKenzie, et al. (1961) and Flinn, et al. (1961).

Only the psychological aspects of these flights will be presented. Variables affecting proficiency that were studied included: the effect of 30-day commitment to the task, the effect of work periods of varying length, the effect of differing signal rates, and the effects of differing times of day. Analysis of the data reveals that only signal rate produces a significant difference. Performance is poorer at the low signal rates. Subjects have reported marked boredom during these low-signal periods. In general, the results on proficiency are like those from the 7-day flights in the one-man cabin, although the flight was four times as long and the tasks considerably more complex. As may be expected, operator reliability can be maintained for long periods of time when there is a regular work-rest schedule and a reasonable amount of activity is programmed. Thus, it appears that we have a great deal of leeway in selecting effective schedules.

Some preliminary observations can be made about interpersonal behavior during the two-man flights. In general, the subjects maintained surprisingly high morale and motivation during the prolonged flights, experienced very little boredom despite the seeming monotony of their routine, and did not show any unusual emotional changes. In each flight, however, some conflicts were revealed. For example, a taciturn individual may be irritated by the continual conversation of a talkative crewmate, while the latter feels rebuffed when his comments are ignored. Or a meticulous, methodical subject may be irritated by the disorganization and untidiness of his crew-mate, while he is considered by the latter to be needlessly slow and obstinate. During such prolonged and inescapable contact with another person, seemingly innocuous habits and mannerisms can eventually become irritating. Such trivialities as a noisy manner of eating, frequent clearing of the throat, or a minor omission in personal cleanliness can in time provoke resentment.

Examples such as these have occurred in the chamber, but it is important to note that they become known *only after the flights*. The antagonistic feelings that the subjects reported in personal diaries or that they described during post-flight debriefings did not affect their interpersonal behavior during the flight. The success of the mission was sufficiently important to them that they consciously refrained from any behavior which might have had a disruptive effect and they continued to work together without open antagonism. Hostility toward monitoring personnel outside the chamber was also observed and at times was openly expressed. It usually centered around the subjects feeling that outside personnel were not giving adequate support.

Physiological data published from those flights (Morgan, *et al.*, 1961) included heart rate, systolic and diastolic blood pressure, body temperature, and respiration rate, each presented as daily averages. No correlations were reported between physiological data and performance measures.

A comparable simulator program is under way at Lockheed Aircraft Corporation's Georgia plant (Adams, *et al.*, 1959). Their program emphasizes the psychological aspects and provides for some psychophysiologic assessment, but minimizes logistic and ecological considerations. This difference in emphasis is important. It is possible that the relatively "neutral" performance results in the SAM studies are the result of greater emphasis on logistical and ecological management. The Lockheed simulator is a five- or six-man advanced flight station mock-up. It is not an altitude chamber, but is otherwise conceptually similar to the SAM space cabin simulators.

The psychomotor section consists of a battery of tasks developed to be "(a) representative of the psychologic factors important to a wide variety of operator performance duties, (b) minimally influenced by specific past experience, and (c) show promise of being sensitive to the experimental conditions to be imposed." Seven tasks, representing perceptual motor coordination, mental computations, pattern discrimination, monitoring, and vigilance, were selected. These were: (1) compensatory tracking, on a standard cross-pointer indicator, (2) arithmetic computation, using "hardware" presentation and response, (3) pattern discrimination, involving matching sequential pairs of patterns, (4) auditory vigilance, in which the subject must detect abnormal delays between "beeps," (5) scale position monitoring, in which the subject must detect meter values that are out of tolerance, (6) warning light monitoring, and (7) probability monitoring, in which the subject must detect biases on continuously moving meter pointers. In this device, there is a good bit of time-sharing of the tasks, since several tasks are monitoring or vigilance tasks. This simulator also has a complex continuous tracking task, a performance dimension never used in the School of Aerospace Medicine programs.

Adams, *et al.* (1959), have reported a series of studies with this simulator on variations in work-rest cycles under conditions of prolonged commitment to the task. Using 12 hours of work per day as the standard requirement, they had crews on work-rest schedule of 2–2, 4–4, 6–8, and 8–8. Though subjects preferred the shorter cycles, there were no performance differences. These studies each lasted 96 hours.

A more extended analysis of work-rest schedules involved a study of the 4–2 cycle over a period of 15 days. Though there were some differences between subjects and across tasks, the major conclusion was that motivated subjects could function effectively under this rigorous schedule for extended periods. Adams and Chiles (1961) also reported some diurnal variations in performance and some adaptation of diurnal rhythms to the working schedule.

After completing two 15-day experiments, they analyzed the daily score of all 11 subjects for each task, dividing the total time into three equal 5-day periods. Figures 8 and 9 present their analysis of such within-day results for the arithmetic computation and the red warning light tasks, respectively. The information in these figures will be referred to later.

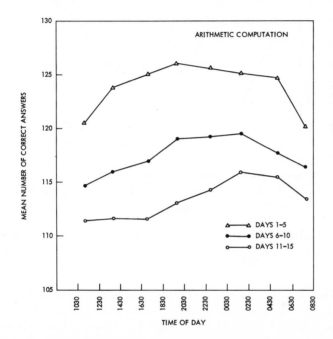

Figure 8. Within-day changes in level of arithmetic task performance during simulated 15-day space flight. (Reported by Adams and Chiles, 1961. Reproduced by permission.)

On these same 15-day experiments, they sampled four physiological measures on two crew members during each 2-hour work period. Four 5-minute samples of physiological data were recorded during each 2-hour work period. The individuals monitored were rotated through the group, so that each crew member was monitored four times daily. Analyzing the basal skin resistance and heart rate based on a 12-hour "rolling mean," Adams and Chiles (1961) presented one point for each parameter each 2-hour work period. Figures 10 and 11 illustrate the strong diurnal pattern observed and the progression to successively higher skin resistance levels as the experiments progressed. This progression can be interpreted as a decreasing level of psychophysiological arousal throughout the experiment.

Only one parameter of one member of the nonvolunteer crew showed

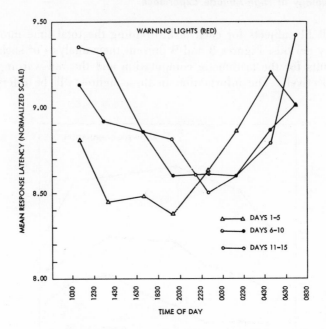

Figure 9. Within-day changes in level of warning-lights monitoring-task performance during 15-day space flight. (Reported by Adams and Chiles, 1961. Reproduced by permission.)

no significant decrease in this psychophysiological level of activation. By contrast, in the more highly motivated volunteer group, five of the 12 trends (six BSR and six heart rate) showed no change. The authors made no mention of any effort to correlate these individual psychophysiological trends with individual performance measures.

Finally, the work at North American Aviation should be discussed. Though only in very early stages, it follows the pattern of the School of Aerospace Medicine and Lockheed program.* The emphasis in their initial flight was equally divided between life-support and psychological problems. This was a three-man, 17-day 2-on–4-off flight. Of particular interest was the fact that effective performance on the psychomotor task could bring considerable monetary reward. Nevertheless, the preliminary results are like those already discussed. In general, no significant differences on long-term variables were obtained. A signal rate effect was evident—performance was poorer at the very low rate, despite the motivation.

It appears that operator performance and reliability can be main-

---

* Personal communication with Mr. Sam Tobey, North American Aviation, Los Angeles.

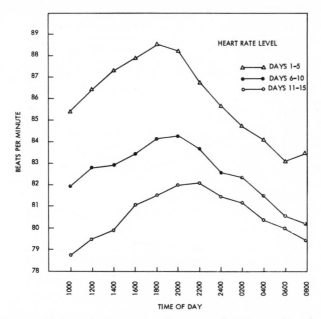

Figure 10. Within-day changes in heart-rate level during simulated 15-day space flight. (Reported by Adams and Chiles, 1961. Reproduced by permission.)

tained over long periods of time under conditions such as are imposed by the space cabin simulators. Serious impairment of proficiency occurs beyond 18 to 20 hours of continuous performance, but there is considerable leeway in choosing suitable work-rest schedules that will permit effective performance of a single operator for at least 7 days. Two operators can remain effective for at least 30 days and with adequate motivation can maintain a satisfactory working relationship. These preliminary observations must, of course, remain tentative until further experience is accumulated with the space cabin simulators and eventually with actual space flight.

V. Psychophysiological Measurements

The previous sections have reviewed experiences relating to high-altitude flight. The psycholoigcal and physiological measurements made during these experiences have been summarized and selected data pre-

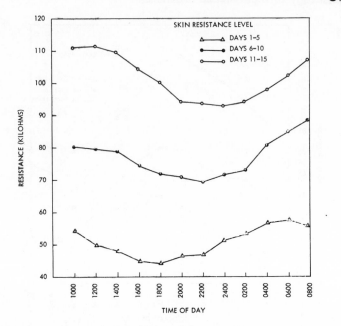

Figure 11. Within-day changes in skin resistance level during simulated 15-day space flight. (Reported by Adams and Chiles, 1961. Reproduced by permission.)

sented. This section attempts to relate the psychological aspects of these experiences to the physiological data available in terms of central nervous system function.

It is becoming more and more widely recognized that the purpose man can serve in space is to perform those mental functions of which man is uniquely capable. This point was emphasized from both the engineering and medical point of view at the 1961 International Astronautical Federation Congress held in Washington, D.C. From the engineering point of view, Karmiol, *et al.* (1961), have emphasized that man would be needed where flexibility and functional sophistication beyond computer technology were required. He presented man as an *integrated* part of the man-machine system. Franks (1961), defined man's role in space as threefold: (1) to exert decisive control of the operation, (2) to observe and learn, and (3) to deal with unforeseen emergencies.

These are clearly the kind of functions that Karmiol, *et al.* (1961), described as sophisticated beyond computer technology.

At the American Rocket Society Space Flight Report to the nation, General Bernard A. Schriever (1961), Commander, Air Force Systems Command, described man's military role in space: "But while satellite-borne instruments can gather a variety of information, they are no sub-stitute for the unique abilities of man to observe, to make judgments, and, most important, to exercise control based on these judgments."

If man ceases to function at this sophisticated level even for short periods, he not only ceases to perform his role but he also endangers the success of the mission and his own survival. If man is included as a sophisticated thinking part of the man-machine system, then there is just as great a need for instrumentation to monitor this function at its required level as for monitoring purely mechanical functions. It is equally im-portant that a malfunction be detected before it approaches the critical mission failure point, not after. Many emergencies, fire, for example, characteristically are readily dealt with when they begin, but quickly grow to catastrophic proportions if undetected or mishandled.

Indices of the level of sophistication at which an individual is (or is still capable of) functioning therefore may be critically important in space missions. The development of such indexes from objective tele-meterable neurophysiological data is especially important because sub-jective pilot reports are unreliable. True psychophysiological experiments of this type will require structuring of the selection, handling, and processing of both the psychological data and the physiological data in ways that permit them to be more meaningfully mated to each other. No high-altitude experiments are known that have done this work in the manner proposed here. First an examination of the selection and proc-essing of psychological behavior data is in order.

It is possible to look at human performance under the stress of high-altitude experience in terms of levels of mental functional sophistication. Some activities apparently require the finely coordinated activity of a much greater portion of the central nervous system than others. The simple reaction time (vigilance) tasks should logically make minimal demands on the central nervous system. They compare neurophysiologi-cally to a simple sensory-motor reflex arc, requiring only the visual recog-nition of the stimulus and the activation of essentially one memory unit to trigger the motor response. There is only one (no choice) possible re-sponse, suggesting minimal mental "effort."

A complex arithmetic computation task such as the one employed by Adams and Chiles (1961) required the subject to mentally compute the algebraic sum of three 3-digit numbers presented as nine evenly spaced digits in a horizontal row. The first two numbers were to be added and the third subtracted. The orientation of the numbers represented a transposi-tion from the customary columnar arrangement. The necessity of adding and subtracting digits that are separated by two other equally spaced digits, of remembering partial sums, and so forth, obviously requires the coordinated activity of many more units of mental function than the simple reaction time task. It would take a far more complex computer to perform this arithmetical computation task. Both tasks are so simple, however, that in a sophisticated space craft whatever flight functions they represented are not likely to be primary functions of the man.

As is obvious, the ability to formulate sound decisions, observe new phenomena, and react to the unexpected will be essential to astronauts. The best engineer is unable to predict all the interactions of the vehicle to the relatively unfamiliar environment of space or all the vehicle's own functional weaknesses (Williams and Hopkins, 1958). The ability of the astronaut to detect and react promptly and appropriately to these unexpected interactions (such as the hyperthermia experience of Lt. McClure on MANHIGH III) may well mean the difference between life and death in space. Initiative is here defined as mental function at this level of complexity. Simple reaction-time (reflex) thinking, or even arithmetical-computation-level thinking, will not suffice. No one has yet built, and few have had the temerity to propose, a computer that can recognize an unprogrammed problem, evaluate its significance, select within itself appropriate memory units to relate all previous experience to this problem, and derive an answer that it will then act on as immediate or future appropriate action.

This task requires the availability of the coordinated memory of all previous experience, which must involve a major portion of the cerebral cortex. But even more significantly, it requires the evaluation of importance, which carries the implication of how much the individual (or computer) cares about the problem. Does it matter? Such emotional responses have their seat in the hypothalamus closely related to the reticular formation and the associated structures between the cortex and brain stem. Thus, initiative-type responses apparently require not only the integrated activity of the entire main computer memory bank—the cerebral cortex—but also the integrated activation of the structures related to more global behavior.

It is not unreasonable to suspect that under the stresses of space flight, the most sophisticated activity, initiative, which requires multiple integration of highly complex central nervous system activity, may suffer serious degradation before arithmetic computation ability, which, in turn, may suffer serious degradation before simple reaction time responses. If analysis of task performance revealed such step-wise degradation in tasks requiring different orders of magnitude of complexity of central nervous system integration, this could prove a most fruitful direction for further investigation.

Although no single experiment is known that observed decrement in performance using measures selected in terms of complexity of central nervous system function, we can draw from two unrelated experiments that provide some evidence in support of this hypothesis. The first concerns a simple reflex-arc level activity devised by Hauty (see Section IV). He described the operator task employed in the one-man chamber experiment as involving functions of spatial discrimination, perceptual judgment, vigilance, and problem solving. For each function, including the problem solving, it was only a matter of several hours until the operator simply recognized a prescribed stimulus pattern and responded with the one and only proper response. The impression one got while operating the system was that fundamentally the only variation required in complexity of central nervous system function was in the degree of complication of the stimulus pattern. One of the three nonpilots who completed the 30-hour experiment showed very little "vigilance" decrement until the last hour of the experiment. Four Air Force pilots completing comparable 30-hour experiments showed no such marked decrement in vigilance. This level of performance appears relatively resistant to acute fatigue stress, possibly more so with acclimatization to it.

At this point, it is of utmost importance to clearly distinguish the "vigilance" described in these Hauty and Adams experiments versus the "vigilance" required in the detection phase of initiative. In these chamber experiments, the subject was thoroughly indoctrinated to look for the specified stimulus situation. Essentially, his task was to recognize whether it was present or absent. From the point of view of the complexity of neurophysiological mechanisms involved, this task is hardly comparable to detecting the unforeseen and recognizing that this novel situation requires a previously unspecified action.

Although the 15-day work situation of the Adams and Chiles (1961) experiment was not comparable in many ways to MANHIGH II flight experiences, their data provide an opportunity to compare changes in performance of tasks requiring two levels of complexity of central nervous system integration under partially simulated prolonged spaceflight conditions. The response latency analysis of the red-warning-light task classified by the authors as a vigilance task represents one of the simplest of recognition-response tasks. The arithmetical task can be thought of as demanding a higher order of central nervous system structural complexity.

Analysis of warning light task data derived from Figure 9 shows that the estimated average mean response latency for the first 5 days was 8.73, rising to 8.83 the second, to 8.96 the third day—a total rise of 3.8 per cent. Estimates derived from the data presented in Figure 8 indicate the average number of correct answers scored on the arithmetic computation test degraded from an average of 123.9 for the first 5-day period through 117.4 for the second to 113.3 for the third 5-day period—a drop of 8.6 per cent. The fact that in this study the arithmetic computation scores showed twice as much decrement as the less mentally demanding red-warning-light test proved nothing in itself. It does suggest a basis for selecting tasks and analyzing results and suggests that this may form a valid basis for structuring behavior tasks.

Figures 10 and 11 illustrate the changes in heart rate and skin resistance noted each successive 5-day period. The progressive increase of skin resistance and decrease of heart rate suggest a progressive decline in level of central nervous system arousal. When this is related to the steady decline in performance in the above tasks, it suggests that the crew members may have been suffering from boredom and deteriorating motivation. The fact that all five subjects of the nonvolunteer group showed significant decrement in the highly demanding arithmetic task, whereas the same trend was observed in only three of the six subjects of the volunteer group, tends to support this interpretation. In the case of the simpler monitoring task, individual trends indicated a greater tendency toward degradation by nonvolunteer subjects. Comparison of individual performance score trends and heart rate basal skin resistance trends would be most interesting.

The evidence of performance decrement primarily due to boredom indicates that prolonged task-commitment experiments as described here may not realistically simulate pioneering space-flight missions. The actual flight experiences to date point up the strong likelihood of major or minor emergencies arising, especially on longer flights. Emergencies not only insure freedom from boredom, but may well convert task-commitment stress to acute fatigue stress in a struggle for survival.

The second experiment, the MANHIGH II flight yielded the only known data attempting to measure initiative in a comparable prolonged high-altitude experience. Figure 5 indicates a marked difference in this measure between the first and the second afternoon of flight. Between 1:00 and 5:30 of the first afternoon, the pilot averaged 16.6 per cent of his time making spontaneous comments to the tape recorder. During the same hours of the second day, no comments were made to it.

This lack of response occurred in spite of numerous situations and subjective experiences worthy of comment. During this second-day period, the capsule passed through a marked haze layer at 70,000 ft. This was a phenomenon that the pilot had been warned might be seen above the tropopause, that had never been reported previously, and that he wished to observe and report in detail. He also was startled during this period by a painful burning sensation on his right arm to discover that the 6-in.

telescope was accidently pointed toward the sun focusing its image on his pressure suit, which was already smoldering. Both of these events, and others like them, certainly would have been the subject of description and some discussion to the tape recorder had they occurred the previous day.

This measure of initiative illustrated in Figure 5 suggests a marked decrement during the first afternoon between 4:00 and 8:30 after 16 hours in the capsule. It is also interesting to note that only one-fourth as much time was spent dictating during sunset as during sunrise after several hours of sleep. Considering the fact that the sunset was the initial experience and the most remarkable, it is likely that this difference reflects a fatigue effect.

Although these two test situations differed greatly, the measure of initiative seemed to degrade much more quickly and more severely than the tasks making simpler demands on the central nervous system. Comparison of these experimental results in terms of neurophysiological complexity of the demands upon the central nervous system suggests that performance measures structured in such terms may show step-wise decrement measure by measure with continued stress. Correlated with appropriate physiological data this could be of fundamental psychophysiological importance.

Behavior obviously is related to levels of arousal and emotion. These are generally considered to be expressed neurophysiologically in the activity of the autonomic nervous system. Certainly, conscious behavior is a function of cortical activity that can be observed physiologically as the electroencephalogram. What functional neurophysiological mechanisms relate cortical activity with those deep-seated central nervous system functions closely allied to autonomic nervous system activity? What neurophysiological evidence is there for a relationship between behavior and physiological measures? Lacey and Lacey (1958) thoroughly reviewed neurophysiological literature to answer these questions following a most interesting psychophysiological experiment.

In their experiment, they studied 28 volunteer adult women under a variety of stressful circumstances while continuously recording their basal skin resistance and their heart rate, measuring the latter with a cardiotachometer. The volunteers were first monitored during a 15-minute relaxation period. They were then given a series of 20 mild electric shocks, each received after a slow countdown to the number 9. Following this, each took the McKinney Reporting Test, a paper-and-pencil test designed to frustrate the examinee. Skin resistance was analyzed in terms of the number of half-minute periods during which sufficient sympathetic autonomic activity occurred to produce a change in resistance of 600 ohms. Half-minute periods during which such a change occurred were considered "bursts" of skin resistance activity. The authors were impressed with the distinctive patterns exhibited by individuals. Some were characterized by "stabile" flat skin resistance records, while "labile" individuals exhibited frequent "bursts."

Corresponding bursts of cardiac activity were scored by comparing the single maximum heart rate in each 5-sec segment and tallying the number of half-minutes that contained two successive 5-sec segments in which the second segment scored a rate at least six beats faster than the preceding segment. This analysis was used to render the scoring of heart rate comparable to the skin resistance measure and to delete sinus arrythmia effects.

Comparing the autonomic activity patterns expressed by the number of skin resistance and cardiac bursts, Lacey and Lacey (1958) found that resting activity shows widespread, reliable individual differences and that an individual tends to emit a relatively constant number of bursts of skin resistance activity at rest, even when experiencing a markedly different level of emotional stress. The resting autonomic activity (number of bursts) was found to be predictive of nonresting autonomic activity levels. Individuals with stabile patterns remained stabile, both resting and active; and those with labile patterns were labile, both resting and active. The Laceys were intrigued by what seemed to them obvious personality differences between, at least, the extremes of their autonomic measures. Individuals with chaotic records during rest and activity differed from those with flat, uneventful tracings. The former seemed overly reactive and the latter unreactive and phlegmatic, but these descriptions were only crude and qualitative with many discrepancies.

The Laceys' paper includes a brilliant review presenting the neurophysiological basis of autonomic system relations to three other central nervous system activities:

1. The levels of sympathetic autonomic activity are clearly related to the electrical activity of the cortex.

2. There is a comparable integration of the autonomic nervous system with the function of skeletal muscles.

3. There is a powerful, homeostatic control relating stimulation of the baroceptors of the carotid sinus with sympathetic and cortical activity.

A summary of key experimental facts supporting each relationship follows.

The Laceys reviewed evidence for both ascending and descending autonomic-cortical coupling. Ascending effects, both positive and negative, are illustrated by (1) the almost complete cessation of cortical brain waves or (2) the appearance of large low-frequency potentials (characteristic of somnolence) in the presence of bilateral hypothalamic lesions.

Stimulation of the hypothalamus, on the other hand, produces an arousal reaction like that produced by stimulation of the ascending reticular activation system of Magoun (1954).

The functional cortical-autonomic relationship is nicely demonstrated by the finding that "stimulation of the hypothalamus with stereotactically inserted electrodes produced excitatory electrical effects on the cortex, *depending on the ability of the stimulated point in the hypothalamus to evoke sympathetic discharge*" (Murphy and Gellhorn, 1945). Of 92 hypothalamic foci that produced pupillary dilatation when stimulated, 88 per cent also produced excitatory cortical effects. On the other hand, of the 40 hypothalamic foci failing to evoke sympathetic responses, 82 per cent were negative for cortical effects.

The cortical effects outlasted hypothalamic stimulation by 20 to 40 sec. The Laceys pointed out that this indicates the excitatory electrical patterns exhibited by the cortex were initiated by hypothalamic impulses, but that the cortex itself sustained the excitation.

The harmony between peripheral sympathetic activity and cortical electrical activity was beautifully demonstrated in curarized animals at sensory rest. Completely parallel spontaneous variations in blood pressure and changes in the frequency of cortical electrical activity were seen. The smoothly ascending and descending lines of the blood pressure tracing were completely in phase with increasing and decreasing cortical frequency. Observing this relationship from another point of view, the Laceys found a report that stimulation of the reticular formation resulted in simultaneous blood pressure increases and shifts to high-frequency electrical activity of the cortex. These observations are nicely summarized:

Two mechanisms thus are revealed in these experiments which result in an exquisite mutual adjustment of autonomic activity and cortical electrical activity. Nonspecific afferents to the ascending reticular activation system simultaneously leads to sympathetic discharge and a cortical arousal reaction, via a direct reticulo-hypothalamic-thalamic-cortical system (Lacey and Lacey, 1958).

The relationship between sympathetic and cortical activity can be an indirect one, starting downward as an autonomic discharge and then return by way of visceral afferent pathways to be fed back through the reticular activation system sometimes helping to maintain the very activity that initiated the response.

Concerning the second type of relationship, the same authors cite experiments by Murphy and Gellhorn (1945) in which hypothalamic stimulus electrodes facilitate cortically induced movement of skeletal muscles depending upon the ability of the stimulated point in the hypothalamus to evoke sympathetic discharge. These results were closely comparable and statistically correspond to the presence or absence of hypothalamically induced EEG responses.

To establish the third relationship, the Laceys cite clear evidence that denervation of the carotid sinus baroceptors causes a sudden transition of cortical electrical activity from a resting rhythm to an extremely rapid rhythm of 30 to 60 cycles per second that maintains itself undisturbed for hours. On the other hand, distension of the carotid sinus positively stimulating the intact baroceptors produces a fall of blood pressure and a simultaneous decrease of cortical electrical activity to a 3-to-5-cycle pattern. This effect is mediated primarily through the nervous system and not indirectly through the drop in blood pressure.

The Laceys point out that, based on these neurophysiological principles, an individual with a low incidence of spontaneous or evoked autonomic fluctuation when stimulated would be expected to produce an increment in the level of cortical arousal that would be self-sustained for a short time. The cortical arousal would be inhibited by any increase in blood pressure caused by the stimulus, with a gradual return to basal conditions. An individual with a high incidence of spontaneous autonomic fluctuation, on the other hand, should show either long sustained high levels of cortical electrical activity or more rapidly occurring cycles of relative cortical arousal and cortical quiescence. This labile individual would be expected to show a higher sensitivity to sensory stimuli and a higher spontaneous motor activity (impulsivity).

Following this review, the Laceys (1958) reported a second experiment on 34 male college students to test this hypothesis. They employed a task that appeared to the subject as a test of reaction time but that included cues that encouraged false responses. Using the same autonomic measures as in their earlier experiment, the Laceys confirmed that autonomic labiles react more quickly and tend to make more false responses than autonomic stabiles. They also found that autonomic labiles (especially with regard to cardiac lability) can maintain maximum "readiness to respond" longer than autonomic stabiles. This experiment strongly reinforces their concept of spontaneous activity. It also suggests that the clearly demonstrated neurophysiological interrelationships between the sympathetic nervous system and the cortex correlate with psychomotor behavior. They emphasize that "small changes rapidly occurring may be more effective as feedback stimuli than large changes occurring slowly." The wealth of psychophysiological information the Laceys derived from two relatively simple experiments by *continuously* monitoring *patterns* of response of the sympathetic nervous system suggests how much is to be gained by more refined analysis of physiological data in psychophysiological experiments.

In the same way that the value of a psychophysiological experiment will be greatly enhanced by a careful selection of the performance tasks, these observations lead to specific guide lines for the selection of physiological parameters and methods for analyzing them. The authors know of no high-altitude experience or experiment that has been fully monitored both psychologically and physiologically. Table 1 shows graphically how incomplete and discontinuous high-altitude physiological data reports have been to date.

Judging by Table 1, heart rate is one of the most popular psychophysiological measures and from the results of the Laceys a potentially valuable one.

Table 1. Period between Data Points

	F-94C	X-15	F-100	MR-3	MH II	MH III	Adams, et al.	Sam Chambers	Lacey and Lacey
Heart rate	I	30 sec	I	15 sec	S	15 min	2 hr	24 hr	30 sec
Blood pressure			I					24 hr	
Respirator rate		30 sec	I	30 sec	S	15 min	I	24 hr	
Basal skin resistance	Cont					15 min	2 hr		Cont
Galvanic skin reflex									30 sec
EEG									
Body temperature			I	15 min		S	I	24 hr	

S indicates sporadic aperiodic data.

I indicates basic measurement made but data not reported or analyzed.

The infrequent use of blood pressure as a source of data is doubtless due to the awkwardness and bulkiness of the necessary equipment. Neurophysiologically it appears to be a most promising psychophysiological measure.

Respiration is a popular measure, but needs methods of measurement and analysis that will more sensitively indicate changes in both rate and volume. It is interesting to note that the gross respiration rate changes reported on the X-15 and the MR-3 flights appeared to be a more sensitive indicator of the emotional strain than the gross heart rate measures.

The skin resistance measures provide one excellent bioelectric indication of autonomic activity but suffer from a number of instrumentation difficulties in operational situations. The Laceys (1958) pointed out that they suspect apparent inconsistencies between their first and second experiments because of the poor resolution of the 30-sec epoch on which their analyses were based. The challenge here is the development of methods of continuous analysis.

It is noteworthy that no human high-altitude experience includes EEG records. Because of the very low signal level, it is a technically difficult parameter to measure; and the amount of information provided by the raw EEG is overwhelming. Some simplifying automatic analysis, that still retains the valuable psychophysiological information is mandatory.

Body temperature is relatively easy to measure, and at this point appears of psychophysiological value primarily to identify the phase relation between the individual's activity and his circadian period. It may also serve as a valuable indicator of thermal stress.

Promising methods of analysis will be discussed briefly for two key neurophysiological measures—EEG and skin resistance.

Burch and Childers (1961) recommend analysis of EEG into major and minor period counts for psychophysiological evaluation. They describe the EEG major period count as the number of EEG waves occurring during a given epoch (usually 1 minute). The waves counted are characterized by the dominant or fundamental frequency familiar in clinical EEG. The minor period count corresponds to the number of superimposed higher frequency waves riding on the dominant frequency. Thus, the minor count measures wave complexity. Burch and Greiner (1960) demonstrated the sensitivity of major and minor period counts to intravenous doses of barbiturate and epinephrine.

Since the level of cortical arousal correlates rather well with both the frequency and the amplitude of the clinical EEG, a method of analysis that considers both and is automatically continuously recorded in real time may offer some advantages. Riehl (1961) has developed such a system. He obtains the activation response factor (U_a) by multiplying the average frequency times the reciprocal of the amplitude of the EEG. Since frequency tends to increase with increasing activation, and amplitude decrease, the factor U_a increases strongly with increasing cortical activation. He has demonstrated changes in the U_a level with gross variations in arousal level as between sleep and wakefulness, as well as dramatic transient responses to more subtle stimuli such as mild electric shock, problem solving, and name-calling.

With respect to the psychophysiological analysis of basal skin resistance Levy, et al. (1961), demonstrated the value of recording BSR on a slowly moving record so that a 24-hour recording is compressed onto a few feet of record. This readily permits pattern analysis. He has presented the basal skin resistance as a general index of arousal. This slow write-out has the advantage of providing an uninterrupted record.

Evaluation of individual galvanic skin reflexes superimposed on the BSR pattern can be measured directly on a sufficiently amplified BSR record as Lacey and Lacey (1958) did it (if the recorder provides sufficient scale to permit this detailed analysis), or it can be obtained in magnified, but distorted form, through capacitive coupling with increased amplification. The latter is the classical technique for recording GSR. However it is obtained, Lacey and Lacey (1958) have argued eloquently for analysis of the frequency of occurrence of changes in resistance rather than analysis of amplitude changes. It is clear that each reflects a different aspect of the activity of the sympathetic nervous system. The electronic techniques developed by Burch and Childers (1961) for EEG major and minor period analysis are readily adaptable to GSR analysis and permit automatic recording for the amplitude, frequency, and active GSR time of the individual reflex resistance changes. Each of these can also be summed in epochs of 1 minute. Continuous analysis of *patterns* of GSR frequency and *patterns* of GSR amplitude conducted in integrated psychophysiological experiments are required to resolve clearly what is the most valuable form of skin resistance data for psychophysiological analysis. It is frustrating to note how few data of this type are available from high-altitude experiences to date.

Obviously, no single physiological parameter in itself provides sufficient information to provide a satisfactory psychophysiological monitoring system. Each parameter contributes helpful information to complete a picture of the psychophysiological status of an individual. As more parameters are measured simultaneously and automatically analyzed with continuous read-out, the possibility of cross-correlating the information greatly expands.

One way to monitor multiple physiological parameters in high-altitude operations is to transmit them from a miniaturized personal telemetry system carried on the individual. This provides four major advantages:

1. The monitored individual experiences minimum encumbrances with wires and wiring harness. He is completely freed of an umbilical cord tethering him to recording instrumentation.

2. Wireless transmission greatly improves the common-mode noise-rejection ratio. In other words, common mode electrical interference (60-cycle power-line hum on the ground, 400-cycle hum in aircraft) is effectively rejected because the radiofrequency telemetry link requires no common ground connection. This arrangement permits high-quality EEG records in locations that would otherwise be prohibited by high levels of ambient electrical noise.

3. When two or more physiological parameters require direct electrode contact with the body (such as ECG, skin resistance measures, and EMG) the common electrical paths frequently create serious mutual interference problems. Using independent battery supplies and making the electronic circuitry of each parameter completely independent until each are combined as video or radiofrequency signals makes it possible

to retain direct-current information without common-path direct-current interference.

4. In psychophysiological experiments, the psychological impact of an individual being wired directly to the experimentor's instrumentation cannot help but influence his attitude toward the experiment and the experimentor. With unobtrusive electronic instrumentation, the wireless link can be quickly forgotten and the subject's attention can be focused on the experiment itself. Thus, the influence of the physiological instrumentation on the psychological aspects of the experiment is minimized.

A one-channel FM/FM EEG transmitter has been developed at the School of Aerospace Medicine that transmits clinical quality EEG records in ambulatory subjects. The unit is a six-channel miniaturized FM/FM telemetry system originally designed and built by Spacelabs, Inc., and subsequently modified by the School of Aerospace Medicine to transmit simultaneously ECG, respiration, BSR, GSR, and temperature.

In summary, it becomes apparent that to conduct a truly psychophysiological experiment, one must tailor the psychological measures and analyses to the structure and function of the central nervous system. Likewise, one must tailor the physiological measures and analyses to neurophysiological response patterns that relate to the behavior of the subject. Implanted electrode studies of the central nervous system are providing the kind of neurophysiological data essential for selecting appropriate measures and analyses. Electronic technology now provides the means for transmitting multiple physiological parameters from miniaturized personal telemetry systems permitting monitoring in operational situations. Although no high-altitude experience to date has been effectively monitored in a psychophysiological sense, it is now possible and should be done. It could herald a new era in aerospace medicine.

References

Adams, O. S., and Chiles, W. D. "Prolonged Human Performance as a Function of the Work-Rest Cycle," ORD 273, Lockheed Aircraft Corp., Marietta, Ga., May, 1961.
———, Levine, R. B., and Chiles, W. D. "Research to Investigate Factors Affecting Multiple-Task Psychomotor Performance," WADC Tech. Rep. 59 120, Wright Air Development Center, ARDC, Wright-Patterson AFB, Ohio, March, 1959.
Augerson, W. S., and Laughlin, C. P. "Physiological Responses of the Astronaut

in the MR-3 Flight." Conference on Results of the First U.S. Manned Suborbital Space Flight, NASA Pub. of papers presented, June 6, 1961.

Burch, N. R., and Childers, H. E. "Physiological Data Acquisition," in *Psychophysiological Aspects of Space Flight*, New York: Columbia University Press, 1961.

———, and Greiner, T. H. "A Bioelectric Scale of Human Alertness: Concurrent Recordings of the EEG and GSR," *Psychiat. Rsch. Reports 12*, Amer. Psychiat. Assn., January, 1960.

Flinn, D. E., Monroe, J. T., Cramer, E. H., and Hagen, D. H. "Observations in the SAM Two-Man Space Cabin Simulator. IV. Behavioral Factors in Selection and Performance," *Aerospace Med., 32*:610–615, 1961.

Franks, W. R. "Homeostatic Compensatory and Failure Patterns in Stress," presented at the Twelfth IAF Congress, Washington, D.C., October, 1961.

Hauty, G. T. "Human Performance in the Space Travel Environment," *AU Quart. Rev., 10*:2, Summer, 1958, Hq. Air Univ. USAF, Maxwell AFB, Ala.

———. "Maximum Effort-Minimum Support Simulated Space Flights," *Aero/Space Engineering, 19*:44–47, 1960.

Karmiol, E. D., Knauff, P. R., and Youtcheff, J. S. "Space Reliability through Man-Equipment Synthesis," presented at the Twelfth IAF Congress, Washington, D.C., October, 1961.

Lacey, J. L., and Lacey, B. C. "The Relationship of Resting Autonomic Activity to Motor Impulsivity," *The Brain and Human Behavior*, XXXVI, Proc. of the Assn. for Rsch. in Nerv. and Ment. Dis., 1958.

Levy, E. Z., Johnson, G. E., Serrano, J., Thaler, V. H., and Ruff, G. E. "The Use of Skin Resistance to Monitor States of Consciousness," *Aerospace Med., 32*:60–66, 1961.

McFarland, R. A. "Operational Aspects of Fatigue," in *Human Factors in Air Transportation*, New York: McGraw-Hill, 1953.

McKenzie, R. E., Hartman, B. O., and Welch, B. E. "Observations in the SAM Two-Man Space Cabin Simulator. III. System Operator Performance Factors. *Aerospace Med., 32*:603–609, 1961.

Magoun, H. W. "The Ascending Reticular Formation and Wakefulness," in *Brain Mechanisms and Consciousness*, Springfield, Ill.: Charles C Thomas, 1954.

Morgan, T. E., Ulvedal, F., and Welch, B. E. "Observations in the SAM Two-Man Space Cabin Simulator. II. Biomedical Aspects," *Aerospace Med., 32*: 591–602, 1961.

Murphy, J. P., and Gellhorn, E. "Influence of Hypothalamic Stimulation on Cortically Induced Movements—Action Potentials of the Cortex," *J. Neurophysiol., 8*:341–364, 1945.

Pearson, R. G., and Byars, G. E., "The Development and Validation of a Checklist for Measuring Subjective Fatigue," SAM Report 56-115, December, 1956.

Riehl, J. L. "An Analog Analysis of EEG Activity," *Aerospace Med., 32*:1101–1108, 1961.

Roman, J. A., Ware, R. W., Adams, R. M., Warren, B. H., and Kahn, A. R. "School of Aviation Medicine Physiological Studies in High Performance Aircraft," presented at the thirty-second Annual Meeting of the Aerospace Medical Assn., Chicago, April, 1961.

Rowen, G. "Biomedical Monitoring of the X-15 Program," AFFTC-TN-61-4, Air Force Flight Test Center, Edwards AFB, Calif., 1961.

Schriever, B. A. "Air Force Systems Command Address to the ARS Space Flight Report to the Nation," Washington, D.C., October, 1961.

Simons, D. G. "MANHIGH II," AFMDC TR-59-28, Holloman AFB, N. Mex.

———. "Pilot Reactions during MANHIGH II Balloon Flight." *J. Aviation Med.*, *29*:1–14, 1958.

———. "Psychophysiological Aspects of MANHIGH," *Astronautics*, *4*:32–34, 1959.

———, McClure, D., Beeding, E. L., and Gildenberg, B. "USAF Manned Balloon Flight into the Stratosphere, MANHIGH III," AFMDC TR-60-16, Holloman AFB, N. Mex., 1961.

———, and Schanche, D. *MANHIGH*. New York: Doubleday, 1960.

Steinkamp, G. R., Hawkins, W. R., Hauty, G. T., Burwell, R. B., and Ward, J. E. "Human Experimentation in the Space Cabin Simulator," SAM Report 69-101, 1959.

von Beckh, H. J. "Human Reaction during Flight to Acceleration Preceded by or Followed by Weightlessness," *Aerospace Med.*, *30*:391–409, 1959.

Williams, A. C., Jr., and Hopkins, C. O. "Aspects of Pilot Decision Making," WADC TR-58-522, Wright Air Development Center, ARDC, Wright-Patterson AFB, Ohio, 1958.

II

SPECIFIC PROBLEM AREAS

6

ISOLATION AND
SENSORY DEPRIVATION

Neal M. Burns and

Space and Armaments Systems
Honeywell Aeronautical Division
Minneapolis, Minnesota

Douglas Kimura

United Aircraft Corporate Systems Center
Farmington, Connecticut

Introduction

OVER twenty years ago, Rear Admiral Richard E. Byrd wrote the following words as he sat, alone, in an Antarctic outpost, ". . . I find that I can't take my loneliness casually; it is too big." Perhaps it would seem fitting to Byrd today if he could see that a multitude of scientific investigators are also unable to take "loneliness casually" (Simons, 1958; Konecci, 1958; Jones, 1956; Levy, *et al.*, 1959; Bamford, *et al.*, 1958; Kinsey, 1953; Ormiston, 1958). Perhaps one of the most poignant expressions of this phenomenon is Burney's report (1952) of his experiences in solitary confinement:

. . . I soon learned that variety is not the spice but the very stuff of life. We need the constant ebb and flow of wavelets of sensation, thought, perception, action and emotion, lapping on the shore of our consciousness, now here, now there, keeping even our isolation in the ocean of reality, so that we neither encroach nor are encroached upon. If our minds are thus like islands, they are of many shapes, some long and straight, others narrow and bent, a few nicely rounded, and yet others round and hard, impervious to the sea and belching from deep unapproachable cones the universal warmth which lies beneath us all. We are narrow men, twisted men, smooth and nicely rounded men, and poets; but whatever we are, we have our shape, and we preserve it best in the experience of many things (Burney, 1952).

It is the purpose of this review to bring together the salient features from a number of studies and reports on confinement and isolation with particular emphasis on the application of these data for further research. To achieve this goal, reference will be made to the literature on animal experimentation, the few controlled studies in which human's have served as subjects in confinement and isolation experiments, and the large number of personal reports on the effects of confinement, isolation, and extreme hazard.

It is interesting to note that some of the primary source material on the effects of extreme isolation have originated from the experiences of naval personnel. Classical descriptions of personal isolation experiences have come from Byrd (1930, 1938), Bombard (1953), and Slocum (1943). These three scientist-adventurers were among the first to face a combination of environmental stress and isolation for a protracted period of time and to record their experiences. The unique combination of hazard and isolation they faced begins to approximate the generally hostile environment that future space voyagers will encounter. In fact, the acceptance of these nautical experiences as an approximation to space travel leads to an interesting prediction. Byrd, Bombard, Slocum, and others found that the greatest threat to their survival was not the hazard of their particular environs, but their aloneness and the monotony of their surroundings. The method these explorers used to cope with this strange kind of psychological trauma, aloneness, was surprisingly similar. A conscious effort was made by each of them to control his own thought processes, to structure his work day rigidly, and to draw into himself for added stimulation and interest. For example, Bombard reported that the freedom from regularity and from the need to perform certain tasks at specific times was detrimental to his well-being. Thus, he directed his efforts in a programmed manner, even allotting very definite periods of time for leisure activity. One of the members of Byrd's 1929 expedition, Chris Braathen, devoted all his spare time to the construction of a model ship (Byrd, 1930). In the chronicle of Byrd's expedition are reports of the way in which each individual member of the group strengthened his existent role structure and became an authority on some particular topic or area of general interest. The evolution of a clear-cut role structure supported these isolated individuals in their efforts to draw on past experiences in order to combat the monotony of the surround.

What general findings can one point to after a review of the experience of these adventures? First, the initial shock of being separated from society causes the newly isolated individual to feel fear; for example, read the description given by Christine Ritter (1900). This feeling, or shock reaction, persists for several days, although the new occupant of this closed system is quite busy with a variety of tasks. Secondly, the monotony of the surround and the lack of the usual sensory inputs reduce the over-all mental efficiency of the isolates. Frequently, this reduction in efficiency is accompanied by feelings of depersonalization and aloneness (for example, Byrd, 1938; Lilly, 1956). In both the anecdotal and the experimental literature hallucinatory experiences accompany these other symptoms. Finally, the isolate, if he is to survive, typically adopts an introspective or internal resilience in order to cope with the terms of aloneness. In group situations, this evolves in the form of a well-defined role structure. In the individual cases, like those of the shipwrecked mariner (Tiira, 1955), the man in solitary confinement (Burney, 1952), or the isolated adventurer (Byrd, 1938), the defense mechanism takes different forms. Typically, these persons acquire a deep-set conviction that they will master the experience; they become highly motivated and devote most of their waking hours to acquiring some new scientific or technical skill (see also Leopold, 1958).

An interesting distinction can be made at this point between two categories of group isolation or confinement experience. The degree of hazard present and the way in which the isolates perceive this hazard can enable us to predict, to some degree, the way in which the group will maintain itself. Although later in the discussion we will consider the simple stimulus properties of the situation, we are speaking here of the subject's knowledge and expectancies of the *outcome* of the isolation experience. This distinction, as presented by Mintz (1951), is between those situations in which a reward structure exists and is perceived by the subjects and those situations where no such probability exists. For example, in theater fires, runs on banks, or hoarding behavior during wartime, a single uncooperative act initiates a series of similar acts and the behavior of the group becomes destructive and chaotic. These kinds of circumstances can be contrasted to coal-mine and submarine disasters, where no exit is available (that is, no reward structure exists). In 1910 a Japanese submarine sank to the bottom of Hiroshima Bay. The crew realized that death was a certainty, and yet there was no panic. The records of those last minutes were recovered later, revealing that each man had stayed on duty and that the captain had accurately recorded all incidents that preceded his death (Baldwin, 1955). Although it might be argued that this group cohesiveness was a function of military training (Wheaton, 1959), similar examples can be found in the behavior of trapped coal miners (for example, see an item in the New York *Times*, March 31, 1947, p. 8). An earlier report by the author (Burns and Gifford, 1960) includes an investigation of one way in which group behavior might be expected to disintegrate based upon the foregoing analysis. Certainly, an examination of those variables involved in group cohesiveness is important in considering the effectiveness of future space-crew members.

Some Definitions

It appears appropriate to pause in the discussion and attempt to formulate some definitions with regard to confinement and isolation. Basically, *isolation, in the present context, results from the removal of the individual from his accustomed environment. Confinement*, as it is used here and in other technical reports, *reduces the freedom of movement that the individual normally enjoys.* Furthermore, there are degrees and combinations of isolation and confinement to which the individual can be subjected and a variety of ways in which these can be achieved. Intertwined with these two variables are the added dimensions of actual and perceived stress. The following classificatory scheme attempts to outline the major techniques that have been used in studies of this nature. The purpose in presenting it at this time is to prepare the reader for the review of the experimental literature that follows and to place the literature into a context of relevance for future research.

Essentially, *confinement* means restriction of movement. This can occur in any one of the following conditions:

1. *Encapsulation.* Included here are solitary confinement in small spaces, long-term flight with cumbersome belts and harnesses, wearing pressure suits, and the like.

2. *Mandatory Restrictions and Perceived Barriers.* These include a fairly large area of social behavior. Examples are such things as the issuance of military orders, observation of curfew regulations, and a variety of societal restrictions. In many instances they serve to prepare individuals to meet more stringent demands.

Carrying this scheme further results in some redundancy. Certainly, the conditions of shipwrecked and solitary sailors overlap with the definitions of both confinement and isolation. To facilitate the classification scheme, however, these situations will be handled in the context of isolation.

Isolation can best be viewed as representing some degree of sensory deprivation, or stimulus paucity. In many instances, as has already been pointed out, isolation and confinement may occur simultaneously. Furthermore, a group of people or a single invididual may be subjected to any of these conditions.

1. *Sensory Deprivation, Single Modality.* In these instances, one sensory channel is blocked. This condition may arise (1) congenitally, (2) with increasing age, (3) as the result of some accident, or (4) it may be induced experimentally.

2. *Sensory Deprivation, Multimodality.* Typically, the following three sensory channels are concerned in examples of this category: visual, auditory, and touch, or physical contact. Examples of these kinds of deprivation may occur in any of the four ways described above.

3. *Absence or Decrease of Input Patterning.* In a normal environment, the individual experiences stimulus density and stimulus variability. The patterning of environmental stimuli is of great importance to adaptive behavior, particularly so since a host of recent investigations have revealed the two-fold function of stimulation: (1) evoking and guiding a specific behavior and (2) nonspecific arousing properties of stimulation *via* the brain-stem reticular formation. Those studies in which the normal patterning of the environment has been altered have frequently employed visual (for example, only diffuse white light is allowed to reach the eye) or auditory (for example, the use of a "white noise" masking tone) manipulations. Certainly other means of altering patterned input are available, the most dramatic of which is probably the work reported by Lilly (1956).

4. *Separation from Normal Environmental Stimuli.* Although in a general sense this is a particular application of categories 1, 2, and 3, it deserves special mention at this point. The specific effects of this aspect of isolation are difficult to assess, although they do manifest themselves in a general manner. Examples of this situation can be found in the soldier stationed overseas away from loved ones or in the prisoner who is denied certain kinds of communication with the outside world (Leopold, 1958). Gewirtz (1957) has analyzed this social deprivation in terms of the dependency response it arouses; this aspect will be considered later in the discussion.

Some Neurophysiology

These definitions and classifications serve as a starting point for a survey of the experimental literature. In order to provide some basic neurophysiological structure to assist in the interpretation of the effects of confinement and isolation, primary consideration should be given the role of the ascending brain stem reticular system. A short description of current concepts of brain stem functions follows. More detailed reviews have been offered by Samuels (1959), Lindsley (1957), and French (1960).

The reticular formation is a mass of phylogenetically old tissue that in higher vertebrates occupies the central brain stem from medulla to thalamus. In primitive phyla it forms the greater part of the central nervous system, but with the development of cerebral and cerebellar tissue, with which it is closely related functionally, only a small portion remains in the spinal cord. Developmentally, the reticular formation engulfs the sensory nuclei of the thalamus. Structures such as the nucleus rubber and substantia nigra, as well as other differentiated hypothalamic and midbrain nuclei, may be its specialized derivatives. The centrally located reticular formation is surrounded by a shell of neural tissue consisting of long fiber tracts and nuclei of specific conduction systems. The dendrites of reticular neurons can cover extremely wide areas, indicating that synaptic contacts with laterally located fibers and nuclei can be made in this fashion, as well as by central convergence of collateral axons from projection systems.

The inputs to the reticular formation are many and varied. Collateral branches leave the main axon trunks of the medial lemniscus and spinothalamic or spinocerebellar tracts as they proceed through the brain stem. There also appear to be cells in the spinal cord that send axons directly to the reticular formation. Interstitial motor cells of the bulb and the quadrigeminal bodies also send fibers to the reticular formation. Corticofugal fibers are another abundant source of reticular formation input and have been traced from the frontal convexity and sensorimotor cortex, particularly the motor region, as well as the cingulate gyrus. Relatively poor sources of fibers are the parietal, lateral, temporal, orbital, and paraoccipital areas. Rhinencephalic structures, particulary the hippocampus and entorhinal area, also appear to have important connections with the reticular formation.

Important anatomical and functional connections exist between the reticular formation proper and the midline and intralaminar nuclei of the thalamus. In turn, connections between the thalamus, considered to be the cephalic portion of the brain stem, and the cortex have been inferred from electrophysiological data. Anatomical connections between the central brain stem and the basal ganglia have not been reported. A major portion of pallidal outflow, however, enters the ventralis lateralis and the ventralis anterior. Reticulopetal fiber tracts also project from the fastigial nuclei of the cerebellum, and important bilateral connections between vermal fastigial structures and the reticular formation and intralaminar thalamic nuclei have been demonstrated.

There is a marked variability in the size of neurons in the reticular formation, some being only 12 microns in diameter and others as large as 90 microns. Since there is a degree of relationship between soma size and axon length, it can be inferred that conduction occurs in short as well as relatively long steps. Since soma size can also be related to axon diameter and conduction velocity, both slowly and rapidly conducting elements are present. The axons often cross the midline and ramify in all directions, both ipsilaterally and contralaterally. Many axons also divide, one branch going cephalad and the other caudad. Collaterals of the branches can extend over long distances, so that a single reticular cell is capable of exerting its influence both in the brain and in the spinal cord.

Potentials evoked in the brain stem by receptor excitation or peripheral nerve stimulation show longer latencies than those recorded more laterally in primary conductive systems. For example, auditory potentials require 9–11 msec to traverse the distance from receptor to lateral lemniscus and 16–20 msec to reach the reticular formation. Such relatively long transport times indicate that short-chain neuron systems are involved in reticular conduction. Since, however, fairly short latency responses can be evoked in the cephalic brain stem when the medullary reticular formation is stimulated, rapid as well as slow cephalic conduction is characteristic. The shape of the potentials evoked in primary sensory systems is a sharp, spike-like initial deflection of 8–12 msec duration; in contrast, the centrally recorded potential is a high amplitude wave of long duration.

The brain stem controls a remarkable variety of bodily functions. Such factors as respiration, vasomotor tone and gastrointestinal secretion, temperature regulation, and neuroendocrine control are under its influence. It also exerts a critical degree of control over motor functions concerned in phasic and tonic muscular control. The role of the reticular system in producing electrographic and behavioral arousal responses and in the maintenance of wakefulness has been amply demonstrated. Recently it has also been shown that the reticular system is capable of modifying the reception, conduction, and integration of all sensory signals to the degree that some will be perceived and others rejected. Although the electrophysiological and behavioral evidence seem to necessitate massive connections with the cortex, they are not clear anatomically. Since cells in the reticular nuclei of the thalamus degenerate after cortical resection, it has been suggested that reticulo-thalamic influences on the cortex are mediated through the reticular nuclei of the thalamus. However, fibers have also been found to course cephalically from the reticular formation in a region ventrolateral to the thalamus. The functional properties of these two routes have not yet been established. Undoubtedly there are other indirect channels, such as through rhinencephalic systems.

Inferences from Behavior

The way in which the brain stem is assumed to operate in complex mental processes (such as attention and thought) is still in large part problematic, although some interesting experimental leads (Fuster, 1958) and theoretical statements (Lindsley, 1957) have recently appeared. Although primary interest is directed to the effects of decreased sensory input, it will serve to good advantage to first consider the action and response of the central nervous system to overstimulation and arousal. One typical response to sudden threat and danger, for example, is immobilization. The subject is startled and "freezes." It can be assumed, then, that in these instances a variety of conflicting inputs pass through the brain stem, resulting in cortical "blocking." The line of reasoning and the accompanying research have been outlined by Malmo in an excellent review (Malmo, 1959). He cites the work of several investigators (Duffy, 1951; Lindsley, 1951; Hebb, 1949; Stennett, 1957) as evidence for what has been called the "inverted U curve" as it pertains to activation. Essentially, this is a

> . . . curve relating level of performance to level of activation . . . from low activation up to a point that is optimal for a given performance or function, level of performance rises monotonically with increasing activation level; but past this optimal point the relation becomes non-monotonic: further increases in activation beyond this point produce a fall in performance level . . . (Malmo, 1959).

A theoretical U-shaped function representing the relationship between degree of central integration and amount of sensory input is offered by both Hebb and Malmo. According to this concept, both very high and very low amounts of sensory input result in disorganization on a central level. The implication here is that a lack of sensory input not only results in a lack of specific sensory data reaching the cortex, but also deprives the cortex of the facilitatory influence it normally receives from the brain stem. Behaviorally, a whole series of phenomena relating to this concept were well documented in a recent text by Fiske and Maddi (1961).

Some pertinent examples of this phenomenon have been well known to military researchers for the past decade. Mackworth (1950) demonstrated that long lapses of attention occur in the absence of sensory variation. In the case of the radar screen observer keeping watch under monotonous conditions, Mackworth found that the observer failed to respond effectively even when some changes in his environment occurred. Subjects in the isolation experiments performed at McGill University (for example, Bexton, *et al.*, 1954) reported that they were unable to concentrate on any topic for a long while. The authors report that because of this difficulty, their subjects were prone to ". . . daydreaming, [they] abandoned attempts at organized thinking, and let their thoughts wander."

Williams, *et al.* (1962), in a study of sleep loss and correlated illusion and hallucinations, reported that when personal concepts of temporal congruity and logical analyses are disrupted (as by sleep loss), the frequency of misperceptions increased. Yet, the subjects in this study became convinced of the reality of these hallucinatory experiences. Williams, *et al.*, speculate that the neurophysiological basis for this increase in hallucinatory behavior can be found in the ratio of specific afferent activity to subcortical activity. When this ratio falls beneath what is considered normal specific afferent input, the "perceptual integrating system" falls under the control of subcortical input. Although this concept appears to disregard the facilitatory role of nonspecific afferent inputs, it should be remembered that both specific and nonspecific inputs normally increase or decrease simultaneously. How strikingly similar these hallucinatory experiences are to those Bombard and Byrd offered as a description of their inability to cope with aloneness.

In the report from McGill are descriptions of the hallucinatory experiences reported by subjects. All 14 subjects in the study had some hallucinatory experience ranging from vivid well-integrated scenes to variations in light or arrangements of dots and lines. Again, the similarity of these experiences to the phantasies of Slocum or Ritter is fascinating, particularly when it is realized that the absence of normal stimulus patterning is common to both of these situations. The McGill subjects wore translucent goggles that transmitted diffuse light but prevented pattern vision. Auditory and tactile cues were also masked, and all such stimulation was kept to a minimum.

Howarth (1955) describes an environment similar in many ways to those experienced by Ritter and Byrd. The patterning of their surround was either without change or so repetitive that it became monotonous. The bulk of their clothing and the accompanying tactile isolation are similar to the heavy gloves and cuffs worn by the McGill subjects. Thus, monotony and a lack of patterning do not provide adequate cues to the individual and also fail to provide the vital nonspecific input on which the cortex depends for normal functioning.

Some Experimental Data

Some of the behavioral and morphological effects of prolonged sensory deprivation during infancy are illustrated in a report on three chimpanzees who were reared under varying conditions of light deprivation (Chow, *et al.*, 1957). Some degree of retardation in visual motor development was present in each subject. Histological examination of the retinas of the three infant chimpanzees revealed that retinal damage also resulted from the deprivation. This study, of course, dealt with deprivation induced shortly after birth. As such, it might be expected to produce more dramatic and long-lasting behavioral and neurological effects. Melzack and Thompson (1956) and Melzack and Scott (1957), in following up other studies (Clarke, *et al.*, 1951; Thompson and Heron, 1954) investigated the effects of restricting the early experience and environment on exploratory behavior and response to pain in dogs. In essence, the behavioral data obtained in these studies support the notion that *early* sensory deprivation and restriction interfere with the emergence of normal patterns of perception and response. Theoretical analyses of the age of the organism, the role of experience, and the time at which deprivation or restriction occurs have been offered (Gelb and Goldstein, 1939; Wolf, 1943; Riesen, 1947; Hebb, 1949; Scott, *et al.*, 1951; Siegel, 1952, 1953).

An interesting indication of the physiological effects of sensory deprivation is found in the length of time *after* deprivation in which abnormalities can be recorded. Heron, Doane, and Scott (1956) found that the EEG taken 3½ hours after the subject was removed from the experimental room still had not returned to normal. Another report (Scott, *et al.*, 1959) based on the same experiment indicated that behavior and cognitive function were also disrupted for several days after the deprivation period. In trying to offer a neurophysiological basis for some of the perceptual deficits and abnormalities resulting from sensory deprivation and isolation, Doane, *et al.* (1959), suggest that this functional deafferentation may cause some parts of the central nervous system to become hyperexcitable and points to the recent report by Evarts (1962) as supporting this hypothesis. It should be mentioned that the notion of central nervous system hyperexcitability does not oppose the neurophysiological interpretation offered earlier in this review. Functional deafferentation may, in fact, cause certain neurones to become hyperexcitable and discharge in some random unpredictable sequence. The representation of this phenomenon on the inverted U curve, however, is still disorganization on a cortical level, since this hyperexcitability supposedly manifests itself as hallucinations, perceptual disturbances, and the like.

A more perplexing result reported in the Doane, *et al.* (1959), study concerned an increase in visual and somesthetic acuity. In a way, this phenomenon may be related to the hyperexcitability concept, a notion the authors themselves support. One consequence of exposure to impoverished sensory environments might well be an increased sensitization to stimulus change or merely to whatever stimuli are available. It is likely that some such neurophysiological process could be the underlying mechanism responsible for the hallucinations of the solitary adventurers discussed earlier in the text.

A more systematic investigation of the effects of stimulus change can be found in the growing number of experiments concerning response patterns accompanying stimulus decrements or increments (Fiske and Maddi, 1961). The former case, that of learned response patterns associated with stimulus decrements, is more commonly called *drive reduction;* as such, that topic will not be discussed in this review. More concern is placed on those cases where increasing stimulation can be used to cue some response or where momentary changes in the environment produce the same effect. The rapidly growing literature on this topic precludes an exhaustive survey; the interested reader can find the pertinent references in the *Annual Reviews of Psychology,* under such topics as exploratory drive and visual exploration. The text by Fiske and Maddi (1961) also has a number of excellent chapters devoted to an interpretation of these phenomena.

Several basic findings, however, deserve mention. First, an increase in illumination can, under the appropriate conditions, reinforce the occurrence of an instrumental response (Henderson, 1953; Marx, *et al.,* 1955; Kish, 1955; Kling, *et al.,* 1956). Secondly, stimulus change also appears to have reinforcing properties and can be used as a means of eliciting and maintaining an instrumental response (Girdner, 1953;

Montgomery, 1954; Butler, 1953; Butler and Alexander, 1955; Butler and Harlow, 1954; Kish and Antonitis, 1956).

Some tentative relationships between stimulus change and sensory deprivation are suggested by these studies. On the one hand, it appears that organisms seek to maintain a given level of arousal. This notion has been advanced by several psychologists recently, the paper by Hebb (1955) being particularly notable. On the other hand, organisms bring to the particular stimulus situation certain expectancies or assumptions about their environment. By expectancies, then, is meant something very close (if not identical) to level of arousal, perhaps placing greater emphasis on the response side of the coin. These expectancies differ from species to species certainly, but also are variable within a species, being largely dependent on two variables: (1) the sum total of the organism's prior experience and (2) the strength of momentary stimulus events that preceded exposure to the present stimulus configuration.

One can interpret an organism's behavior in confinement or isolation as an attempt to maintain some level of arousal. As the length and stringency of the confinement-isolation period increases, the behavior of the organism in that environment is quite likely to change. Several examples can be used to illustrate this point. Glickman (1958) found a consistent within-days and between-days decrement in the amount of exploratory behavior displayed by his animals. In support of his data, Glickman referred to the work of Sharpless and Jasper (1956), who demonstrated that with repeated presentation an auditory stimulus lost its ability to arouse the brain stem reticular formation. The research on exploratory behavior and drive has, however, failed to demonstrate conclusively which conditions produce a decline in such stimulus-seeking behavior and which conditions will increase or maintain that behavior. Nevertheless, the habituation phenomenon described by Sharpless and Jasper does provide the beginnings of a neurophysiological explanation for the gradual failure of a stimulus to evoke a response. The optimal level of excitation concept (Hebb and Thompson, 1954) is also strengthened by studies like that of Sharpless and Jasper, Fuster, Stennet, and Lindsley, and loses some of its *ad hoc* character.

Some Comments

Earlier in this chapter the conditions pertaining to several categories of isolation and confinement were described. Basically, this scheme defined certain degrees of stimulus change and stimulus density. The two preceding paragraphs have outlined the relationships of the stimulus to the organism. Now, it is proposed to examine the relationships of any particular stimulus to the total stimulus complex. In other words, attention will be directed to the ways in which the number and variability of available stimuli affect the confinement-isolation environment. In addition to direct physical manipulation of the stimulus content of the environment, the symbolic and social effects of restriction will be considered.

Limiting the number of stimulus elements in an organism's environment has two immediate consequences. First, the number of primary responses that are directly cued by the presence of the stimulus element is reduced. Secondly, the number of associative (or S-S) responses that are indirectly initiated by the presence of the stimulus element is also reduced. With the passage of time, a third response to this limited environment can also occur; generally speaking, this response takes the form of illusory or hallucinatory experiences. The organism now attends to certain less well-defined aspects of the particular stimulus (such as shadows, shading, or certain incongruities) and "reads into" the environment other stimuli that physically do not exist. Furthermore, some individuals under particular circumstances appear predisposed to behaviors such as have been just described. To some extent these misperceptions may even be positively rewarding to the subject in that they provide stimulus variability in an otherwise unchanging environment. Perhaps the errors of commission (as opposed to omission) on the part of radarscope observers can be explained, in part, by this phenomenon.

Limits on stimulus variability and intensity are also potent means of altering behavior patterns and frequently occur concomitantly with decreases in stimuli density. The loss of environmental variety as it was produced in the McGill study has profound effects on problem-solving, perception, and organized thought processes. An investigation similar to the McGill study was conducted at Princeton (Vernon and Hoffman, 1956; Vernon and McGill, 1957) with considerably different results. These differences, however, are attributable to the methodologies used in the two studies, which indicate that in many respects the procedures used in the Princeton investigations reduced the severity of the experiments. The reader is referred to the review by Wheaton (1959) for additional comment on this matter. In Lilly's investigations (1956) the inputs to almost all sensory channels were drastically reduced and the effects were generally similar to those observed in the McGill study. The speed of onset of these effects, however, was considerably different. Lilly's report described many of the same kinds of phenomena that were observed in the McGill study, except that in Lilly's experiment they occurred after only two or three hours had passed; in the McGill experiment, on the other hand, somewhere in the vicinity of 24 hours was required to produce a noticeable change in perception or performance (Scott, *et al.*, 1959).

Several tentative relationships emerge from this analysis. First, the severity of the deprivation-isolation environment and the length of exposure to such an environment can be assumed to combine in a predictable manner. Secondly, the variability associated with the component stimuli in the environment contribute to mitigating the severity of the environment. Variability, here, means stimulus change and is dependent on the properties of the stimulus per se and the prior experience of the subject with the stimulus element in question. Thirdly, the subject himself uses every means available to structure and restructure his stimulus field. His efforts in this direction have an experiential basis and are also influenced by momentary central excitatory and inhibitory states.

The symbolic or social effects of isolation and confinement are so diverse that they preclude exhaustive review at this time. Recently, however, psychiatric examinations concerned with prisoners of war and methods used in forceful indoctrination ("brain washing") have illustrated the importance of this problem. Lifton (1954; 1956) and Schein (1956) have presented some unique data that were obtained after the Korean conflict. Two concepts of importance to the present discussion that emerge from these presentations of those of *milieu control* and *lack of consensual validation*. Milieu control is defined by Lifton (1956) as representing manipulation of all communication with the environment. Schein (1956) goes slightly further in his analysis by suggesting that isolation-confinement environments remove the consensual validation to which we are accustomed and dependent on in a normal unrestricted environment.

Examples of extreme socio-environmental control are found not only in POW camps, but in penitentiary environments as well (Stennett, 1957; Gaddis, 1958). Leopold (1958) has provided a very readable analysis of his prison experiences, which illustrates the effect of such extreme communication control on social behavior. In Leopold's case, it can be noted that the absence of adequate information from the "outside world" makes his need for consensual validation increasingly acute. Finally, Leopold adopts *in toto* the mores of convict behavior and, in fact, becomes very well liked by his fellow prisoners. In the papers by Lifton and Schein referred to earlier (see also Dean, 1954), the effects of milieu control and lack of consensual validation on the American POW is even more dramatic. As external points of reference are removed (such as letters from home, information about other prisoners, and the state of the war) the POW begins to seek some authoritarian structure to replace those means of validation which he has lost. In a subtle and gradual manner, the Communist interrogator and the philosophy he represents perform this function. They provide a new social milieu for the prisoner, a milieu in which he can seek and obtain validation and ego satisfaction.

Another factor that may operate in some of these instances is the stimulus-or information-seeking behavior referred to earlier. When the usual forms of stimulation and information are removed, the subject apparently becomes so bored that he will attend to material he would normally avoid. In fact, such endeavors become rewarding to the subject. Thus, when the complete sensory environment is reduced and controlled, the occupant of such an environment becomes predisposed to receive stimuli of almost any sort (for example, Scott, *et al.*, 1959). Therefore, this factor plus the need for consensual validation combine to insure the success of methods of forceful indoctrination.

The effects of consensual validation are also applicable to experimental studies. The improved performance of the isolated subjects in the Princeton experiment, for example, may be due to the repeated stimuli presentations as Wheaton (1959) suggests, or even other factors (such as increased attention in the absence of sensory variation). A more reasonable explanation to use, however, is that by using the method of anticipation, Vernon and his co-workers presented their subjects with the very thing they were trying to keep away—that is, an opportunity for consensual validation. Knowledge of results is almost immediate in serial anticipation lists, and the subject has an excellent opportunity to test his hypotheses. In the McGill work, such an opportunity was not available. Mentally checking arithmetic multiplication products is not too satisfactory in terms of positive feedback. Similarly, performance on digit-span tests does not provide immediate knowledge of results. The subject in all of the tests used in the McGill studies never had a real opportunity to find out how well he had performed. In Vernon's studies, such an opportunity was regularly provided as part of the experimental procedure.

In the results of our investigations (Burns, 1959; Burns and Gifford, 1960), these variables of knowledge of results and ego involvement appeared to be the continuum on which to place the data on cognitive and intellectual functioning. Problem solving was not impaired, and tests involving some competition between S and E also sustained good performance. In both these tasks positive feedback was provided and ego involvement was high. Moreover, consensual validation was available to the subject. Routine tasks without these qualities deteriorated and failed to elicit acceptable levels of performance.

The multiplicity of variables operating simultaneously in a confinement situation make assignment of dominant or major sources of influence rather arbitrary. Loss of information about external events is certainly important to the isolate. Cues as to diurnal variation and temperature changes contribute to the hypodynamic aspects of the isolate's environment. Lack of knowledge of the activities of others (such as friends and family) also contributes to the separation of the isolate from his normal environment. Finally, inadequate information with regard to the isolate's performance on various tasks or with regard to his perception of certain stimuli increase his feeling of detachment and add to his insecurity. This last group of factors contributes to the lack of consensual validation; and, to a certain extent, this lack is part and parcel of almost every aspect of the isolate's confinement. When analyzed in this fashion, any way in which the confinement or isolation experiment is interrupted can be interpreted to provide an opportunity for consensual validation.

These occasions take different forms in different studies. For example, scheduled menus help in that their appearance in a confinement chamber may validate the isolate's hypothesis with regard to time of day. Requests for an opportunity for body waste elimination may require the experimenter's assistance and thus assure the isolated subject that the experimenter is still there. This list can be elaborated and, in fact, gets rather lengthy for some of the experiments that have been done in the past. The constant source of consensual validation in the experimental literature with regard to confinement and isolation, however, is the psychological test procedure that is introduced. In every instance, the procedure involves the subject making some response to a stimulus the experimenter has presented. Test procedures, however, differ with regard to the degree of consensual validation they incur. Knowledge of results and extent of ego involvement are the two major agents in deciding on the opportunity the subject has had for consensual validation.

This distinction remains to be tested in a single study, although the experimental paradigm required is not difficult to establish. Current research is being directed to this goal. Until such time, the effectiveness of consensual validation in a confinement situation is still, quite obviously, hypothetical. The differences in procedures in all the work in this area make direct comparison of obtained data quite tenuous. Studies that employ groups of subjects make the problems of experimental conduct and interexperimental comparison even more complex. Hopefully, attempts at generalization will lead to better defined studies and a clearer emergence of the dominant variables.

In Closing

Thus far in the discussion, the commentary on isolation and confinement has been extended to a broad range of reports and investigations, with an attempt to preserve some degree of specificity. It is felt, however, that the omissions from the review are in some ways more striking than the inclusions. An adequate theoretical framework for handling the concepts involved in the area of isolation and confinement will depend on the utilization of data that have already been accumulated in a number of ancillary areas. The data on childhood separations, for example, provide some striking examples of the human behavior dynamics involved in social and emotional deprivation (Bowlby, 1953; Goldfarb, 1945; Spitz, 1954). Gewirtz and Baer (1958a, 1958b) have provided excellent reviews of this material plus a theoretical framework with some implications for the present topic.

The critical age studies and the effects of early environments on behavior (Luchins and Forgus, 1955; Thompson, 1955) are two other areas of significance in the construction of a unified theory. The imprinting investigations by Lorenz (1950), Tinbergen (1951), Hess (1959), and others present excellent examples of response development in controlled environments that may eventually help to define the basic operating factors in behavioral alterations that result from sensory deprivation and confinement. The recent accumulation of data in the field of psychopharmacology and the behavioral effects of many hallucinogenic agents (Garattini and Ghetti, 1957; Ross and Cole, 1960) are also of more than just casual importance to discussions of sensory deprivation. Thus, the listing of peripheral but related topics could go on endlessly until almost every area of psychology had at least some representation. Yet, it is only after an interdisciplinary synthesis has been attempted and completed that the psychological processes involved in isolation and confinement will be understood.

We feel that the general class of rhythmic behavior can also be viewed as part of the commentary on isolation and confinement. Many aspects of biological rhythms seem to parallel daily changes in light or temperature. To take a fairly simple example, there are nocturnal and diurnal animals. Even plants have been found to exhibit persistent rhythms in such processes as sporulation, growth rate, leaf movements, and phototaxis. Daily rhythmic variations also occur in the degree of alertness, body temperature, catechol amine excretion, blood sugar levels, and so on of man and other higher animals.

In addition to such long-term rhythms, variations involving shorter time segments also occur. These are illustrated by the ability of human subjects to estimate short time durations rather accurately and by the fact that animals can be taught to estimate the passage of time through various behavioral techniques. Although the operations of the short- and long-term timing processes are usually studied separately, a single neural mechanism seems to mediate such long-term cyclical behavior as sleep, as well as short-term time estimation. Such a mechanism will be proposed after we have considered some characteristics of time behavior.

Probably the most profound influence on both short- and long-term timing behavior is the nature of the intra- and extra-organismic environment. The fruit fly, for example, in its normal habitat leaves its pupal shell at dawn. When the larvae are raised in continuous darkness, however, the fruit flies emerge at random. On the other hand, if the larvae are exposed to a relatively brief interval of light, the flies will emerge 24 hours after the exposure.

In most human subjects under normal conditions there is a tendency to underestimate the passage of time. The intervals we have studied (Burns and Gifford, 1960, Burns and Gifford, 1961; Kimura, *et al.*, 1962) range from 15 to 300 sec, and the results have been consistent through three separate experiments. The timing behavior of a subject is quite stable and has the same configuration for all intervals tested. Shifts in response characteristics can be produced by controlling extra-organismic variables, such as the testing method and the level of the ambient stimulus conditions, and intra-organismic variables such as subject anxiety. Thus, the accuracy and stability of short-term timing also depends on the characteristics of the stimulus input.

Of interest here is the striking effect of reducing the level of ambient stimulus conditions. In a restrictive and confining environment simulating the conditions found in space vehicles, the characteristic change is in the direction of underestimating the passage of time. Time may therefore appear to pass rather quickly for the astronaut on an extended space voyage, assuming all goes well.

Now, let us examine in some detail an interesting form of rhythmic behavior—sleep—and the remarkable degree to which it is under the control of environmental variables.

First, we shall consider neural theories of sleep, which fall into two categories, those which imply separate sleep and waking centers and those which postulate only a waking center. It is generally assumed that the waking center includes the brain stem reticular formation of Magoun and Moruzzi (1949). A sleep center was hypothesized by Nauta in 1946, when sleeplessness was observed in animals with lesions in the anterior hypothalamic area. A sleep center was also proposed by Hess, who found that low-voltage stimulation at 4 to 12 cycles per second of the midline thalamus above the interior hypothalamic area was followed by sleep. In such theories the sleep center is thought to exert a direct inhibitory effect on the waking center.

The concept of the sleep center is considered to be superfluous by Bremer, who suggests that sleep may be initiated by synaptic fatigue in the cortex or in the activating system itself. Our view, expressed in detail in a paper published in 1957 (Burns, 1957), is similar to that of Bremer. It was suggested that Nauta's lesions, which destroyed the anterior hypothalamic area, disrupted parasympathetic processes, leaving the animal in a state of chronic sympathetic elevation. This, in effect, produces a great change in the characteristics of the internal environment of the animal. Since the bodily processes of the animal are now in a continuously heightened condition, those bodily stimuli normally associated with sleeping no longer occur, and the animal accordingly exhibits less sleep behavior. The effects of Hess's low-voltage, low-frequency electrical stimulation can be interpreted similarly. The current may either stimulate the parasympathetic system, producing stimuli associated with sleeping such as the lowering of blood pressure and heart rate, or it directly produces similar effects. In either case, the effects of the intra- and extra-organismic stimulus antecedents of sleeping may be cumulative, eventually culminating in sleep. The importance of external and internal stimulus conditions is also clear to anyone who has tried to sleep in a strange place or after too much or too little food.

While sleeping is generally conceded to be basically a physiological regenerative process, it would be erroneous to think that physiological necessity is all that governs sleeping. For example, one less obvious factor is that to a great degree we sleep because we like to sleep. If a change occurred in the way in which we perceive sleep, alterations in sleep behavior would be sure to follow. In the case of the man living in an hypodynamic environment, it is conceivable that sleep becomes less rewarding. As the reinforcing value of sleep decreases, the behavior of sleep will be emitted for progressively shorter periods, the limit being defined by the minimal amount necessary to accomplish regenerative functions.

Up to now we have been speaking as if being asleep and being awake were discrete states. Under ordinary conditions this way of talking is acceptable, but the fact that sleeping and waking are conventionally defined areas along a continuum becomes clear when describing an individual living in a hypodynamic environment. The electrical activity of his brain shows little of the conventional sleep pattern, and behaviorally sleeping and waking are difficult to distinguish, apparently because sleeping is so light. It is as if the range between sleeping and waking had shrunk until the two states are practically indistinguishable. In this state, neither fully awake nor fully asleep in the usual sense, it appears that activity is maintained at such a level that physiological breakdown is just balanced by regeneration. In a hypodynamic environment, therefore, it appears that not only can sleep become less rewarding, but because of reduced physiological activity, *normal* sleep actually becomes unnecessary.

In our opinion these findings indicate that cyclical behavior—sleep and waking and timing behavior—is regulated largely by environmental factors. Variations in sensory input appear to be the main factor governing normal rhythmic processes, broad-based cyclical changes as well as short-term events. Unlike Brown's hypothesis (Brown, 1960), which favors an external clock whose forces spring from stable geophysical rhythms, we suggest a neural pacemaker whose activity varies as a function of stimulus conditions. Our hypothesis requires a complex central neural pool that receives inputs from many sensory systems and that controls the level of activity in the central nervous system as a function of the sensory input. This seems to point to the brain stem reticular activating system of Magoun and Moruzzi, which was discussed earlier, as the central regulating mechanism. As is well known, the reticular activating system receives collaterals from afferent neurons, exerts profound influences on the activity of the cerebral cortex, and is decisive in the regulation of sleep. The behavioral activity level of animals as well as perceptual factors also appear to be functions of the condition of the reticular activating system. Such data suggest that experimental work on this problem may increase our understanding of the neural mechanisms by which extra- and intra-organismic environmental variables exert their controlling influences on the basic and short-term rhythmic processes of higher organisms.

The problems of submarine habitability as described elsewhere in this volume represent another set of problems that will be encountered in space flight. An interesting commentary on the similarity of the problems of submarine and space travel is provided by the following two quotations, which are separated in time by the passage of ten years. Darrow and Henry (1949) in their report on undersea warfare stated:

The unavoidable rigors of life on a submarine patrol subject men to conditions of severe psychological and physiological stress and demonstrate an endurance which bears testimony to the remarkable capacity of the human organism for adaptation, for compensation, and for acclimatization to conditions.

Brody (1959), while participating in a symposium on the psychiatric problems of man in space, reported

> . . . in any event, man's psychological plasticity is a matter of record, and if workable and habitable space ships are constructed, I am sure that effective pilots can be found to use them.

Thus, it would appear that even after a decade of human factors research and development at least one of the philosophical guide lines in this research area remained unchanged: "Man's plasticity would see him through." Although such a philosophy may be reassuring to many, the present investigators are more encouraged by the point of view expressed by Brown (1959). After first pointing out that human capabilities are presently being pushed to capacity if not beyond it, Brown suggests that designing operational craft to function at this potentially incapacitating level is not in the best interest of mission success and operator safety. Rather, he suggests that in order "to use the pilot most effectively, we must conduct a thorough engineering study of his sensory and motor capabilities under changing conditions of acceleration and design the equipment which he will use accordingly."

Suitable emphasis must be placed on the selection and training of crews for space and orbital flight. Included here, too, are the more immediate operational requirements such as may be involved in global surveillance missions, antisubmarine warfare reconnaissance, and long-term nuclear submarine voyages. Each of these circumstances possesses, to a certain degree, some of the properties of an isolation or confinement experience.

As many of these contemplated missions will involve crew complements of more than one man, the area of group cohesiveness and team effectiveness under stress will assume new importance. Self-sustaining, regenerative, life-support systems for space vehicles are designed to control entropy. Redundant control inputs are provided both internally and externally to yield a stable, highly organized environment. The psychological milieu must have regulation of a similar sort in order to combat the behavioral entropic increase in closed-loop systems. It has been shown that when the intensity and quality of external stimulation is reduced, responses and central processes become disorganized. Yet, a space-cabin environment does have certain advantages *if* proper inputs are maintained. Specific role structures emerge for each man and become highly developed. Individual inadequacies are perceived by the other crew members and corrected, thus helping to strengthen the group as a whole. Feedback in the form of consensual validation and ego-involvement will operate to establish and maintain a value system. Finally, many investigators are concerned with the effects on motor development and organization of future generations raised under conditions of zero or minimal gravity; the kind of conditions, for example, that might be anticipated in long-duration celestial migrations. During such a flight, the normal proprioceptive stimulation that accompanies growth would be absent. Children raised under conditions of gravity that are different from those which exist on earth will almost certainly not have the muscular tonus and sensorimotor development common to terrestrial beings.

The behavioral scientist is still somewhat handicapped in his approach to the psychological problems of space flight, since he has so little experimental data. Nevertheless, as the data reviewed here demonstrate, his experiences in closely related areas and his knowledge of existing concepts enable him to contribute something more than an educated guess.

References

Baldwin, H. W. *Seafights and Shipwrecks*, New York: Doubleday, 1955.

Bamford, H. E., Hanes, L. F., Ritchie, M. L., and Wilson, S. E. *The Operation of Manned Spacecraft*, Wright-Patterson AFB, Ohio: Wright-Air Development Center, 1958 (Tech. Rep. 58-225).

Bexton, W. H., Heron, W., and Scott, T. H. "Effects of Decreased Variation in the Sensory Environment, *Canad. J. Psychol.*, 8:70–76, 1954.

Bombard, A. *The Voyage of the Heretique*, New York: Simon and Schuster, 1953.

Bowlby, J. "Critical Phases in the Development of Social Responses in Man," *New Biol.*, 14:25–32, 1953.

Brody, E. B. Discussion in Symposium on space psychiatry, *Amer. J. Psychiat.*, 115:1112–1113, 1959.

Brown, F. A., Jr. *Cold Spring Harbor Symp. Quant. Biol.*, 25:57–72, 1960.

Brown, J. L. The Bio-dynamics of Launch and Re-entry. *Naval Res. Rev.*, May, 1959, 8–15.

Burney, C. *Solitary Confinement*, London: Clerke and Cockeran, 1952.

Burns, N. M. "Apparent Sleep Produced by Cortical Stimulation," *Canad. J. Psychol.*, 11:171–181,1957.

——. *Environmental Requirements of Sealed Cabins for Space and Orbital Flights: A Second Study. Part 1. Rationale and Habitability Aspects of Confinement Study*. Naval Air Matériel Center, Philadelphia: Air Crew Equipment Laboratory, 1959 (Project TED NAM AE-1403, Report NAMC-ACEL-413).

—— and Gifford, E. C. *Environmental Requirements of Sealed Cabins for Space and Orbital Flights: A Second Study. Part 2. Effects of Long Term*

Confinement on Performance. Naval Air Matériel Center, Philadelphia: Air Crew Equipment Laboratory, 1960 (Project TED NAM AE-1403, Report NAMC-ACEL-414).

—— and ——. "Time Estimation and Anxiety," *J. Psychol. Stud., 12*:19–27, 1961.

Butler, R. A. "Discrimination Learning by Rhesus Monkeys to Visual-Exploration Motivation," *J. Comp. Physiol. Psychol., 46*:95–98, 1953.

—— and Alexander, H. M. "Daily Patterns of Visual Exploratory Behavior in the Monkey," *J. Comp. Physiol. Psychol., 48*:247–249, 1955.

—— and Harlow, H. F. "Persistence of Visual Exploration in Monkeys," *J. Comp. Physiol. Psychol., 47*:258–263, 1954.

Byrd, R. E. *Little America.* New York: G. P. Putnam's Sons, 1930.

——. *Alone.* New York: G. P. Putnam's Sons, 1938.

Chow, K. L., Riesen, A. H., and Newell, F. W. "Degeneration of Retinal Ganglion Cells in Infant Chimpanzee Reared in Darkness," *J. Comp. Neurol., 107*: 27–42, 1957.

Clarke, R. S., Heron, W., Fetherstonhaugh, M. L., Forgays, D. C., and Hebb, D. O. Individual Differences in Dogs: Preliminary Reports on the Effects of Early Experience, *Canad. J. Psychol., 5*:150–156, 1951.

Darrow, C. W., and Henry, C. E. "Psychophysiology of Stress," in *A Survey Report on Human Factors in Undersea Warfare,* Washington, D.C.: National Research Council, 1949, pp. 417–439.

Dean, W. F. *General Dean's Story,* New York: Viking Press, 1954.

Doane, B. K., Mahatoo, W., Heron, W., and Scott, T. H. "Changes in Perceptual Function after Isolation," *Canad. J. Psychol., 13*:210–219, 1959.

Duffy, Elizabeth. "The Concept of Energy Mobilization," *Psychol. Rev., 58*: 30–40, 1951.

Evarts, E. "The Physiological Basis of Hallucinations," in L. J. West (ed.), *Hallucinations: A Symposium,* New York: Grune and Stratton, 1962.

Fiske, D. W., and Maddi, S. R. *Functions of Varied Experience,* Homewood, Ill.: Dorsey Press, 1961.

French, J. D. *Handbook of Physiology and Neurophysiology,* Washington, D.C.: American Physiological Society, *2*:1281–1305, 1960.

Fuster, J. M. "Effects of Stimulation of Brain Stem on Tachistoscopic Perception," *Science, 127*:150, 1958.

Gaddis, T. E. *Birdman of Alcatraz: The Story of Robert Stroud.* New York: Signet Books, 1958.

Garattini, S., and Ghetti, V. (eds.). *Psychotropic Drugs,* New York: Elsevier, 1957.

Gelb, A., and Goldstein, K. "Figural Blindness," in W. D. Ellis (ed.), *A Source Book of Gestalt Psychology,* New York: Harcourt, Brace, 1939, pp. 315–325.

Gewirtz, J. L. "Social Deprivation and Dependency," paper read at American Psychological Association, New York, September, 1957.

—— and Baer, D. M. "The Effect of Brief Social Deprivation on Behaviors for a Social Reinforcer," *J. Abnorm. Soc. Psychol., 56*:49–56, 1958a.

———— and ————. "Deprivation and Satiation of Social Reinforcers as Drive Conditioners," *J. Abnorm. Soc. Psychol.*, *57*:165–172, 1958b.

Girdner, J. B. "An Experimental Analysis of the Behavioral Effects of a Perceptual Consequence Unrelated to Organic Drive States," unpublished doctoral dissertation, Duke University, 1953.

Glickman, S. E. "Effects of Peripheral Blindness on Exploratory Behavior in the Hooded Rat," *Canad. J. Psychol.*, *12*:45–51, 1958.

Goldfarb, W. "Effects of Psychological Deprivation in Infancy and Subsequent Stimulation," *Amer. J. Psychiat.*, *102*:18–33, 1945.

Hebb, D. O. *The Organization of Behavior*, New York: Wiley, 1949.

————. Drives and the C.N.S. (Conceptual Nervous System), *Psychol. Rev.*, *62*: 243–254, 1955.

———— and Thompson, W. R. "The Social Significance of Animal Studies." in G. Lindzey (ed.), *Handbook of Social Psychology*, Reading, Mass.: Addison-Wesley, 1954, pp. 532–561.

Henderson, R. L. "Stimulus Intensity Dynamism and Secondary Reinforcement," unpublished doctoral dissertation, University of Missouri, Columbia, Mo., 1953.

Heron, W., Doane, B. K., and Scott, T. H. "Visual Disturbances after Prolonged Perceptual Isolation," *Canad. J. Psychol.*, *10*:13–18, 1956.

Hess, E. H. "Imprinting," *Science*, *130*:133–141, 1959.

Howarth, D. *We Die Alone*, New York: MacMillan, 1955.

Jones, M. B. *Personal Autonomy and Confinement in the Naval Service*, Pensacola, Fla.: U.S. Naval School of Aviation Medicine, 1956 (Proj. No. 001 108 109, Report No. 5).

Kimura, D., Burns, N. M., and Snyder, Deborah L. "Experimental Method as a Factor in Temporal Judgment," Unpublished Manuscript, The Decker Corporation, Bala-Cynwyd, Pa., 1962.

Kinsey, J. L. *Report of Psychiatric Studies on Operation Hideout*, U.S. Naval Submarine Base, Conn.: U.S. Naval Medical Research Laboratory, 1953 (Report No. 230).

Kish, G. B. "Learning When Onset of Illumination Is Used as Reinforcing Stimulus," *J. Comp. Physiol. Psychol.*, *48*:261–264, 1955.

———— and Antonitis, J. J. "Unconditioned Operant Behavior in Two Homozygous Strains of Mice," *J. Genet. Psychol.*, *88*:121–129, 1956.

Kling, J. W., Horowitz, L., and Delhagen, J. E. "Light as a Positive Reinforcer for Rat Responding," *Psychol. Rep.*, *2*:337–340, 1956.

Konecci, E. B. "Human Factors and Space Cabins," *Astronautics*, *3* (1), 42–43, 71–73, 1958.

Leopold, N. F., Jr. *Life Plus 99 Years*. New York: Doubleday, 1958.

Levy, E. Z., Ruff, G. E., and Thaler, V. H. "Studies in Human Isolation," *J. Amer. Med. Assoc.*, *169*:236–239, 1959.

Lifton, R. J. "Home by Ship: Reaction Patterns of American Prisoners of War Repatriated from North Korea," *Amer. J. Psychiat.*, *110*:732–739, 1954.

————. "Thought Reform" of Western Civilians in Chinese Communist Prisons," *Psychiat.*, *19*:173–197, 1956.

Lilly, J. C. "Effects of Physical Restraint and of Reduction of Ordinary Levels of Physical Stimuli on Intact, Healthy Persons," Symposium No. 2: Illustrative Strategies for Research on Psychopathology in Mental Health, in *Group for Advancement of Psychiatry*, 1956–1959, pp. 13–20 (GAP Publ. Office, 104 E. 25th St., New York).

————. "Mental Effects of Reduction of Ordinary Levels of Physical Stimuli on Intact, Healthy Persons," *Psychiat. Res. Reports*, 5:1–9, 1956.

Lindsley, D. B. "Emotion," in S. S. Stevens (ed.), *Handbook of Experimental Psychology*, New York: Wiley, 1951, pp. 473–516.

————. "Psychophysiology and Motivation," in M. R. Jones (ed.), *Nebraska Symposium on Motivation*, 1957. Lincoln: University of Nebraska Press, 1957, pp. 44–105.

Lorenz, K. Z. "The Comparative Method in Studying Innate Behavior Patterns," *Symp. Soc. Exper. Biol.*, *4*:221–268, 1950.

Luchins, A. S., and Forgus, R. H. "The Effect of Differential Post-Weaning Environment on the Rigidity of an Animal's Behavior," *J. Genet. Psychol.*, *86*: 51–58, 1955.

Mackworth, N. H. *Researches on the Measurement of Human Performance.* London: H. M. Stationery Office, 1950 (Med. Res. Council. Special Report Series No. 268).

Malmo, R. B. "Activation: A Neuropsychological Dimension," *Psychol. Rev.*, *66*:367–386, 1959.

Marx, M. H., Henderson, R. L., and Roberts, C. L. "Positive Reinforcement of the Bar-Pressing Response by a Light Stimulus Following Dark Operant Pretests with No Aftereffect," *J. Comp. Physiol. Psychol.*, *48*:73–76, 1955.

Melzack, R., and Scott, T. H. "The Effects of Early Experience on the Response to Pain." *J. Comp. Physiol. Psychol.*, *50*:155–161, 1957.

———— and Thompson, W. R. "Effects of Early Experience on Social Behavior." *Canad. J. Psychol.*, *10*:82–90, 1956.

Mintz, A. "Nonadaptive Group Behavior," *J. Abnorm. Soc. Psychol.*, *46*:150–159, 1951.

Montgomery, K. C. "The Role of the Exploratory Drive in Learning," *J. Comp. Physiol. Psychol.*, *47*:60–64, 1954.

Moruzzi, G., and Magoun, H. W. "Brain Stem Reticular Formation and Activation of the EEG," *EEG Clin. Neurophysiol.*, *1*:455–473, 1949.

Ormiston, D. W. "The Effects of Sensory Deprivation and Sensory Bombardment on Apparent Movement Thresholds," *Dissertation Abstr.*, *12*:2200–2201, 1958.

Riesen, A. H. "The Development of Visual Perception in Man and the Chimpanzee," *Science*, *106*:107–108, 1947.

Ritter, Christine. *A Woman in the Polar Night*, New York: The Century Company, 1900.

Ross, S., and Cole, J. O. "Psychopharmacology," *Ann. Rev. Psychol.*, *11*:415–438, 1960.

Samuels, Ina. "Reticular Mechanisms and Behavior," *Psychol. Bull.*, *56*:1–25, 1959.

Schein, E. H. "The Chinese Indoctrination Program for Prisoners of War," *Psychiat.*, *19*:149–172, 1956.

Scott, J. P., Fredricson, E., and Fuller, J. L. "Experimental exploration of the Critical Period Hypothesis," *Personality*, *1*:162–183, 1951.

Scott, T. H., Bexton, W. H., Heron, W., and Doane, B. K. "Cognitive Effects of Perceptual Isolation," *Canad. J. Psychol.*, *13*:200–209, 1959.

Sharpless, S., and Jasper, H. "Habituation of the Arousal Reaction," Brain, *79*:655–680, 1956.

Siegel, A. I. "The Effects of Deprivation of Visual Form Definition upon the Development and Transfer of Simple Form Definition in the Ring Dove," unpublished doctoral dissertation, New York University, 1952.

———. "A Motor-hypothesis of Perceptual Development," *Amer. J. Psychol.*, *66*:301–304, 1953.

Simons, D. G. "Pilot Reactions during 'Manhigh II' Balloon Flight," *J. Aviat. Med.*, *29*:1–14, 1958.

Slocum, J. *Sailing Alone around the World*, New York: Blue Ribbon Books, 1943.

Spitz, R. A. "Unhappy and Fatal Outcomes of Emotional Deprivation and Stress in Infancy," in I. Galdston (ed.), *Beyond the Germ Theory*, New York: Health Education Council, 1954, pp. 120–131.

Stennett, R. G., "The Relationship of Alpha Amplitude to the Level of Palmar Conductance," *EEG Clin. Neurophysiol.*, *9*:131–138, 1957.

Sykes, G. M. "Men, Merchants, and Toughs: A Study of Reactions to Imprisonment," *Soc. Prob.*, *4*:130–138, 1956.

Thompson, W. R. "Early Environment—Its Importance for Later Behavior," in P. H. Hoch and J. Zubin (eds.), *Psychopathology of Childhood*, New York: Grune and Stratton, 1955, pp. 130–139.

——— and Heron, W. "The Effects of Early Restriction on Activity in Dogs," *J. Comp. Physiol. Psychol.*, *47*:77–82, 1954.

Tiira, E. *Raft of Despair*. New York: Dutton, 1955.

Tinbergen, N. *The Study of Instinct*. London: Oxford University Press, 1951.

Vernon, J., and Hoffman, J. "Effects of Sensory Deprivation on Learning Rate in Human Beings," *Science*, *123*:1074–1075, 1956.

Vernon, J. A., and McGill, T. E. The Effect of Sensory Deprivation upon Rate Learning, *Amer. J. Psychol.*, *70*:637–639, 1957.

Wheaton, J. L. *Fact and Fancy in Sensory Deprivation Studies*. Brooks AFB, Texas: School of Aviation Medicine, 1959 (Report No. 5-59).

Williams, H. L., Morris, G. O., and Lubin, A. "Illusions, Hallucinations and Sleep Loss," in L. J. West (ed.), *Hallucinations: A Symposium*, New York: Grune and Stratton, 1962.

Wolf, A. "The Dynamics of the Selective Inhibition of Specific Function in Neurosis: A Preliminary Report," *Psychosom. Med.*, *5*:27–38, 1943.

7

OPERATOR PERFORMANCE IN ACCELERATION ENVIRONMENTS

Randall M. Chambers

Aviation Medical Acceleration Laboratory
Naval Air Development Center
Johnsville, Pennsylvania

ONE of the most interesting classes of environments that influence human behavior and physiology is that produced by acceleration stress. Acceleration environments that influence human behavior and physiology are of great interest because man is frequently required to perform tasks and survive physiologically during exposure to them. The spectrum of acceleration environments is extremely large, comprehending not only relatively routine and frequent activities, such as driving automobiles and many types of sporting activities, but also less frequent but more stressful activities such as flying airplanes and spacecraft.

Most people have experienced simple accelerations of very short duration and low magnitude while engaged in relatively routine activities such as driving automobiles and boats. In flying airplanes, however, the acceleration exposures are potentially more severe, and symptoms such as "grayout," "blackout" and vertigo are well known to aviators. Spins, dives, tumbles, rolls, banks, skids, buffeting, landing, egress, or impact produce a variety of physiological and psychological symptoms, some of which still pose unsolved problems. During flight in space vehicles, however, man may encounter an even greater variety of accelerations during launch, insertion, orbital and interplanetary flight, re-entry, impact, and recovery phases. There are also many types of possible abort conditions that may be encountered during any given space flight maneuver; and consequently the types of accelerations can vary greatly in terms of amplitude, duration, direction, rates of onset and decline, and frequency parameters. The acceleration experiences that man in space may encounter appear to be virtually unlimited.

The following survey of the scientific literature was conducted in an attempt to summarize the results of experiments in which human behavior has been studied during exposure to acceleration. Most of the published experiments have been concerned with a relatively limited number of acceleration conditions. Consequently, since the emphasis of this chapter is primarily on human behavior rather than on acceleration or physiology per se, the author has attempted to categorize human behavior and then to review the effects of acceleration conditions on these dimensions of behavior. Thus, after a brief summary of various types of acceleration environments, their effects on man's sensory and perceptual abilities are reviewed. Then, effects on simple and complex psychomotor performance and on higher mental abilities are summarized. Personality, emotional, and motivational aspects are then reviewed. Recent work in using acceleration facilities to conduct space flight simulation studies, astronaut training, and tests of displays, controls, and restraint systems are also reviewed. Problems of protecting man against the adverse effects of acceleration without limiting his performance capabilities are reviewed, some general principles concerning human performance capabilities during exposure to stressful acceleration environments are presented, and problem areas requiring further investigation are identified.

A major portion of the current interest in the effects of acceleration on human performance arises from the requirements for providing the human pilot of high-performance aircraft and spacecraft with the capabilities for maintaining control of his vehicle and for performing various tasks during exposure to the more physiologically and psychologically adverse acceleration conditions he may encounter. These are important problems to the pilots and astronauts who must pilot these vehicles and also to the passengers, who may also be required to perform and survive within these environments.

I. Acceleration Environments

The study of human performance in acceleration environments is a complex endeavor, involving principles of physics, engineering, physiology, and psychology in the description of the acceleration variables and in the prediction of human tolerances and behavioral changes. An acceleration environment may be described in terms of (1) the magnitude of the acceleration force; (2) its rate of onset and decline; (3) the duration of the peak acceleration; (4) the total exposure time; (5) the complexity of the acceleration profile and the way in which the various linear and angular acceleration vectors combine to produce resultant forces; (6) the direction of the acceleration force with respect to the human body, and (7) the frequency and amplitude characteristics of the acting forces.

During exposure, the human subject may approach blackout or unconsciousness, he may experience pain and discomfort, and his eyes, heart, and musculature may show specific symptoms in response to the acceleration stress. Similarly, the ability of the human subject to perform perceptual, motor, and intellectual tasks may be impaired as a result of mechanical, physiological, or emotional events that occur before and during the acceleration exposure. Whereas there is at the present time a major interest in the effects of acceleration on both physiology and behavior, there is a severe shortage of quantitative information on the effects of most types of acceleration environments. Before the performance of man within acceleration environments can be presented, it is necessary to review some of the major types of acceleration environments and the nomenclature which is used to describe them. Also, some of the basic physiological concepts and some of the major means for protecting man's physiological functioning during acceleration exposure are summarized. These are the foundations upon which man's performance capabilities largely depend.

A. ACCELERATION NOMENCLATURE

To date, a standard terminology for describing acceleration and its various components has not been adopted by engineering, biological, physiological, and psychological groups. Since there is much variation in nomenclature, it is important to describe the major systems of nomenclature briefly before proceeding to a review of the effects of acceleration on human performance.

Acceleration may be defined as the rate at which the velocity of a body changes per unit time. If the velocity of the body is constant, its acceleration is said to be zero, and acceleration may increase or decrease, according to the increase or decrease in velocity of the body. The concept of acceleration due to gravity is based on the law of physics that declares that every mass is attracted by every other mass with a force varying as the product of the masses, and inversely as the square of the distances between them. Thus, there is an attractive force between the earth and any body near it. Mathematically, this relationship is

$$F = g\,\frac{m_1 m_2}{r_2}$$

where g is a gravitational constant. For bodies whose mass is small compared with that of the earth, the magnitude of the force depends primarily on the earth's mass and the distance of the body from the center of the earth. The value of this force near the surface of the earth is such that it causes any body, in the absence of other forces, to be accelerated towards the center of the earth at the rate of about 32.2 ft/sec^2 in accordance with Newton's Second Law,

$$F = ma$$

which states the amount of force F required to produce in a given mass m, a given acceleration a, which is the rate of change of velocity. At a given location, the gravitational force on any body is directly proportional to the mass of that body. The ratio F/m has the same constant value for all bodies when the force F is due to the earth's gravity. This ratio,

$$a = \frac{F}{m}$$

when describing the acceleration of gravity, is given the special symbol g. Although difficulties arise from the fact that g varies slightly over the earth's surface, the standard value of g has been defined as approximately 32.2 ft/sec^2 and is used in calculations involving the acceleration due to gravity on or near the earth's surface. The force due to gravity that the earth continuously exerts on a body is conveniently called the *weight* of the body and is denoted by the symbol W.

It is important to note that the symbol g is used only for the acceleration due to gravity, while the G used in aviation medicine is considered a unit of reactive force (Gauer and Zuidema, 1961). The upper-case letter G has been in use for a considerable period of time and in a variety of ways to denote force and acceleration, as indicated by such expressions as "ability to tolerate accelerative forces," "subjecting an individual to accelerative forces," or "subjecting an individual to G." These expressions, though not entirely accurate, have commonly accepted meanings in the literature of the physiology of acceleration. The symbol G refers to the force and acceleration occurring in a given situation. When it is stated that a body is experiencing a certain amount of G, one can determine the actual amount of force in units if he multiplies the given value of G by the standard weight W of the body,

$$F = GW$$

In physiology and aviation medicine, it is convenient to measure any acceleration as a multiple of the standard acceleration, g, and any force F as a multiple of the standard weight W of the body upon which F is acting. However, because of the physiological importance of the *position* of the human body with respect to the acceleration force, the directional aspects of the acceleration quantity are considered differently from those used in physics. In physiology and aviation medicine, only the magnitudes of the vectors g and W are employed. The directions of the vectors a and F are independent of the fixed directions of the physical quantities g and W. It is desirable to employ a single symbol to represent the common ratio formed by normalizing F and a with respect to standard gravitational values. Thus, G is defined as a ratio of forces, or, as a ratio of accelerations, as follows (Dixon and Patterson, 1953, 1961):

$$G = \frac{F}{W} \qquad \text{or} \qquad G = \frac{a}{g}$$

More detailed discussions of the problems of acceleration nomenclature may be found in Dixon and Patterson (1961), Gauer (1961a), and Clark, *et al.* (1961). In this chapter, the G System of Units proposed by Dixon and Patterson (1961) is used, although it is recognized that there is much confusion in the field regarding terminology. In practice G is considered as a unit of force, and actual forces are expressed as "so many Gs." Terms such as "G units" or "a force of 5 G" are frequently used, the latter meaning, for example, a force whose magnitude is five times the weight of the body in question.

Several nomenclature systems that have been used are summarized in Table 1. On the left is listed a current vehicle displacement nomenclature that refers to the center of gravity displacement with respect to the vehicle axis. Listed adjacent to this is a physiological displacement

Table 1. Summary of Acceleration Nomenclatures Frequently Used

VEHICLE DISPLACEMENT (ACTION WITH RESPECT TO VEHICLE AXES)		PHYSIOLOGICAL DISPLACEMENT (HEART REACTION WITH RESPECT TO CHEST OR SKELETON)		ACTION DISPLACEMENT (RESULTANT ACTION OF VEHICLE WITH RESPECT TO BODY)		ACCELERATION FIELD (INCLUDING BODY POSITION AND REACTIVE FORCE)	
Symbol	Maneuver	Symbol	Response	Direction	Direction	G Field	Body Position
$+a_x$	Catapulting or launch	$+G_x$	Heart moves towards spine	Forward	Sternumward	Transverse G	Supine
$-a_x$	Arresting	$-G_x$	Heart moves towards chest	Backward	Spineward	Transverse G	Prone
$+a_y$	Yaw right	$+G_y$	Heart moves to left	Right	Sideward, right	Lateral G	Right-to-left
$-a_y$	Yaw left	$-G_y$	Heart moves to right	Left	Sideward, left	Lateral G	Left-to-right
$+a_z$	Push over	$-G_z$	Heart moves towards head	Footward	Tailward	Negative G	Seat-to-head
$-a_z$	Pull up	$+G_z$	Heart moves towards feet	Headward	Headward	Positive G	Head-to-seat
$+\dot{p}$	Roll right	$+\dot{R}_x$	Heart rolls left	—	—	—	—
$-\dot{p}$	Roll left	$-\dot{R}_x$	Heart rolls right	—	—	—	—
$+\dot{q}$	Pitch up	$+\dot{R}_y$	Heart pitches down	—	—	—	—
$-\dot{q}$	Pitch down	$-\dot{R}_y$	Heart pitches up	—	—	—	—
$+\dot{r}$	Yaw right	$-\dot{R}_z$	Heart yaws left	—	—	—	—
$-\dot{r}$	Yaw left	$+\dot{R}_z$	Heart yaws right	—	—	—	—

nomenclature that refers to the displacement of the heart with respect to the human skeleton. Two types of action displacement systems follow, each of which have had wide usage for giving a general statement of the human subject's position within an acceleration environment. The last two systems refer more to the traditional classification of transverse, positive, negative, and lateral acceleration fields.

When dealing with simple acceleration problems, it is customary to consider three kinds of acceleration: linear, angular, and radial (McCormick, 1957). Linear acceleration occurs in a straight line, angular acceleration occurs during rotatory movement (as when an aircraft is in a tailspin), and radial acceleration occurs when the direction of movement continuously changes (as when an aircraft is pulling out of a dive or making a turn).

It is also convenient to consider acceleration in descriptive terms such as positive G, negative G, transverse G (supine), transverse G (prone), fluctuating G, and zero G. Examples of these are shown in Figure 1. Positive acceleration occurs when the human body is positioned so that the force of inertia acts on it in a head-to-foot direction. Negative acceleration occurs when the body is positioned so that the force of inertia acts in a foot-to-head direction. Transverse G (supine) refers to an accelerative force from chest to back, and transverse G (prone) refers to an accelerative force from back to chest. Fluctuating G (or "jostle") refers to an unstable, uncontrolled acceleration profile that may vary greatly in complexity, as illustrated in the figure. "Zero gravity" refers to a situation in which there is a complete absence of gravitational effects on the human body, when, for example, the gravitational attraction of the earth is exactly counterbalanced by inertial forces. This condition occurs during the execution by an aircraft of the proper parabolic flight path or in the case of an orbiting satellite.

This terminology, though descriptive, is not exact enough to describe acceleration forces as they act along the various axes of the vehicle or of the human body. Among the systems of nomenclature used by aerodynamicists, one of the most widely used is a modification of that originally proposed by Bairstow (1920) in terms of vehicle displacement acceleration. Generally, this refers to aircraft displacements over the ground with respect to three vehicular axes, X, Y, and Z. Figure 2 and Table 2 present a summary of this system of acceleration nomenclature, in which positive X is forward, positive Y is to the right, and positive Z is downward (Clark, *et al.*, 1961). Reverse directions are indicated by the negative sign. The acceleration axes refer to the center of gravity of the aircraft with the X-axis in the longitudinal direction, the Y-axis in the wing direction, and the Z-axis in the vertical direction. The acceleration

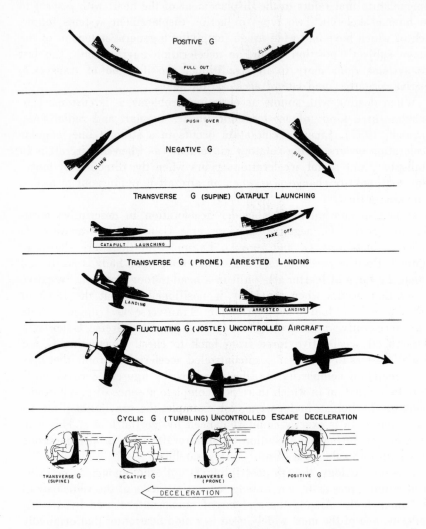

Figure 1. Examples of some G-environments. Accelerations encountered in flight and escape. (Official photograph U.S. Navy.)

unit is feet per second per second (ft/sec^2) regardless of direction. At any given instant, the total linear acceleration of the center of gravity of the aircraft is the vector sum of these three components. Angular acceleration components about any given linear axis are expressed in radians per second per second with $\dot{p}$, $\dot{q}$, and $\dot{r}$ being given positive or negative signs to indicate directions of rotation. The equations of motion

Table 2. Nasa Airplane Axis System
(Vehicle Displacement)

LINEAR ACCELERATION MODES

Description of Aircraft Motion	Symbol	Unit
Acceleration forward (surge)	$+a_x$	ft/sec² or g
Deceleration (Accelerate backward)	$-a_x$	ft/sec² or g
Downward Acceleration	$+a_z$	ft/sec² or g
Upward Acceleration (heave)	$-a_z$	ft/sec² or g
Straight and level flight at constant speed	$a_z = O$	
Acceleration to right (sway)	$+a_y$	ft/sec² or g
Acceleration to left	$-a_y$	ft/sec² or g

$a = a_x + a_y + a_z$

ANGULAR ACCELERATION MODES

Angular acceleration about X-axis (roll right)	$\dot{p}$	rad/sec²
Angular acceleration about Y-axis (pitch up)	$\dot{q}$	rad/sec²
Angular acceleration about Z-axis (yaw right)	$\dot{r}$	rad/sec²

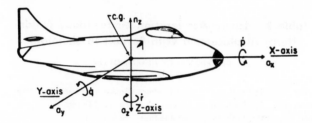

Figure 2. Airplane axis system for describing linear and angular acceleration environments. (Official photograph U.S. Navy.)

of the aircraft can then be written in terms of vector notations using the six vectors as indicated in Figure 2.

Although appropriate transformations of this nomenclature are available for use in physiological research (Dixon and Patterson, 1953), which take into account seat angles and other geometric factors, this procedure has disadvantages (see Clark *et al.*, 1961). Consequently, a system more compatible with the various physiological terms already in use has been proposed (Clark *et al.*, 1961). This system is summarized in Figure 3 and Table 3. It can be seen that this terminology emphasizes body reactions to the accelerations. The positive directions along the axes are directions of reactive displacements and are consequently expressed by a different symbol from that used in Figure 2. Positive G_x means that the heart is pulled from chest to back with respect to the skeleton, and the physiological X-axis is positive toward the back and

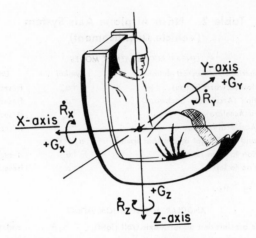

Figure 3. Physiological displacement nomenclature used in describing the physiological effects of acceleration. (Official photograph U.S. Navy.)

Table 3.   Linear Acceleration Modes (Body Fluids, Heart Displacement With Respect to Skeleton)

DESCRIPTION OF HEART MOTION

Actual	Other Descriptions			Symbol	Unit
Towards spine	Eye-balls-in	Chest-to-back	Backward facing	$+G_x$	g
Towards sternum	Eye-balls-out	Back-to-chest	Forward facing	$-G_x$	g
Towards feet	Eye-balls down	Head-to-foot	Headward	$+G_z$	g
Towards head	Eye-balls-up	Foot-to-head	Footward	$-G_z$	g
Towards left	Eye-balls-left	—	Rightward	$+G_y$	g
Towards right	Eye-balls-right	—	Leftward	$-G_y$	g

$$N(G) = \frac{a}{g} = N_1G_x + N_2G_y + N_3G_z$$
$$N^2 = N_1{}^2 + N_2{}^2 + N_3{}^2$$

ANGULAR ACCELERATION MODES

Acceleration about X-axis (roll axis)	$\dot{R}_x$	rad/sec^2
Acceleration about Y-axis (pitch axis)	$\dot{R}_y$	rad/sec^2
Acceleration about Z-axis (yaw axis)	$\dot{R}_z$	rad/sec^2

(Angular acceleration is positive or negative by right hand rule)

negative toward the chest. Positive G_y means that the heart moves to the left with respect to the skeleton. The positive physiological Y-axis is right to left. If the heart moves to the right with respect to the skeleton, this is called negative G_y. Positive G_z means that the heart is displaced caudally along the spine, and negative G_z means that the heart is displaced toward the head.

Similarly, the angular acceleration movement about the X-axis, Y-axis, and Z-axis are also described in this diagram. Acceleration about the X-axis means that the acceleration forces are causing the heart to roll left in the chest. This is designated by $+R_x$. Acceleration about the Y-axis means that the acceleration forces are causing the heart to pitch down within the chest and is designated by R_y. Acceleration about the Z-axis means that the acceleration forces are causing the heart to yaw left in a direction about the Z-axis, and this is designated by $+R_z$. The negative sign is used to indicate conditions in which the acceleration forces are causing the heart to be displaced in the opposite directions around the X-axis, Y-axis, and Z-axis. More detailed comparisons and discussions of the nomenclature are described in Clark, *et al.* (1961); Gauer and Zuidema (1961); and Gell (1961). Figure 4 and Table 4 describe the relationship of physiological accelerations to the acceleration environment.

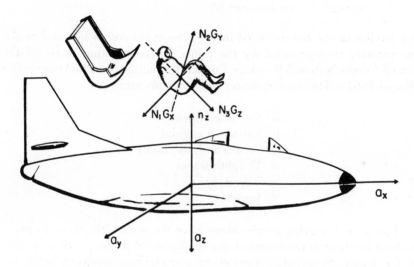

Figure 4. Relationship of physiological acceleration to description of acceleration environments. (Official photograph U.S. Navy.)

In this chapter, this physiological displacement system is used throughout. It is noted that this procedure may be conveniently used to describe vibratory, oscillatory, and impact vibrations also, and consequently has advantages over the other systems.

B. BASIC TYPES OF ACCELERATION ENVIRONMENTS

Acceleration environments may be classified according to basic types. Whereas many attempts have been made in the past to classify accelera-

Table 4.

Linear Acceleration Modes

DESCRIPTION		SYBMOL	
Aircraft	Physiological	Aircraft	Physiological
Forward	Supine G	$+a_x$	$+N_1G_x$
Backward	Prone G	$-a_x$	$-N_1G_x$
Upward	Positive G	$-a_z$	$+N_3G_z$
Downward	Negative G	$+a_z$	$-N_3G_z$
Straight and level flight at constant speed		$a_z = 0; n_z = 1g$	$N_3G_z = 1G_z$
To right	Lateral G	$+a_y$	$+N_2G_y$
To left	Lateral G	$-a_y$	$-N_2G_y$

Angular Acceleration Modes

Roll right	The heart rolls left	$+\dot{p}$	$+N_4\dot{R}_x$
Pitch up	The heart pitches down	$+\dot{q}$	$+N_5\dot{R}_y$
Yaw right	The heart yaws left	$+\dot{r}$	$-N_6\dot{R}_z$

tion environments, the one used in the present chapter is identical to the one recently recommended by the Panel on Acceleration Stress of the Armed Forces National Research Council Committee on Bio-Astronautics (Bates, 1961). These acceleration environments are:

  a. Sustained linear
  b. Sustained angular
  c. Zero G and subgravity
  d. Weightlessness
  e. Vibratory
  f. Impact

Linear and angular accelerations have the same definitions as given to them in classical mathematics and as discussed in the previous section of the paper. Steady-state motion on a centrifuge produces linear acceleration as far as the human subject is concerned. In this situation, radial acceleration is used to simulate linear acceleration. However, changes in rotational speed of the centrifuge or motions of a gimbal-mounted gondola produce concurrent angular accelerations.

Zero gravity and subgravity are as described in the previous section. Weightlessness, however, is defined as that condition in which the person has the psychological feeling of no weight, as when suspended in a fluid of equal specific gravity, but in which the full force of gravity is actually still acting on him. These three conditions are reviewed in another chapter. For the purposes of this chapter, impact accelerations are regarded as abrupt, physiologically severe stresses. These usually last less than one second, but have extremely rapid rates of onset and decline, and very high magnitudes.

Vibration (oscillation) is the rapid variation in acceleration with time when the displacement is alternately greater and smaller than the reference. The planes of vibration may be defined with reference to the human body as the following: *vertical* (up-down); *transverse* (side to side), and *longitudinal* (fore-aft). The amplitude of displacement at a point is the largest value of displacement that the point attains with reference to its equilibrium position. The number of cycles completed per unit time is the frequency of vibration. Acceleration, within the vibration context, refers to the rate of change of the velocity of the point. It is expressed in G units of intensity. Whereas man can endure high acceleration loads, it is sometimes assumed that accelerations at very low intensity may be of no consequence to performance. As will be shown in this chapter, however, vibrations having G values that are a fraction of the tolerated acceleration levels are sometimes of major consequence to human performance.

The severity of any particular acceleration environment is dependent upon many physical, physiological, and psychological variables, among the most important of which are the physical characteristics of the accelerations themselves. In flying an airplane, for example, a pilot may experience a complexity of mild linear, angular, and radial accelerations during various piloting maneuvers, such as take-off, banks, turns, rolls, skids, side slips, dives and pull-outs, spins, tumbles, buffeting, landing, egress, crash, or impact. Within spacecraft, an even greater number of maneuvers may be experienced by the astronaut, and in these cases the severity and complexity of acceleration stresses to which he may be exposed is virtually unlimited.

Several acceleration fields are of major interest in space operations. The launch accelerations may be small in magnitude and prolonged in duration or large in magnitude and short in duration, depending on the specific characteristics of the booster rocket. Boosters may have one, two, three, or four stages, and they vary greatly. Most of the boosters for any manned-craft system can be engineered to meet the physiological limits of man, provided that the physiological limits of man are known (Hessberg, 1961a, 1961b). During the orbital (flight) phase, the major acceleration aspects are concerned with subgravity or reduced gravity environments. The minor accelerations produced by reaction controls for vehicle orientation during orbital flight are of a very low G magnitude and are not considered of any physiological significance, except as they may possibly effect the vestibular function when superimposed over subgravity conditions. The re-entry accelerations imposed on spacecraft pose problems, largely because these accelerations may easily approach the physiological limits. They appear to pose serious problems also because of the possibility that subgravity during orbit may greatly lower man's tolerance to re-entry G.

The landing phase, or impact with the earth, also depends upon the system involved. This may extend to as high as 40 G for less than one second (Hessberg, 1961a). The accelerations associated with emergency egress and escape may vary greatly in complexity and severity. These accelerations cannot be catagorized, because there are many methods and conditions for escape. A final type of acceleration field is that characterized by vibrations (oscillations). If superimposed on high linear or angular accelerations, they may pose severe physiological and psychological problems.

There are many different types of devices which produce acceleration environments in which man is required to perform and survive. Aircraft and spacecraft are perhaps of most interest at the present time. Unconstrained motion within aircraft and spacecraft involves six degrees of freedom, which may be conveniently expressed in terms of six components, three of which are linear accelerations and three of which are orthogonal angular accelerations. For any given aircraft or spacecraft, some of these components are more important than others, and the ways in which these are combined determine largely the complexity of the environment in which man may find himself.

For descriptive purposes, it is desirable to express the environment of man within these types of vehicles in terms of a standard nomenclature. It is possible to express these linear and angular accelerations in terms of the amplitude and direction of stress on man. The physiological displacement nomenclature presented in Table 1 approximates a comprehensive description of the acceleration environment with respect to the human pilot exposed in a six-degree-of-freedom acceleration environment.

A centrifuge capable of simulating several of these acceleration conditions at any given instant is located at the U.S. Naval Air Development Center's Aviation Medical Acceleration Laboratory (AMAL), Johnsville, Pennsylvania. This centrifuge has a radius arm of 50 feet with a 10-by-6-foot oblate spheroid gondola mounted at the end. The gondola is mounted within a double gimbal system that can continuously position a pilot within the gondola with respect to the direction of any resultant acceleration vector, as the arm turns at any desired velocity up to 173 miles per hour, producing radial accelerations up to 40 G. The angular accelerations can reach 10 radians/sec^2 and angular velocities can reach

2.8 radians/sec. Given this power capability and the proper control, it is possible to simulate the three linear acceleration components of flight continuously and some of the angular accelerations; however, the angular accelerations of the centrifuge with only three degrees of freedom of control cannot simulate all of the possible flight accelerations (see Figure 5).

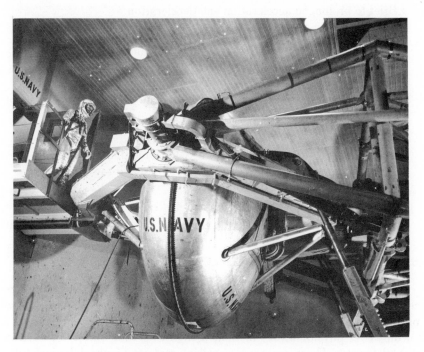

Figure 5. Pilot in space suit entering AMAL human centrifuge during complete mission training and simulation exercises in preparation for Mercury Redstone and Mercury Atlas flights. (Official photograph U.S. Navy.)

There are, however, requirements in human factors research for studying man's behavior in acceleration environments that involve less than four degrees of freedom. Other devices are shake tables and vertical accelerators that can provide oscillations, usually in one degree of freedom. Rocket sleds and drop towers (Stapp, 1961; Eiband, 1959) are used for producing acceleration environments having extremely short duration and very high amplitude.

The following acceleration devices are used in experimental research on human subjects:

Abrupt acceleration, deceleration, and impact

Drop towers   Inclined test facilities
Rocket sleds   Swing devices
Vertical decelerator towers   Catapult and arresting devices
Ejector seat devices

Brief to prolonged acceleration and deceleration

Centrifuges   Spin tables
Rotating rooms   Pitch and roll chairs
Angular accelerators   Special motion simulators
Small rotary devices   Variable stability aircraft
Tumbling devices   Special purpose flight simulators

Brief to prolonged vibration and oscillations

Shake tables   Variable stability aircraft
Vertical vibration devices   Random vibration devices
Horizontal and lateral vibrator
    devices

C. PHYSIOLOGICAL TOLERANCE TO ACCELERATION STRESS

One of the most important and complex concepts in acceleration research is physiological tolerance, the ability of the human subject physiologically to withstand varying degrees of acceleration stress. It encompasses physiological functions as well as a wide variety of environmental factors. There are some excellent reviews of physiological tolerance (Eiband, 1959; Swearingen, *et al.*, 1960; Clark, 1961; Clark and Faubert, 1961; Bondurant, 1961; Gauer, 1961a, 1961b; Gauer and Zuidema, 1961; Kornhauser, 1961; Leverett and Zuidema, 1961; and Stapp, 1961).

Since physiological G tolerance is a function of many variables, it has not been possible to construct a single simple graph which adequately summarizes G tolerance. Also, there has been no systematic work in which the same subjects have been exposed to a sufficiently wide variety of conditions using reasonably comparable tolerance criteria. G tolerance may be expressed as a function of at least five primary acceleration variables, and a complex multidimensional graph would be required to show all of the relationships, even if the complete data were available. These variables are as follows:

a. The direction of the primary of resultant G force with respect to the axes of the human body.
b. The rate of onset and decline of G.
c. The magnitude of peak G.
d. The duration of peak G.
e. The total duration of acceleration from time of onset to termination.

Other conditions influence a human subject's tolerance. Some of them, in addition to the ones already presented earlier, are as follows:

a. The types of end points used in determining tolerance.
b. The types of G protection devices and body restraints.
c. The type of environment in which the subject is tested, such as temperature, ambient pressure, noise, and lighting.
d. Age.
e. Psychological factors, such as fear and anxiety, competitive attude, willingness to tolerate discomfort and pain.
f. Previous acceleration training and accumulative effects.
g. The types of acceleration device used for exposing the subject to acceleration.
h. Muscular control, tensing, and effort.

Many different criteria have been used to describe G tolerance. These include EKG abnormalities, cardiovascular response, survival time, carotid pressure, chest pain, blackout, and unconsciousness. However, human tolerance to positive G is usually measured in terms of the visibility of lights, usually two peripheral lights and one center light. If the subject fails to signal to the presence of peripheral lights, this failure is characterized as loss of peripheral vision and sometimes called "grayout." Failure to respond to the central light is called "blackout." The next step in severity is unconsciousness. For negative G the criteria are generally severe visual malfunctions, such as redout, blurred vision, excessive pain and excessive tears. For transverse G, the criteria are usually visual dimming or loss of peripheral vision, excessive blurring or difficulty in focusing, excessive tearing, chest pain, excessive pain or discomfort in the extremities, extreme fatigue, and extreme difficulty in breathing.

The rate of onset and duration of G are of great significance in impact acceleration. Impact accelerations are encountered in collisions, drops, catapults and arrestments, and a number of experimental test devices. Rocket sleds, drop towers, and swing devices are the most frequently used devices for experimental work. One of the highest impact studies on human subjects was that reported by Beeding and Hessberg (1958), in which Beeding, riding as a subject, experienced 82.6 G at a rate-of-onset of 3,826 G per second for a duration time of 0.040 second. He reported that at impact he experienced a searing pain from the coccyx up to L-3, and feared that these vertebrae would crumble if he moved. He had highly impaired vision and a severe headache. He was hospitalized for three days and was in traction for the first day. The first six meals following the exposure resulted in severe stomach pains.

The tolerance criteria for impact studies are unclear. Using drop towers, Headley, *et al.* (1960), conducted some forty-six vertical impact experiments on human subjects in the seated position and variously re-strained. Acceleration loadings extended up to 35 G for a fraction of a second. The only post-test clinical finding was a microscopic hematuria that lasted one month. Similarly, using swing devices to simulate crash-type mechanical forces, Lewis and Stapp (1958) found that all subjects were bruised and complained of abdominal and epigastric pain. In these studies, abdominal G ranged from 4 to 22 G for durations ranging from 0.001 to 0.003 second.

Although the physiological and anatomical consequences of impact have received intensive study, it is not possible to derive suitable physio-logical tolerance criteria. Similarly, very little is known about the emo-tional, perceptual, and intellectual changes or impairments that may occur. In impact acceleration the skeletal system remains relatively rigid,

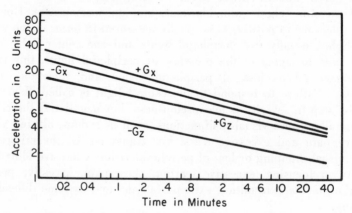

Figure 6. Average acceleration tolerance for positive acceleration $(+G_z)$, negative acceleration $(-G_x)$, transverse supine acceleration $(+G_x)$, and transverse prone acceleration $(-G_x)$. (Official photograph U.S. Navy.)

whereas the tissues and internal organs, being more elastic, react violently.

Figure 6 shows some of the most important relationships for magnitude of acceleration and duration time for positive acceleration $(+G_z)$, negative acceleration $(-G_z)$, and transverse accelerations $(+G_x$ and $-G_x)$. The figure includes both impact accelerations and sustained accelerations. The plot is partially theoretical, since data along some of

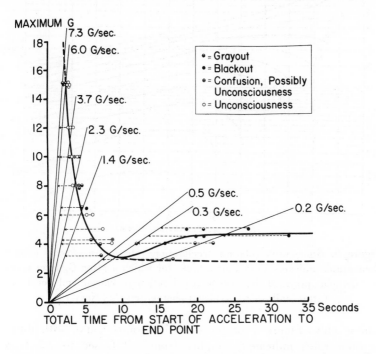

Figure 7. Human tolerance to positive G_z for varying rates of onset, G—amplitudes, and exposure times (after Stoll, 1956). (Official photograph U.S. Navy.)

the intermediate points are not available. Most of the curves in this chart are based on summaries reported by Duane, *et al.* (1953); Beckman, *et al.* (1954); Eiband (1959); Gauer and Zuidema (1961a); and Creer, *et al.* (1960). Lateral G has not been plotted, since there has been insufficient research to date to place on a graph of this type.

Figures 7 and 8 summarize an analysis conducted by Stoll (1956), in which the physiological end points of over 300 experiments were studied. These acceleration tolerance curves are for positive (G_z) ac-

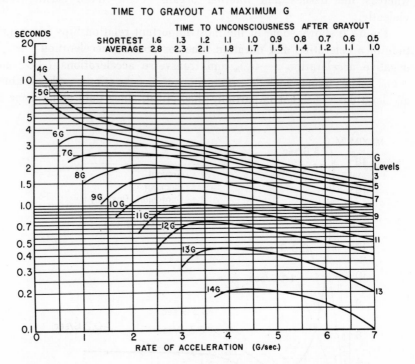

TIME TO GRAYOUT AT MAXIMUM G

Figure 8. Nomograph relating acceleration rate to time-to-end point. Nomograph indicates approximate times for which a given G_z level may be tolerated, provided the rate of acceleration is known and constant (after Stoll, 1956). (Official photograph U.S. Navy.)

celerations only. Figure 7 presents a G tolerance curve with different acceleration rates indicated, ranging from 0.2 G/sec to 7.3 G/secs. Figure 8 presents an acceleration nomograph for positive G.

The above figures represent averages and not necessarily maximum tolerance levels. To portray some of the tolerance runs achieved to date, Table 5 has been prepared to show some maximum acceleration exposures that human subjects have endured. This table does not necessarily mean that the subjects who made these runs could not have endured higher accelerations for longer time periods. It simply attempts to report the results of tests that have been made in unusually adverse acceleration environments and that for the most part represent record runs in terms of peak acceleration value and endurance.

Table 5, and Figures 6, 7, and 8 suggest that man's highest tolerances are along the G_x direction, with $-G_x$ next, then $+G_z$, and finally $-G_z$.

**Table 5. Some Maximum Acceleration Exposures Endured
by Human Subjects**

Type of G Field	Type of Maneuver	Peak G	Exposure Time (sec)	Type of Device
$+G_x$	Abrupt deceleration	$82.6G_x$	0.04	Deceleration sled
(Transverse G,	Abrupt deceleration	$55G_x$	0.01	Deceleration sled
sternumward)	Abrupt deceleration	$35G_x$	0.12	Deceleration sled
	High-G re-entry	$25G_x$	5	Centrifuge
	Re-entry simulation	$15G_x$	5	Centrifuge
	Tracking and endurance test	$14G_x$	127	Centrifuge
	Tracking and endurance test	$10G_x$	210	Centrifuge
	Tracking and endurance test	$6G_x$	555	Centrifuge
$-G_x$	Abrupt deceleration	$-60G_x$	0.01	Deceleration sled
(Transverse G,	Abrupt deceleration	$-38G_x$	0.12	Deceleration sled
spineward)	Endurance test in water capsule	$-31G_x$	5	Centrifuge
	Endurance test in water capsule	$-28G_x$	5	Centrifuge
	Re-entry simulation	$-15G_x$	5	Centrifuge
	Prolonged tracking and endurance test	$-10G_x$	71	Centrifuge
	Prolonged tracking and endurance test	$-6G_x$	350	Centrifuge
$+G_z$	Ejection escape	$+20G_z$	0.1	Ejection tower
(Positive G)	Endurance, tracking	$+9G_z$	6	Centrifuge
	Endurance, tracking	$+8G_z$	26	Centrifuge
	Endurance, tracking	$+7G_z$	90	Centrifuge
	Endurance test	$+5G_z$	240	Centrifuge
$-G_z$	Ejection escape (downward)	$-10G_z$	0.1	Ejection tower
(Negative G)	Push over	$-4.5G_z$	5	Airplane
	Endurance test	$-3G_z$	32	Centrifuge

Gauer and Zuidema (1961) provide excellent reviews of some of the physiological tolerance studies that have been made along these acceleration axes.

In addition to physiological G tolerance, an important concept is that of G protection. There are many kinds of G protection devices, the most common of which are form-fitted contour couches, net couches, G suits, water suits, a large variety of straps and restraining equipment, and the binding of body members. The kind of G protection equipment used is also important because it influences the kinds of tasks that a person can perform during acceleration exposure, since, in addition to providing support, it restrains and restricts the subject's movements. G protection equipment may either facilitate or impair performance, depending on how it is designed with respect to the man and the acceleration environment.

The G protection system that is receiving most intensive study at the present time is the form-fitted contour couch. For performing piloting tasks when in a pressure suit and in the G_x or in the G_z position, the form-fitted couches shown in Figures 9 and 10 have been found to be satisfactory. A more portable, adjustable restraint system that is designed to provide protection from the major types of acceleration vectors and that does not require individual fitting has also been developed (Smedal, *et al.*, 1961, Figure 11).

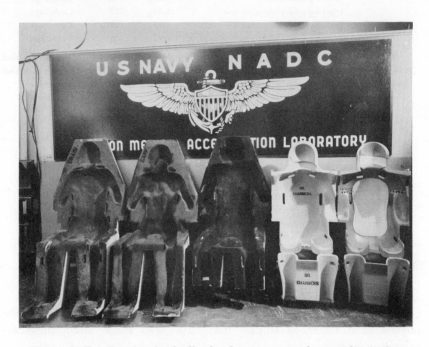

Figure 9. Family of individually fitted contour couches used in pilot performance studies on the AMAL human centrifuge. (Official photograph U.S. Navy.)

Figure 12 is a graph that compares some unusually outstanding time-tolerance to acceleration centrifuge runs along several acceleration vectors. This particular figure represents results of prolonged high-G acceleration tests in which experienced pilots served as subjects. They continuously performed piloting tasks in acceleration fields during steady-state G exposures in which performance proficiency as well as physiological tolerance were used as tolerance criteria. The data are based on results of studies conducted on the Aviation Medical Acceleration Labora-

Figure 10. Subject in inflated pressure suit in contour couch prior to acceleration exposure. The figure illustrates a condition in which the administration of any of the standard psychological tests to measure mental functioning would be very difficult. (Official photograph U.S. Navy.)

tory Human Centrifuge, utilizing the best restraint equipment available at the times the studies were conducted.

A variety of unusual restraints, such as water-tanks, water-capsules, and procedures for completely foaming the human subject, are reviewed by Bondurant, Blanchard, Clarke and Moore (1958); Clark and Gray (1959); Gray (1960); Weaver, *et al.* (1961), and Leverett, *et al.*(1961).

In closing this section, it should be emphasized that marked individual differences in G tolerance exist, and extreme caution is necessary in attempting to generalize tolerance data from one person or groups of persons to any given individual subject within an acceleration environment. The problem of individual differences is analyzed in later sections of this chapter.

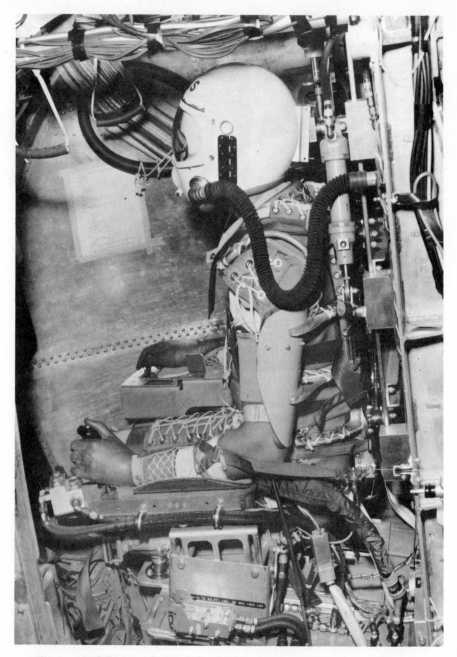

Figure 11. Pilot in advanced G-protection and restraint system, developed by NASA and tested at the AMAL human centrifuge. This system was designed to provide protection for $+G_x$, $-G_x$, and $+G_z$ accelerations. It is adjustable, portable, and comfortable. This system provides maximum protection against performance decrement during exposure to high sustained accelerations. (Official photograph U.S. Navy.)

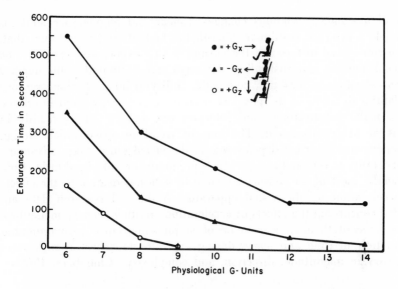

Figure 12. Summary of time-tolerance centrifuge endurance tests in which pilots were exposed to high prolonged $+G_x$, $-G_x$, and $+G_z$ steady-state accelerations. The pilots wore special G-protection equipment and were all experienced centrifuge riders. They were required to maintain satisfactory tracking performance continuously during exposures to the physiological G-stress. (Official photograph U.S. Navy.)

II. Sensation and Perception

There are several ways in which acceleration affects human performance. First, performance changes may be direct effects that the accelerative forces have on sensory receptors. Secondly, the autonomic nervous system may be so affected that the control and coordination of component activities of different parts of the body are influenced. Thirdly, these changes may be the result of physical forces acting on the body members themselves, without involvement of neural and sensory systems. Finally, there may be interactions among these effects. The purpose of this section is to summarize the research on the ability of man to sense and perceive stimuli during exposure to acceleration. These concern the vestibular, kinesthetic, proprioceptive, visual, and auditory senses. Research on the effects of acceleration on complex perceptual processes required for time and spatial orientation is also reviewed.

During exposure to acceleration stress, the human subject's perception of a standard stimulus changes. Linear and angular accelerations themselves produce vestibular, kinesthetic, tactual, and visual cues that, when considered in terms of the normal $+1\ G_z$ experience, appear to be unusual, unique, and misleading. Although man is limited in the number of senses which he may use, he has the ability to integrate these sensory modalities in terms of the physical environment, employ them in unique ways, make substitutions, and interpret his sensory inputs readily in terms of his environment. The current trend in space-vehicle design considers man's normal dependency on the visual sense, takes advantage of his ability to see, and assigns him a predominance of visual tasks. Consequently, most of the sensory research to date has dealt with the effects of acceleration on the visual apparatus. Additional research data are needed concerning the effects of acceleration on other sensory modalities, since some of them appear to be of major importance in maintaining orientation in time and space during exposure to acceleration vectors that vary in magnitude, direction, and complexity (Chambers, 1962b).

A. VESTIBULAR, KINESTHETIC, AND PROPRIOCEPTIVE SENSES

The senses of motion, position, pressure, and vision are important indicators of acceleration conditions. However, the human subject seems incapable of differentiating the components of a G field to which he is exposed. He can appreciate only the effects of the various forces in terms of their common resultant. There are a number of illusions associated with the kinesthetic and vestibular senses, and extensive work has been done on some of these illusory phenomena.

Exposure to acceleration has a manifold effect on the vestibular and kinesthetic senses of man. Most of these effects are produced during linear accelerations and decelerations and by the angular accelerations that may be superimposed. During zero gravity (see also the chapter by Loftus and Hammer) and high acceleration stress, the perceptual and motor performance of a human pilot depends largely upon the muscle, pressure, and posture senses. The abilities to position a limb, to orient one's body or any part of the body, to manipulate tools, or to perform piloting tasks are all subject to the vestibular and kinesthetic senses.

The perception of the position and movement of the human body is controlled by the labyrinthine system, consisting primarily of the semi-circular canals and the otolith portion of the vestibular organ, and the extralabyrinthine system, consisting of the muscle spindles, Pacinian corpuscles, nervous plexuses, and Meissner corpuscles (Geldard, 1953; Gerathewohl, 1958). The generally accepted theory concerning the way in which vestibular organs function to maintain balance is that the otolith organs respond to linear accelerations and to gravity and that the six semicircular canals respond to angular accelerations. The theory of the functional relationships between the semicircular canals and otolith organs has been challenged (Gray, 1960), but the importance of these structures in maintaining balance is well established (Guedry and Graybiel, 1961).

The muscle spindles provide information about movements and positions of the body. The Pacinian corpuscles compose the posture sense. The nervous plexuses and Meissner corpuscles compose the pressure sense, which provides information on tactile orientation. The otoliths, muscle spindles, Pacinian corpuscles, nervous plexuses, and Meissner corpuscles are frequently called "gravireceptors" or "graviceptors," since they are all involved in the perception of the effects of gravitational forces.

The vestibular and kinesthetic senses are active during acceleration. The reaction of the vestibular apparatus is proportional to acceleration, although the human subject is not capable of differentiating the components of the accelerative forces to which he is exposed. For example, in many instances judgments concerning the attitude of the aircraft based on "feel" while flying have been shown to be incorrect (Clark and Hardy, 1961). Similarly, some disorientation follows exposure to combinations of high G vectors, and also when the G is reduced suddenly, as from 15 G_x to 1 G_x (Brown, 1957).

Variations in tension within the body and of the pressures in contact with the body can create misleading impressions regarding motion (Schafer, 1951; Stewart, 1945). These variations are also a function of the direction of the acceleration load on the body.

Research results (Stewart, 1945; Christensen and Johnson, 1959) show that the sensitivity of the body to changes in gravity varies as a function of the amount of gravitational force being exerted. At a range from +1 to +2 G, a person can sense small changes of 0.1 G and lower. From +2 to +3 G, this sensitivity to change decreases to 0.2 G, above +4 G, the sensitivity to change is approximately 1 to 2 G, and above 6 G, this sensitivity is between 2 and 3 G. Also, subjects could perceive a reduction of G from 9 to 6 or from 6 to 4, and they were aware that considerable residual G remained after both of these reductions. In some cases, however, a reduction from a high G to 2 G resulted in failure of the subject to recognize that he was still exposed to accelerative forces in excess of gravity.

Sensations reported by subjects experiencing positive $(+G_z)$ accelerations acting on the body are increased pressure of the buttocks on the seat; heaviness of the head, body, and limbs; downward pull of the diaphragm, jaw, and skin of face; congestion in the lower segments of the body; and the loss of peripheral and possibly central vision. Depending upon the severity of the acceleration, there may be pain in the toes, the feet, the ankles and the gastrocnemius muscle. There may be feelings of fullness in the lower extremities, and breathing may be difficult and tiring.

During exposure to negative accelerations $(-G_z)$, the sensations reported by subjects are pronounced even at low G levels: sensations of fullness, pressure, throbbing, and possible pain in the head area; upward displacement of the internal organs and thorax; pressure against the shoulder and seat belt restraints; difficulty in breathing, speaking, and swallowing; marked difficulty in vision; and pain in and possibly damage to the eyes, such as conjunctival hemorrhage.

The aftereffects of G are small compared with the aftereffects of negative G, which include dizziness, facial congestion, distension of the arteioles, and conjunctival and subcutaneous hemorrhages that may last for days. Confusion, headache, and loss of muscular coordination may persist for several hours.

Sensations reported by subjects during transverse $(+G_x)$ accelerations are pressure on the chest and possible substernum pain; difficulty in breathing; sensations of pressure along the dorsal part of the body, especially the back, hips, neck, and head; some blurring of vision; and the loss of visual acuity, accompanied by difficulty in keeping the eyes open. Some loss of peripheral vision is also frequent.

The effects of transverse $(-G_x)$ accelerations include feelings of fullness and pain along the anterior surface of the body, especially the face, fingertips, and toes; pressure points along the chest and face; congestion in the nose; marked ease of inhalation; blurring of vision accompanied by tears and possible temporary distortion of the eyeball; and pain along the anterior surface of the eye and associated musculature.

Research on the vestibular, kinesthetic, and proprioceptive senses has not progressed to the extent that the specific effects of acceleration on these sensory systems may be precisely reported. The technology and procedures that would lend a more quantitative nature to the qualitative descriptions given above are not yet available. Similarly, the degree to which acceleration may act on these senses to indirectly affect performance under acceleration is unknown.

B. VISION

During exposure to higher positive, negative, and transverse accelerations, visual disturbances occur. During positive acceleration, these disturbances result primarily from retinal ischemias. However, mechanical distortion of the eye may also occur in severe cases. Generally, a period of grayout exists before blackout occurs (see Figure 7). Grayout is characterized by a general dimming, blurring, and tunnel vision, and occurs approximately 1 G unit below the level at which blackout occurs. Grayout symptoms usually appear at approximately $+4G_z$. In the case of blackout, the arterial pressure equals or is less than intra-ocular pressure, and so blood is not supplied to the retina. Consciousness is retained during blackout, but unconsciousness will follow if there is an increase in G amplitude. In the case of negative G, there is an increase of arterial and venous blood pressure in the head, resulting in extracranial pooling of the blood. Serious damage to the visual apparatus may occur if more than $-2\ G_z$ are sustained for more than 10 seconds (Sieker, 1952; Henry, 1950). Primary visual symptoms during negative G are: disminished vision, difficulty in focusing, conjunctival hemorrhage, tear secretion, "red out," and a tendency for the lower lid to overlap the upper lid.

During exposure to high transverse accelerations, the effects on the visual system depend largely on whether the acceleration force is $+G_x$ ("eyeballs in") or $-G_x$ ("eyeballs out"). When the accelerations are $+G_x$, no major visual disturbances have been reported up to loads of 14 G_x for 5 seconds' duration at peak. At levels between $+6$ and $+12\ G_x$, however, there may be some tearing, apparent loss of peripheral vision, and difficulty in keeping the eyes open. For $-G_x$ ("eyeballs out") accelerations, some pain may be experienced and small petechia may occur on the lower surfaces of the eyelids, and vision may be temporarily impaired. Conjunctival hemorrhaging may persist for several days, although to date no internal damage has been reported for accelerations as high as $+12\ G_x$ (Gauer and Ruff, 1939; Clark, *et al.*, 1945; Code, *et al.*, 1947; Gauer, 1950; Martin and Henry, 1950; Buhrlen, 1937; and Duane, *et al.*, 1953). In the case of $-G_x$ accelerations, however, the kind of restraints provided for the face, eyeballs, and anterior surface of the body is a major consideration, since levels higher and longer than this may be achieved by using appropriate protective devices.

The problem of maintaining vision under transverse acceleration appears to be largely a mechanical problem, due partly to mechanical pressures on the eyes, musculature, and the accumulation of tears. In addition to G amplitude and the direction of the primary G vector, the duration at peak G is of major importance. Total time during which a human subject can endure exposure to acceleration stress and maintain good vision depends primarily on his system for G protection. For positive acceleration, G protection is needed which will retain as much blood as possible in the head region. For transverse $(+G_x)$ accelerations, the G protection system must provide comfortable and evenly-distributed protection to the posterior surface of the body. For transverse $(-G_x)$ accelerations G protection should be provided for the anterior surface of the body, musculature around the eye sockets, and if possible, the eyeballs themselves. Vision remains adequate for performing a continuous perceptual-motor tracking task during exposure to positive and transverse steady-state accelerations for the following durations: 90 seconds at $+7$ G_z; 127 seconds at $+14$ G_x, and 71 seconds at -10 G_x. These record runs were conducted using restraint systems. These do not necessarily establish limits of visual performance, since the relationship between amplitude of G and duration at peak G has not been established. For example, in an earlier experiment by the author, one subject, using a contour-couch restraint system, was able to perform a visual task during $+25$ G_x for 5 seconds.

The end points for vision are much more clearly established for positive acceleration. Cochran, et al. (1954), tested 1,000 subjects who were seated in the upright body position on a human centrifuge. Using responses to peripheral and central lights as their criteria, they found the mean threshold for loss of peripheral vision to be $+4.1$ G_z, the mean threshold for blackout to be $+4.7$ G_z, and the threshold for unconsciousness to be $+5.4 G_z$. The standard deviations for these means were: $+0.7$ G_z, $+0.8$ G_z, and $+0.9$ G_z, respectively. Marked individual differences were shown for the range within which the subjects experienced loss of peripheral vision and blackout. For loss of peripheral vision, the range for the 1,000 subjects was $+2.2$ G_z to $+7.1$ G_z. For blackout, the range was from $+3.0$ G_z to $+8.4$ G_z. Subjects who tensed their muscles and who had G suits were able to maintain vision to somewhat higher levels of positive acceleration. In a recent series of tests at AMAL test pilots who were given maximum G protection and practice trials could maintain good vision within a range of between 6 and 8 positive G for approximately 30 seconds without blacking out.

Visual acuity decreases progressively as the magnitude of G increases (Enoch, 1957; Frankenhaeuser, 1957a; White and Jorve, 1956). This occurs during exposure to both positive and transverse accelerations. As G increases, a given level of visual acuity may be maintained by increasing the size of the target or the amount of illumination. White and Jorve (1956), for example, found that at $+7$ G_x, a target had to be twice as large as at 1 G in order to be seen. In another study, White (1958) observed that a test light had to be nearly three times as bright at $+4$ G_z as at $+1$ G_z in order to be seen.

Ability to read dials is influenced by both acceleration and illumination. At high luminances, the impairment due to G is not as great as it is for the same G at lower levels of luminance. At marginal levels of illumination, acceleration and luminance interact to produce a relatively large increase in errors. A significant and progressive effect on threshold occurs at all luminance levels, and this decrease in visual acuity is greater under conditions of low luminance levels (Warrick and Lund, 1946; White, 1958a; White and Riley, 1956). In testing visual reaction time in a central and a peripheral region of the retina, Brown and Burke (1957) used test light luminances of 4,500 millilamberts and 0.025 millilambert. Vision was maintained more effectively in the foveal region when the brighter light was used. When, however, the brighter light was placed in the peripheral visual field, peripheral vision could be maintained even though foveal vision of the dim light was lost.

Luminance threshold of the fovea (cones) increases as a function of acceleration. Within moderate tolerance limits, increasing the amplitude of positive acceleration increases the absolute foveal visual thresholds (Howard and Byford, 1956; White, 1958).

The severity of visual loss is highly dependent upon the rate of onset of the positive acceleration. A rate of onset of 7 G per second to a maximum of $+8 \ G_z$ sustained for only a fraction of a second may not produce any visual symptoms, whereas a rate of onset of 1 G per second to $+5 \ G_z$ may produce grayout and blackout in approximately 3 seconds. Research on the rate of onset has been extensively reported (Gauer and Henry, 1953; Edelberg, *et al.*, 1956; Stoll, 1956). Repeated exposure to acceleration may increase the visual threshold, i.e., result in a decline in visual sensitivity (White, 1958b).

As acceleration increases, an increase in contrast is required to detect a target. A recent study by the author and Braunstein and White at AMAL showed that more contrast was needed during positive acceleration than for transverse acceleration. For example, 16 per cent contrast between a target and its background was required at $5 \ G_z$, and 12 per cent contrast was required at $7 \ G_x$. For the static condition, an average of approximately 8.5 per cent contrast was required.

Visual brightness discrimination was studied for four levels of background luminance at four levels of positive acceleration and five levels of transverse acceleration. Figure 13 presents the mean contrast requirements for the four positive acceleration conditions. For each of the four positive acceleration conditions, the required mean contrast increased as the background luminance decreased. Also, for any given background luminance level, the higher acceleration levels required more brightness contrast. Similar results were shown for the transverse G exposures, although the differences due to background luminance were more than those due to acceleration level. When transverse and positive acceleration

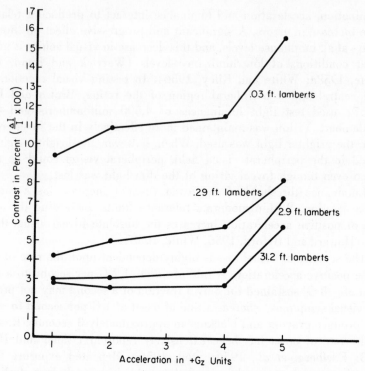

Figure 13. Effects of positive acceleration $(+G_z)$ on brightness discrimination thresholds for perceiving an achromatic circular target against each of four background luminances. (Official photograph U.S. Navy.)

loads are compared, the positive acceleration stress consistently required more contrast than did the transverse acceleration stress.

During exposure to positive acceleration, the visual field narrows rapidly as G increases (Hallenbeck, 1946; Brown and Burke, 1957). During positive G a narrowing of the visual field from 90 degrees at 1 G to an average of 46 degrees at 4.4 G was reported by Hallenbeck (1946). This narrowing continues as G is increased, until blackout occurs.

The effects of transverse acceleration on the visual field are less clear. In recent work by Chambers at AMAL, good peripheral vision was noted at loadings as high as $+12$ G_x. It is believed that such phenomena as tearing and pressure on the eyeball, rather than grayout, cause most of the visual decrement during transverse G. Data on central vision up to $+25$ G_x suggests that vision is not the limiting tolerance factor for transverse accelerations. Unless external eye protection is provided for $-G_x$

transverse accelerations, however, symptoms of blurring, tearing, and poor focusing occur after levels of -4 G_x. Given adequate eye protection, test pilots have maintained for a short time good peripheral and central vision to as high as -14 G_x.

It appears that visual reaction time increases during exposure to positive acceleration (Burmeister, 1939; Canfield, *et al.*, 1949; Brown and Burke, 1957). Brown and Burke (1958), for example, found that subjects exposed for more than 5 seconds to peak loads of 3 to 6 G responded more slowly to a visual stimulus than did other subjects at 1 G.

The study of the oculomotor and neural systems on human subjects exposed to acceleration has included the reflexly produced ocular nystagmus (Graybiel, 1952; Gray, 1956), photographic measurements of pupillary size during acceleration (Wilson and Canfield, 1951), volutional and involutional ocular motility, the optokinetic reflex, the ability to follow visually a moving target during acceleration exposure (Westheimer, 1954), consensual light reflex, the application of negative pressure over the eyes, and studies of corneal distortion. Decreased retinal circulation (Duane, 1954) and associated hypoxia have been established as one of the primary responsible causes of visual loss (White, 1961; Brown, 1961). Beckman, *et al.* (1961), found that the application of 30–35-mm Hg negative pressure over the eyes via a modified under-water swimmer's mask could restore vision following grayout and black-out to nearly normal. Also, they found that the optokinetic reflex and the ability to follow a target was restored by this procedure, although the pupils remained dilated. They suggest that in addition to the commonly acknowledged retinal failure during blackout, there is also a cerebral cortical dysfunction that occurs during positive acceleration at the blackout level. Lambert (1945) had earlier documented the fact that the application of pressure to the orbits could be used to change the visual threshold for blackout. Keighley, *et al.* (1951), found that flicker-fusion frequency was changed when suction was applied to the orbits of subjects exposed to acceleration.

Corneal distortion under acceleration has been studied at AMAL by filming reflections from the cornea and measuring distortions. To date, the results have been inconclusive because of the excessive tearing, but the data suggest that the cornea is distorted at levels of $+8$ G_x.

Ocular motility becomes limited during high positive acceleration. Although these limitations may be overcome by voluntary effort, the movements are ataxic. Voluntary eye movements disappeared at approximately the acceleration level that produced a loss of peripheral vision. The optokinetic reflex disappears concomitantly with blackout and the limitation of ocular motility, and the ability to follow a moving target also becomes impaired. Pupillary dilatation occurs (Wilson and Canfield, 1951; Beckman, *et al.*, 1961) as the visual fields constrict during positive acceleration, and is maximal when central vision is lost.

Ocular motility is of importance in performing visual tasks under acceleration, since fixation of the eyes in the primary position may occur, making it difficult for the pilot to change his point of visual fixation to another part of the instrument panel. This problem appears to be related to, but different from, the basic problem of seeing under conditions of acceleration.

Preliminary results (Chambers, *et al.*, 1962) suggest that positive pressure breathing protects vision to some degree during the more severe acceleration stress levels. Experienced test pilots report that the ability to see an instrument panel and perform a tracking task was improved by positive pressure breathing of 100 per cent oxygen at levels of 8, 10, and 12 G_x. These results were based upon the subjective opinions of the pilots. In a second study, the effects of positive pressure breathing on brightness discrimination were evaluated for both positive and transverse acceleration stress. Subjects breathed normal air, 100 per cent oxygen, and 100 per cent oxygen under pressure. With a background level of 0.03 ft-lambert the subjects were required to continually operate a switch to maintain a target at the minimum brightness contrast level. The results for positive acceleration exposures of 90 seconds' duration each are shown in Figure 14 for the $+1$, $+2$, $+3$, and $+5$ G_z levels. Figure 14 suggests that at $+3$ and $+5$ G_z levels, the positive pressure plus 100 per cent oxygen condition required less visual contrast than did the other two conditions. Similar results were found for the transverse G loads. Visual brightness was maintained at a constant level for both the 100 per cent oxygen and the 100 per cent oxygen plus positive pressure conditions, whereas for the normal air condition without positive pressure breathing an increasing amount of contrast was required as G increased. These results, although preliminary, suggest the possibility that visual performance may be increased by the positive pressure conditions plus 100 per cent oxygen.

Because of the importance of the visual sense during acceleration of stress produced within high-performance aircraft, there has been extensive research on the effects of positive acceleration on vision. More recently, largely because of the utilization of transverse acceleration profiles in proposed manned spacecraft, extensive research programs have been established to study the effects of transverse acceleration on vision. Although a brief summary of the results of experiments has been

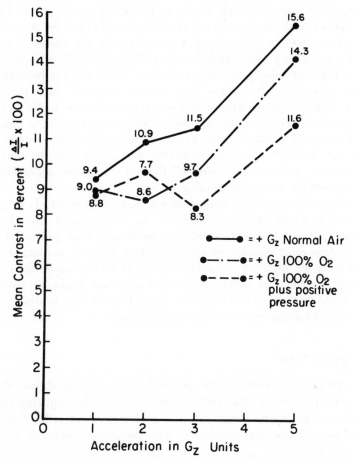

Figure 14. Comparative effects of breathing normal air, 100 per cent oxygen, and 100 per cent oxygen plus positive pressure breathing on brightness discrimination during exposure to positive acceleration. (Official photograph U.S. Navy.)

presented, the reader is directed to some of the more exhaustive treatments of this subject, especially White (1961b), Brown (1961), Brown, *et al.* (1961), and Chambers (1962a).

C. HEARING

Hearing remains unaffected even at very high levels of acceleraton, long after vision fails (Beckman, *et al.*, 1954, 1961; Cope and Jensen, 1961). Although it was found that auditory reaction time increases as positive acceleration amplitude increases (Canfield, *et al.*, 1949), Brown (1961) challenged this conclusion on the grounds that the increase in reaction time may be a result of a decrement in the motor response. Preliminary data by Cope and Jensen (1961) showed an increase in response time in adding aurally presented numbers. Preliminary unpublished laboratory data show that hearing continues during at least the early stages of unconsciousness (as interpreted from EEG) induced by positive acceleration. Although more evidence is needed to quantify the auditory end points during exposure to positive, transverse, and negative acceleration stress, all available data show that the auditory sense continues to function during all three acceleration modes beyond the end points for visual functioning.

One important practical consideration may be mentioned. In flight conditions in which grayout, blackout, or other visual disturbances might be expected to occur, as during prolonged high positive G, or during certain short profiles, or during certain types of prolonged $-G_x$ accelerations, the auditory channel would still be operative, even after the visual channel had failed. Some consideration might be made to provide flight signals via the auditory channel in vehicles in which these types of accelerations may be expected to occur.

D. TIME PERCEPTION

Four major categories of time perception are of interest: the ability to judge the passage of time, the performance of skills requiring timing of component parts and sequences, the performance of tasks requiring time-sharing, and the maintenance of psychological orientation in time (Chambers, 1958a).

Studies of the effects of acceleration on time perception are difficult because many variables are involved. For example, the number of stimulus events to which a person is responding (Chambers, 1958), one's internal chemical state (Dews and Morse, 1958; Goldstone *et al.*, 1958), the degree of confinement and aggravation (Burns and Gifford, 1960; Ross, 1959; Simons, 1958b; Hanna and Gaito, 1960) have all been found to affect one's ability to judge the passage of time.

Frankenhaeuser (1958), using the psychophysical method of fractionation, asked subjects to reproduce the duration of random time units by pressing a button. Comparisons of the measures obtained at rest and during centrifugation (maximum of $+3$ G_z for 10 minutes per run) showed that the time settings were shorter during centrifugation than before or after. Also, the standard stimulus was underestimated more during exposure to acceleration than during normal conditions. Her results indicate that subjects underestimated the passage of time during positive acceleration. Other studies tend to agree with this finding (Frankenhaeuser, 1956, 1957a, 1957b).

Chambers and Eggleston (1959), using the method of verbal estimation, required test pilots to make time judgments in G fields ranging from $+1$ G_z to $+8$ G_z. This work indicates that although the amount of error was unpredictable, the direction of error at the $+3$ G_z and at $+4$ G_z levels were similar to that reported by Frankenhaeuser for $+3$ G_z. At the $+6$, $+7$ and $+8$ G_z levels, however, the subjects overstimated the passage of time.

There are many reports from centrifuge subjects that their time perception becomes distorted in varying ways during exposure to acceleration. It has not been possible, however, to get comparative data for positive and transverse acceleration loads, nor to compare the effects of rate of onset, duration, and peak amplitude. Quantitative data are also needed that indicate the degree and direction of the effects that acceleration has on the other categories of time perception, for example, the execution of the components and sequences of tasks, the performance of time-sharing tasks, and the maintenance of time orientation.

It has been questioned whether there are any post-accelerative effects on time perception. Frankenhaeuser (1956, 1957b, and 1958) and Chambers and Eggleston (1959) have not reported any such effects, even after record-breaking runs involving transverse acceleration loads as high as 23 G_x and 25 G_x. Similarly, time judgment was found to be unaffected even after prolonged immersion in water (Chambers, *et al.*, 1961). The water immersion technique is thought to simulate zero gravity effects.

E. DISORIENTATION AND ILLUSIONS INDUCED BY ACCELERATION

Under some conditions acceleration can adversely affect orientation (Brown, *et al.*, 1957; Ham, 1943) and may produce illusions of vision, motion, and bodily position. Angular and linear acceleration may be perceived incorrectly with a relatively high reliability in terms of frequency of occurrence. Man, within his normal 1 G environment, uses his visual, vestibular, kinesthetic, and associated cues to perceive his motion, and his position with respect to his environment. However, in a centrifuge, rotating room, or space capsule, for example, he does not always have the availability of reliable vestibular, kinesthetic, tactual, and visual inputs. Disorientation due to acceleration occurs to experienced subjects (Brown, *et al.*, 1957, Ham, 1943). Disorientation may result from false or incorrect impressions of one's position and direction of motion. These may be temporary in nature, or, in the case of physiological damage to parts of the sense organs themselves during extremely prolonged or intense accelerations, they may persist. There is some evidence that disorientation following exposure to transverse acceleration up to $+20$ G_x may be reduced following repeated exposure (Collins, *et al.*, 1958). Duane, *et al.* (1953), found that after exposure to 15 transverse G for 5 seconds, some subjects reported vertigo each morning for up to 40 days following the test experience. The question of damage to the vestibular apparatus during high G or long G exposure is unanswered. Armstrong (1961) suggests that vertigo implies a state of confusion, in which the subject either lacks, ignores, or misinterprets his sensory inputs. Factors other than exposure to acceleration may be involved.

Illusions of vision and motion that occur during exposure to accelerations are the Coriolis effect, the oculogravic illusion, the oculoagravic illusion, the oculogyral illusion, sensations of falling or floating, and false sensations from banks and turns. The Coriolis effect refers to the case where the subject has sensations of spinning or tilting when he rotates his head while within a rotating system. It results from vestibular stimulation and occurs when an object on a rotating device moves in a direction that is not parallel to the axis of rotation (Johnson, 1956; Johnson, *et al.*, 1960; Gray, *et al.*, 1961). Some recent work (Guedry and Montague, 1961) indicates that the magnitude and direction of the "vestibular Coriolis reaction" can be measured. Related work (Graybiel, Zarriello, *et al.*, 1959; Graybiel, *et al.*, 1961) has demonstrated that the reaction diminishes fairly early within a series of trials.

The oculogravic illusion is characterized by the apparent movement or displacement of a visual stimulus. For example, during the onset of chest-to-back accelerations $+G_x$ on the centrifuge, a person may experience a sensation of tilting backwards. A target observed under this condition would appear to be displaced upwards. The degree of displacement corresponds to the angle between the resultant force and the normal vertical. Conversely, during deceleration, the displacement of the target may appear to move downwards. Sometimes the person, rather than the visual field itself, appears to be tilted (Graybiel and Patterson, 1954). Graybiel concludes that the illusion is due to the stimulation of the otoliths in the utricle of the inner ear. Schafer (1951) lists four types of oculogravic illusions frequently encountered in flying aircraft.

Graybiel and Patterson (1954) used the term "oculoagravic" illusion to refer to an illusion that occurs during subgravity and zero gravity states. For example, luminous targets seen in the dark appeared to be displaced in an upward direction. Gerathewohl and Stallings have reported than an induced after-image moved upward during weightlessness, and downward during acceleration.

The "oculogyral" illusion produces the sensation that the visual field is spinning about the body axis (Graybiel and Hupp, 1946). In darkness, a weak stimulation of the labyrinth causes apparent motion, which may persist after all other sensations of the rotation have disappeared. If the subject fixes his eyes on a lighted target that turns as he turns, the target appears to turn as the subject turns. It may appear displaced during rotation; and when rotation stops, the target may appear to continue to move for a short time. The oculogyral illusion experience is complex: the sensations of angular speed and displacement may seem discordant, the plane of apparent bodily rotation may shift, visual illusions occur, nystagmus may occur, and motion sickness and disturbing vegetative reactions may occur. Eighteen distinct sensations representing variations in the oculogyral illusion have been listed by Gray and Crosbie (1958). Schafer (1951) has listed three types of oculogyral illusions encountered in flying aircraft.

One of the most interesting studies involving the oculogyral illusion was by Graybiel, *et al.* (1961), in which four healthy males were exposed to tilts in a small rotating room for 64 hours. Great variations among the subjects were reported, but all subjects showed some adaptation.

The study suggested that the oculogyral illusion and associated disturbing vegetative reactions may be eliminated during the course of continual rotation. In a related study, Clark and Graybiel (1961) studied the psychological performance of six subjects during adaptation to the stress of rotation for two days in the room. Rotations varied from 1.71 to 10.0 rpm. A detrimental effect was produced on the motivation of the subjects, but the subjects were able to maintain their performance levels on psychological tasks which required muscular coordination, steadiness and computation.

There are several disorientation problems. These have been excellently described by Armstrong (1961) and may be summarized as sensation of climbing while turning, sensation of diving during recovery for a turn, sensation of diving beyond the vertical, illusion of turning, the unperceived banks, sensation of opposite tilt in a skid, overestimating the degree of bank, and sensation of being tilted following gradual recovery from a roll. In contrast with these is an illusion described as a false sensation of body movement, such as falling, tumbling, rolling, and floating. Gauer and Haber (1950), Gerathewhol (1956, 1958), and others

have theorized and conducted experiments regarding the premise that in
the absence of gravity, many may experience false sensations of body
movement, due largely to the absence of the gravity to which he has so
long been accustomed.

The etiology and preventive measures regarding illusions and false
perceptions induced by changing gravitational fields and superimposed
accelerations are complex. Individuals vary greatly in their sensitivity to
illusions. The position of the body with respect to angular and linear
accelerations, the structure of the visual field, prior experience, practice,
sensitivity thresholds, information feedback, and psychological expectancy
are some of the variables upon which much research is needed. Illusions
of vision and motion are of major importance in the design and utilization of rotating space stations. If a human within a rotating capsule of
sufficient velocity tilts his head only a few times relative to the axis of
rotation, even though the accelerations involved are extremely small in
magnitude, he may perceive apparent rotations that may produce disorientation, confusion, and possibly nausea. The need for data on the
vestibular, visual, and kinesthetic performance characteristics in response
to angular accelerations occurring about several axes within a rotation
system—for example, illusions of vision and motion produced by acceleration—pose serious problems in the design of space stations
(Guedry, Graybiel, *et al.*, 1959; Graybiel, *et al.*, 1961; Lansberg, 1955b;
Niven and Hixon, 1961; and Schubert, 1954; Brown, *et al.*, 1961). Much
research, particularly on ameliorative measures, is needed.

III. Simple Psychomotor Performance

Acceleration affects psychomotor skills as well as sensory and
perceptual processes. The distinctions between simple and complex psychomotor performance are somewhat arbitrary. Complex psychomotor
performance is conceived as involving the continuous operation of several task-components simultaneously, to the extent that discriminations
and responses are continuously required on each of the task components.
The operator is required to continuously relate his performance to the
stimulus and response events immediately preceding, thus taking into
account not only the immediate task requirements but also those which
have already occurred as well as those which are expected to occur as
a result of his performance. Assuming appropriate measurement pro-

cedures, it is usually possible to measure complex psychomotor performance in terms of both the total task proficiency and in terms of task-component proficiency on each of the components (Chambers, 1958b, 1959). Finally, in measuring the effects of acceleration on psychomotor performance, complex psychomotor tasks usually require much prior practice and learning in order that stable base lines may be established, whereas mere familiarization is usually sufficient for performance of simple psychomotor tasks.

A. APPLYING FORCES DURING EXPOSURE TO G

Acceleration influences the amount of force that a person can exert, which depends upon the magnitude and direction of the primary acceleration vector, the direction of application of the exerted force, and the position of the body member within the acceleration field. There are major individual differences in the amount of force various subjects may exert. (Canfield, *et al.*, 1948a; Lombard, *et al.*, 1948; Wells and Morehouse, 1950; Brown, 1960). G may be expected to be minimal under conditions in which the exertion of force by the subject is perpendicular to the direction of the G vector. However, the force that a subject can exert on a control may be severely limited when the required direction of the force requires opposition to the forces of acceleration. The amount of force that a pilot can exert in certain directions changes with the amplitude, duration, and magnitude of G.

By sitting in an aircraft seat and being exposed to various transverse and positive acceleration loads, investigators have been able to get approximations of the magnitudes at which it is just possible to make head, limb, or feet motions in specified directions. Clark and Hardy (1959) for example, have reported an interesting sketch in which the vehicle accelerations are specified at which it was just possible to make certain movements. Figure 15 presents this sketch. The subject, wearing a standard helmet, low-cut shoes, and flight suit, is seated in an aircraft seat. The arrows indicate the movements of the body that are just possible at the vehicle accelerations listed. The values reported here are approximations, since it was not possible to get precise quantitative measurements. They are subject to many variations, according to the strength of any particular subject, prior acceleration experience, and the rates and durations of the accelerations.

When the subject is in the prone position, his ability to make movements is different than when he is in the seated position. A much higher level of acceleration can be tolerated in the prone position than in the

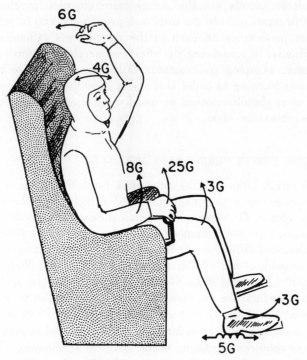

Figure 15. Movements of the body are just possible under the conditions indicated in this diagram. (Official photograph U.S. Navy.)

seated position without gross impairment of vision or consciousness, and consequently acceleration forces become sufficiently high so as to interfere with movements of the limbs before there is any failure of the sensory systems. Clark, *et al.* (1945), found that the body, legs, and arms could not be lifted at $+8 G_x$ or above and that the unsupported head could not be lifted above $+9 G_x$. They could maintain their breathing at $+12 G_x$; and at this G level the ability to pull against controls with the arms, flex and extend the ankles against rudder pedals, move the forearm when the elbow is bracketed, and move the hand and fingers were only slightly impaired. Lambert, *et al.* (1945), showed that the subjects were capable of rolling their heads from side to side, and that they could operate a switch with the fingers up to $+10 G_x$. At the higher transverse G levels, it may be impossible for the subject to provide enough muscular force to his limbs to make the required reach in order to apply control maneuvers. For example, Clark, *et al.* (1959), reported that one subject whose hand slipped off the tracking control during a 16.5 G_x run was unable to reach the instrument again until the acceleration was reduced to approximately 10 G. Studies have also been done to determine levels at which a subject can hold various portions of his body stationary during exposure. Brown, *et al.* (1955) demonstrated that up as high as 5 positive G, subjects could hold their heads in a fixed, forward-tilted position. The duration of exposure is critical, however, since the onset of fatigue during G is extremely rapid when a subject attempts to hold his head, arm, leg, or foot in a fixed, unsupported position. Subjects supported by a form-fitting couch (Collins, *et al.*, 1958) could manipulate a small right-hand stick with the fingers in a plane normal to the line of accelerations as high as $+20$ G_x, and even to $+25$ G_x (Collins, *et al.*, 1959), although there was some question of the accuracy with which he was positioning the stick with respect to the signal lights of the task.

Using a more complex, three-axis hand-control device, Chambers (1961) found that subjects had difficulty in making coordinated precise movements satisfactorily at 15 G. They were unable to make full-throw control movements along all three axes, and there was a loss of sense of control feel that, combined with the physical forces involved, made it very difficult to make precise control movements.

Using an electromyographic technique, Wells and Morehouse (1950) attempted to separate that component of force resulting from voluntary muscular exertion under acceleration and that component arising from the acceleration loading of the limb itself. By having the subjects maintain a spring scale at constant deflection, the total force on the control was held constant, and the amount of acceleration was varied from run to run. Their findings suggest that muscular exertion varies with changes in acceleration such that the voluntary muscular exertion offsets increases or decreases in forces resulting from changes in weight of the limb due to acceleration.

The ability of human subjects to exert and control their muscles in order to exert the proper amount of force to counteract the accelerations during low-frequency high-amplitude vibrations poses interesting problems. One of the most interesting reports in the literature is that by Hornick, *et al.* (1961), in which an attempt was made to measure the ability of subjects to maintain a constant foot pressure during exposure to side-to-side and longitudinal (fore-and-aft) whole-body vibrations using vibration intensities of 0.15, 0.25, and 0.35 G and various vibration frequencies. The greatest decrements occurred at the highest G levels and at 1.5 to 2.5 cycles per second; error decreased at higher frequencies. Decrement was immediate with the onset of vibration, and recovery was complete following exposure.

B. DISTANCE, LOCATION, AND ACCURACY OF GROSS MOTOR MOVEMENTS

The distances through which a pilot is capable of moving various parts of his body vary with the position of the pilot with respect to the gravitational force, the amplitude of acceleration, the rate of acceleration, and its direction (Clark, *et al.*, 1945; Lambert, *et al.*, 1945; Buhrlen, 1937; Code, *et al.*, 1947; King, *et al.*, 1947). Acceleration forces that are within tolerance limits affect simple motor performance (Canfield, *et al.*, 1949). Speed and accuracy of the reaching movements are impaired as G increases, whether it be negative, positive, or transverse. Walking, crawling, and moving along a ladder against the force of acceleration at $+2$ G are seriously restricted in the untrained subject (Code, *et al.*, 1947), and these gross movements become impossible at $+4$ G. The direction of the G obviously has a major influence on the accuracy, amount of effort required, and speed with which a person can make gross motor responses.

Studies of reaching movements have attempted to define distance, location, and accuracy during exposure to various acceleration fields. Canfield, *et al.* (1953), reported that reaching movements were seriously impaired at 3 positive G and that the amount of impairment increased with G magnitude. Impairment was greater for the preferred hand (right or left, as the case may be) than for the other hand. Also, movements below the normal rest position were more accurate than movements in other directions. The size of objects to be reached was important, and it was found that the sizes of objects to be grasped or pushed had an influence on accuracy.

Accuracy of making reaching movements and in performing various tasks is seriously impaired as G increases, whether the G be negative, positive, or transverse. In addition to the magnitude of the acceleration, its direction with respect to the body has a major influence on the accuracy component of the task. Willmorth and Green (1950) found that accuracy in making reaching movements decreased significantly with increased G. Similarly, Zuidema, *et al.* (1956) found accuracy decrements in both a continuous and discontinuous motor task at high G levels. Frankenhaeuser (1958) found that accuracy of movement in performing a continuous pursuit-task decreased significantly during exposure to 3 G_z as compared with performance at 1 G_z.

Kaehler and Meehan (1960) studied the effects of transverse accelerations on the ability of subjects to reach and operate a horizontal lever, a vertical wheel, a rotating knob, a push button, and a toggle switch. They found that subjects can reach and adjust these types of controls with accuracy at transverse levels up to 8 G_x and -4 G_x regardless of control location, within a total reach distance of 30 inches. The study also demonstrated that the vertical wheel and rotating knob were more difficult to operate for both types of accelerations than were the horizontal lever, toggle switch, and push button. Response times were important, and these are reviewed in the section on speed of movement.

It is extremely difficult to sense and perform precise motor responses at high G levels (Chambers, 1961). This is a complicating factor in addition to the mechanical effects of acceleration. There have been a number of studies to determine the limits in which a pilot can be expected to manipulate his controls (King, *et al.*, 1947; Meehan and Jacobs, 1958; Kaehler and Meehan, 1960). In many practical situations, these boundaries are affected by factors other than the acceleration loads themselves, such as the type of restraint system, the presence or absence of a pressure suit, and the type of suit and its inflation pressure. Most of this work is yet unpublished, since it tends to pertain to specific problem situations and is not amenable to the derivation of general principles. Meehan and Jacobs (1958) and Kaehler and Meehan (1960) have provided extensive data on the effects of acceleration on the operation of simple control devices as a function of workplace orientation within acceleration fields. Distance, location, and accuracy variables appear to show a significant effect on motor performance as acceleration increases. Shapes, sizes, locations, and modes of operation of any specific type of device within a pilot-restraint system all exert an interacting effect with the characteristics of the acceleration force. Consequently, few general principles have been derived which pertain to specific parameters taken independently.

Recent research on the effects of prolonged angular acceleration on the performance of motor movements has stimulated much interest (Clark and Graybiel, 1961). Perceptual and motor skill proficiency appears to be impaired during prolonged exposure in slow rotating rooms, but the degree to which this may occur appears to be largely dependent upon physiological and motivational processes. Research on the problems involving rotating rooms and space platforms has recently been reviewed (Clark and Graybiel, 1961; Hardy, Clark, and Gray, 1959; Clark and Hardy, 1961; Guedry and Ceran, 1959; Guedry, *et al.*, 1958).

C. SIMPLE RESPONSE TIME IN PERFORMING MOTOR TASKS

Time required for the human subject to accomplish simple motor responses may vary as a function of the magnitude and direction of the acceleration force, the rate of onset of G, the orientation of the person with respect to the acceleration force, the type of response being performed, the type of control device which the subject is using, its location and distance, and the type of restraint and suiting equipment the subject is wearing. Of major concern here is the problem of determining the degree to which the mechanical effect of acceleration itself affects response time. Although the measurement of response time as a function of acceleration has been complicated because of the large number of other factors which have been present in most experiments, it is generally agreed that response time for performing simple motor response increases as acceleration increases in magnitude. It has not always been possible, however, to identify the specific determining factors to account for this relationship.

Studies have been conducted on time required for subjects to perform manual tasks such as moving the hand from a reference position to a target, moving from a reference position to a toggle switch and manipulating the switch, and moving from a reference position to a rotary switch and adjusting the switch for a predetermined meter reading (Bryan, *et al.*, 1951; Canfield, 1950a, 1950b; Willmorth and Green, 1950). Up to $+5\ G_z$ movement time increased with increased acceleration. The amount of increase in movement time varied with the direction of motion, and was greatest when the direction of the required motion was opposite to the direction in which the arm tended to move as a result of acceleration. These findings agree with other observations which show an increase in the time required for the execution of various motor tasks (Burmeister, 1939; Kerr and Russell, 1944; Canfield, *et al.*, 1948a, b; Canfield, *et al.*, 1949; Comrey, *et al.*, 1950; Canfield, *et al.*, 1950; Brown and Burke, 1958). It should be emphasized, however, that these effects are not related solely to mechanical effects of acceleration, since sensory and perceptual processes were also included in the intervals which were measured. The time required to reach a control varies with its position within the person's control-reach boundaries for any given acceleration field (King, *et al.*, 1947; and Meehan and Jacobs, 1958). Reach time appears to increase significantly with increased acceleration for certain control locations, but shows no change for other locations (Cochran, 1953; Hunter and Weiss, 1953; Brown, 1957). Time required for some movements, such as those required for operating ejection controls varies with the type of control, the orientation of acceleration forces, and the level of acceleration (Hill and Brown, 1958; Brown, 1960).

There have been relatively few experiments on the effects of low-frequency, high-amplitude, whole-body vibrations on performance of motor tasks. One detailed study, however, has been conducted by

Hornick, *et al.* (1961), in which side-to-side vibrations and fore-and-aft vibrations utilizing frequencies from 1.5 to 5.5 cycles per second, with intensities of 0.15 to 0.35 G were studied. These vibrations characteristics significantly affected performance.

One of the most comprehensive studies on the effect of $+G_x$ and $-G_x$ transverse accelerations on the performance of simple motor tasks was accomplished by Kaehler and Meehan (1960). Time required to operate each of five representative aircraft-type controls—horizontal lever, a vertical wheel, a rotating knob, a toggle switch, and a push button—was carefully measured in more than $900+G_x$ and $500-G_x$ runs on the Human Centrifuge at the University of Southern California. By carefully controlling the positioning and sequencing of the tests and using three chronometers during test runs, they were able to measure the following parameters of motor performance: response time, reach time, adjustment time, activation time, and total mean manipulation time. Front-to-back accelerations $(+G_x)$ ranged from $0\ G_x$ to $+8\ G_x$; back-to-front accelerations ranged from $0\ G_x$ to $-4\ G_x$.

They found that the mean response time (defined here as the time between the appearance of a stimulus light and the removal of a subject's hand from his lap switch) increases as a function of the amplitude of both $+G_x$ and $-G_x$ accelerations. For $+G_x$, the mean response time was increased from 0.23 second at rest to 0.33 second at $+8\ G_x$. For $-G_x$, the mean response time was increased from 0.22 second at rest to 0.28 second at $4\ G_y$. Similarly, the mean reach time (defined as the elapsed time between the removal of the subject's hand from the lap switch until he touches the control device) was increased proportional to the magnitude of $+G_x$ accelerations. For $-G_x$ accelerations, the reach time was in the same general direction of change, but not as great. The mean reach time was affected more for consoles located directly in front of the subject, requiring a reaching motion in direct opposition to the accelerative force, than for consoles located perpendicular to the accelerative force. Mean reach time increased proportionally to the magnitude of $+G_x$.

The mean activation time (defined as the total elapsed time between the removal of the subject's hand from the lap switch until the complete operation of the control is completed) for both the toggle switch and the push button increased from approximately 0.4 second at rest to 1.0 second at $+8\ G_r$. For $-G_x$ accelerations, the time increase was in the same general direction but not as large. Best adjustment time (defined as the time elapsed between the first touch of a designated control and the final proper positioning of the control) was achieved when the controls were located in the direction of the accelerative force and required control motions in the plane perpendicular to the accelerative force. Consequently, both the reach time and the adjustment time for a control device were differentially affected by the direction of the G force. For both $+G_x$ and $-G_x$, controls located directly in front of the subject and nearest to him required the least amount of adjustment time and were the least affected by the increased accelerative force.

Under conditions of $+G_x$ accelerations, the total mean manipulation time increased proportionally with the magnitude of the accelerative force. This same tendency was shown for $-G_x$ accelerations. From least to most time required for total manipulation of the controls used in this experiment for both $+G_x$ and $-G_x$ accelerations were as follows: toggle switch, push button, horizontal lever, rotating knob, and vertical wheel. During $+G$ accelerations, the human subject could perceive a visual stimulus, reach and adjust controls such as a toggle switch, push button and horizontal lever in a mean time of approximately 1.0 seconds at $+8\ G_x$. Controls such as the rotating knob and vertical wheel, which were more difficult to operate under normal conditions, could be fully manipulated in a mean time of approximately 1.5 seconds at $+8$ G. Similarly, $-G_x$ accelerations, the toggle switch, push button, and horizontal lever could be operated faster than could the more difficult rotating knob and vertical wheel (Kaeler and Meehan, 1960).

It should be emphasized that body position, control shape, and control position all affect reaction speed in performing a task within any given G field (C. W. Brown, 1948; Weitz, 1944, 1945, 1951). Generally, response time increases when G increases and when a controlled movement is required. Control positions found to be optimum for executing responses under ordinary static conditions may be impossible to execute within required time limits under some acceleration conditions. Similarly, a motor response which is optimum in difficulty during static conditions may be impossible to operate within required time limits during some acceleration conditions. Also, even though response time for actuating a switch or turning a knob in a high $-G_x$ field may be very short, the operation of this same switch or knob in a high G_x field may be impossible. Similarly, the activation of a control switch in a high G_y field may take much longer than the activation of the same control switch in a high G_y field.

It has been found that learning is an important variable in time required to perform motor responses. In the Mercury astronaut training projects conducted at the AMAL (unpublished), response times which were much longer during acceleration conditions than during static conditions early in a training project eventually became the same under both static and acceleration conditions, as a result of intensive practice. A major portion of the effects of practice results from learning how to breathe, strain, monitor, and control other aspects of the situation in which the astronaut is experiencing the acceleration. These observations were especially conclusive in training programs in which the use of pressure suits in the inflated and deflated conditions were involved. The pressure suits themselves posed special problems, such as response restriction, uncomfortable temperature and stiffness conditions to which the astronauts were required to become accommodated under conditions of acceleration.

D. PERFORMANCE OF MOTOR RESPONSE SEQUENCES UNDER G

The magnitude, direction, duration, and steadiness of the G and the rates of onset and decline have a marked effect on the performance of sequential tasks. A series of movements requiring interaction with G from different directions increases this difficulty greatly. The accuracy of the forces that a pilot can exert on a series of control switches and buttons and knobs is severely limited when some of his required operations are in directions parallel with the primary G, but others are perpendicular, transverse, or in opposition to the primary G vector. This type of situation may result from the location of the controls, from the fluctuation of the G field itself, or both.

A number of experiments have been conducted to study the effects of acceleration on a pilot's ability to perform the sequences of actions necessary for ejection (Cochran, 1953; Hunter and Weiss, 1953; Hill, Brown, and Peck, 1957; Hill and Brown, 1958; Hill and Webb, 1959; Clark, 1961a, 1961b). The pilot's ability to perform these tasks is severely limited when the required direction of the force is in opposition to the primary G vector. Most of these studies were conducted under conditions of sustained acceleration at a fixed orientation. Subjects on the centrifuge were brought up to a given level of acceleration, which was held constant, and then given a signal to execute the ejection procedure. When the acceleration was positive, that is, so oriented that it tended to pull the subject down into the seat, some subjects failed to complete the ejection procedure with a face curtain at $+5$ or $+6$ G_z. When the acceleration tended to pull them forward out of the seat against restraining straps, almost all subjects were unable to pull the face curtain at $+6$ G_z. Accelerations that forced the subject against the seat back did not cause as much difficulty.

Using a Martin-Baker Mark J5 ejection seat installed tangentially on a centrifuge and using an open-loop centrifuge simulation of the Army YAO-1 "Mohawk" airplane, Clark (1961a) studied the body displacement and performance impairment effects of lateral acceleration loads up to $+5$ G_y. In general, it was found that lateral accelerations interfered with ejection seat sequence operations, beginning at approximately $+3$ G_y. The restraint equipment used, as well as the acceleration loads endured, resulted in disturbing displacements of the body, shoulder, hips, head, arms, and legs, as well as some oculogravic illusions, bruises, and petechiae. These displacements resulted in the requirement for more time to initiate ejection operations. Times required for ejection were not dissimilar to those reported by Hill (1957) and by Hill and Webb (1959) for other acceleration loads.

Another problem is the effect of accelerations encountered during aircraft catapulting on a pilot's subsequent ability to fly his aircraft. An analysis (Brown, 1957a) of required performance indicated that the most critical task immediately after launching was control of the aircraft in pitch and roll. Pilots were therefore required to stabilize disturbances of an aircraft attitude indicator in pitch and roll immediately following exposure to transverse accelerations acting in the same direction as catapult accelerations. No decrement in performance was found even after short exposure to accelerations of nearly $+12$ G.

Several experiments have studied sequential performance during patterns of acceleration that varied in a manner and degree representative of uncontrolled flights (Hunter and Weiss, 1953; Hill, 1959; Snyder, 1961). Performance during conditions of fluctuating uncontrolled acceleration conditions pose interesting problems to the pilot. The best example of these problems are found in an open-loop centrifuge simulation of 12 different types of spins characteristic of the A3J-1 airplane. Snyder (1961) studied the ability of pilots to perform a series of ordered sequences of tasks which were required for successful recovery from these spins. During the initial five turns of a simulated spin, the pilot made preparations for a spin recovery, but was instructed not to attempt recovery until the fifth spin was completed. For the next three turns the pilot had a specific order of prescribed tasks to perform in order to effect recovery. If neither the pilot's performance nor the limited aircraft response stopped the spin, the pilot had two more spin turns available in which to operate his spin recovery rockets. If these did not produce the desired results, he had one spin turn left in order to determine the efficacy of the emergency spin chute. This was the last means available for spin recovery; and if this failed, the pilot had to eject.

In this study (Snyder, 1961), failure of the pilot to perform appropriately caused the pilot to endure the entire G-time spin profile, whereas a successful recovery brought the centrifuge to a smooth stop. It was found that G values to -3.25 G_x did not decrease performance time, but that it did limit the ability of the pilot to fully move his controls. At levels above -4 G_x, the pilots reported difficulty in thinking and reacting clearly; and in some runs, the pilots failed to make the control movements or moved them in the wrong direction. Because of the narrowing of the visual fields, the pilots were unable to respond to the peripherally located spin direction lights; and because of the restraint system, they were unable to reach some of the controls during the more difficult maneuvers. The study, even though based on only two subjects, illustrates some of the difficulties in studying complex response sequences during exposure to complex acceleration profiles.

E. EFFECTS OF ACCELERATION ON DISCRIMINATION REACTION TIME

Although it is generally agreed that some acceleration environments do influence discrimination reaction time behavior, it has been practically impossible to measure the mechanisms that account for the effects. During acceleration, the results could be due to the impairment in a variety of places: the peripheral sensory systems in perceiving the stimulus, the central nervous system in processing the stimulus and initiating discriminatory choice, the neuromuscular system in coordinating the response, the motor components that effect the response and manipulate the appropriate control device, or, as in the case of some studies, the indirect effects of protective equipment and related components of the situation in which the tests were conducted.

Burmeister (1939) found an increase in mean reaction time to a visual signal during 30-second exposures to $+3$ and $+4.5$ G_z, as compared with performance under normal conditions. Subjects were required to pull a stick as quickly as they could in response to a light stimulus. Exposure times were 30 seconds in duration. In an experiment by Kennedy, *et al.* (1944), no significant effects of acceleration levels below grayout were found on reaction time. These authors found longer reaction times at higher acceleration levels, but considered that these were due to "inattention" rather than a change in reaction time itself.

Warrick and Lund (1946) observed a decrease in reaction time during G exposure. A significant increase in reaction time to a visual stimulus was reported by Canfield, *et al.* (1949), during positive acceleration loads of 3 and 5 G, although Canfield, *et al.* (1950), found only transient decrements in discrimination reaction time in a similar experiment.

Frankenhaeuser (1958), using red, green, and white light signals, measured choice reaction times during exposure to $+3$ G_z and found that subjects took significantly longer to respond at $+3$ G_z than under normal $+$ G_z conditions. This was true for exposures of both 2 minutes' and 5 minutes' duration. Her conclusion was that visual choice reaction time was increased by positive acceleration.

Brown and Burke (1958) found highly significant effects of positive acceleration on discrimination reaction time. They required subjects to depress a switch lightly with the forefinger in response to visual stimuli. These centrifuge tests, which were at maximum G for 10 seconds, demonstrated that reaction time was significantly prolonged as acceleration increased and that the increase in reaction time was greatest during the last five seconds of the 10 second peak G exposure. Since they found that reaction time for a lower luminance light stimulus was nearly 50 per cent longer than that of a higher luminance stimulus, they concluded that at least part of the response time increase was due to the effects of the acceleration on the visual system.

Cope and Jensen (1961) developed an auditory reaction time task in order to avoid the problem of visual decrement of grayout and blackout and consequent loss of the stimulus, during exposure to positive G. The task required the subject to add pairs of numbers that he heard *via* an auditory magnetic tape system and then to decide and press small buttons according to whether the sum was "odd" or "even." Preliminary work with this testing apparatus during positive G_z exposures to grayout levels indicates that the time required to make these responses increases during exposure to positive acceleration.

To study the effects of transverse acceleration on discrimination reaction time, an apparatus was developed that consisted of four small stimulus lights, a small response handle containing four small response buttons, and a programmer that could present a large variety of random sequences to subjects on the centrifuge (Chambers, *et al.*, 1961). Tests conducted statically and under water indicated that subjects responded reliably on this device. When the device was mounted on the centrifuge, however, it was found that transverse acceleration exposures influenced performance on the task. As the lights came on, the subject was required to press the appropriate buttons on his right-hand stick as fast as he could. Following pre-acceleration training to achieve a stable base-line performance level, twelve blocks of 25 responses per trial responses during the experience of 6 G for 5 minutes per subject were presented. Each subject received three such acceleration trials. Since speed and accuracy were both involved in the behavior, time and errors were normalized and then added. During the first trial, the mean response scores were slower than the grand mean; during the second trial, the response scores were even slower than the first trial; but during the third trial under G, the performance scores improved significantly. The results suggest that acceleration impaired performance during the first and second acceleration runs, but that during the third acceleration run, the subject had learned how to maintain his physiology and his performance under acceleration stress, and consequently his discrimination reaction time scores improved. This shows that learning how to perform during exposure to acceleration stress is a very important factor in evaluating the differences between static and acceleration results.

Recent improvements in this device (Cope and Chambers, 1961) show promise for continuously monitoring the subject's performance. It has been suggested by the medical personnel that the device shows major promise as a useful medical indicator of the subject's well-being during exposure to high G stress, since it is assumed that changes in cerebral functions would occur prior to changes in the physiological functioning of the subject, such as indicated by the respiration and electrocardiographic responses.

Some of the most interesting research on the effects of transverse acceleration on discrimination reaction time have been observed during some of the Mercury astronaut training programs conducted on the AMAL human centrifuge. During early phases of training, transverse accelerations were found to have significant effects on the time required by the astronauts to perceive malfunction indicators on their instrument panel, and to decide and initiate appropriate motor response maneuvers. The stimuli were presented on a "tele-light" panel (see Figure 29). The astronauts were required to monitor this panel of indicators and when certain light signals occurred (such as "on," red, green, or "no-light") during specific times during the simulated flights, they were required to take appropriate corrective action. During the early portion of their training, there were major differences in the discrimination response times for the conditions which were produced under acceleration as compared to those that were control static runs. After extensive practice the effects of acceleration disappeared. It has been concluded by the author that the effects of transverse acceleration on these discrimination reaction times were eliminated by the learning and practice which the astronauts experienced. It is not known whether a similar principle would hold for the effects of positive acceleration on discrimination reaction time.

Whereas there is little information available concerning the effects of transverse and longitudinal whole-body vibrations on choice reaction time, the tentative conclusion seems to be that the effects, if any, are few. Hornick, *et al.* (1961) found that vibrations at frequencies ranging from 1.5 to 5.5 cycles per second and intensity ranging from 0.15 to 0.35 G had no significant effects on discrimination reaction time performance during the vibration exposures of 30 minutes. However, there were significant decremental effects on the post-exposure test results, showing a highly significant lengthening of discrimination reaction time following 30 minutes' exposure to the whole-body vibrations in both transverse and longitudinal test conditions.

IV. Complex Psychomotor Performance

The effects of acceleration on complex psychomotor performance are not greatly different from the effects on simple tasks, although performance decrement is usually related to task difficulty. By extensive practice it is possible to eliminate many aspects of performance error, and it is frequently reported that highly practiced subjects perform better under moderate acceleration conditions than they do under static conditions. Even at the higher acceleration levels, which are near the limit of physiological tolerance, the subject's proficiency during stress may be highly dependent upon his stage of practice. Finally, the performance decrement may be directly related to artifacts produced by the kind of restraint system, control device, and information display the pilot uses during the acceleration exposure tests. Many of these variables are reviewed in the following sections, and studies that have attempted to measure the interactions among these variables within acceleration environments are discussed.

A. PSYCHOMOTOR TRACKING PERFORMANCE

The ability to perform a relatively simple two-dimensional tracking task is impaired by exposure to transverse accelerations. In one experiment the subject operated a control device to perform coordinated pitch-and-roll tracking maneuvers that were programed on the face of an oscilloscope. Steady performance levels for the horizontal and vertical components of the tracking task prior to G exposure were recorded. When $+8\ G_x$ was reached, decrements in both components were obtained. As acceleration returned to normal, performance in both components also returned to normal shortly thereafter. Following submersion in water to the neck level for 12 hours (Chambers, *et al.*, 1961), these subjects showed approximately the same performance curves, suggesting the rela-

tive stability of the decrement during the second trial, even following a
rather unusual and prolonged intervening experience.

Using the free-swinging cab of the Wright Air Development Center
(WADC) human centrifuge, Clarke, *et al.* (1959), studied tracking
ability and several physiological variables of subjects exposed to G_x
accelerations ranging to $+16.5$ G_x in runs extending to 170 seconds'
duration. During exposure to $+16.5$ G_x, dual pursuit tracking performance for two subjects dropped from approximately 93 per cent time on
target at $+1$ G_x to approximately 12 per cent time on target at $+16.5$ G_x.
In performing the dual pursuit tracking task with the target twice as large
(7.0 mm instead of 3.5 mm), however, performance dropped from approximately 99 per cent time on target at $+1$ G_x to approximately 58 per
cent at $+16.5$ G_x. In none of the tests was there any evidence of impairment immediately following the termination of the acceleration run. These
results confirm and extend earlier findings by Preston, *et al.* (1955)
that subjects could perform similar tasks during three-stage $+G_x$ accelerations characteristic of a launch vehicle.

The Aviation Medical Acceleration Laboratory (AMAL) centrifuge
was used to simulate sustained re-entry tracking control problems. It was
demonstrated that well-trained test pilots could successfully perform a
moderately complex tracking task, while being subjected to relatively
high and varied accelerations for prolonged periods of time. A special
restraint system (Smedal, *et al.*, 1960) was used to minimize physiological discomfort. In this particular study, tracking efficiency was calculated in percentage units based on the accumulated tracking error
divided by the accumulated excursions of the target. Pitch-and-roll control inputs were made with a small two-axis pencil controller, and the
yaw inputs were made with a toe pedal operated by flexion and extension
of the foot about the transverse axis of the ankle joints. In these studies
the rate of onset for all accelerations was approximately 0.1 G per second.
Each tolerance run was preceded by a static run intended to serve as a
base line. As was predicted, tracking performance was impaired at the
higher G levels. However, the pilots were able to maintain proficiency
above a level considered necessary for aborting the run, as measured
on a percentage scale that could vary between -100 and 100 per cent
proficiency. Smedal, *et al.* (1960), concluded that a properly restrained
subject can withstand the acceleration stresses produced by re-entry from
circular velocity.

In a more recent study, pilots were observed to maintain a relatively
high level of performance proficiency on a complex tracking task during
very high G. The most striking centrifuge run for $+G_x$ steady-state
accelerations was $+14$ G_x for 127 seconds. The outstanding runs for $-G_x$

steady-state accelerations was $-10\ G_x$ for 71 seconds. This was accomplished by using special restraint equipment (Smedal, *et al.*, 1961).

Concentrating on the effects of positive acceleration on tracking performance, Fletcher, *et al.* (1958), found that accuracy in tracking was better with shorter durations of exposure and at the lower levels of exposure. Run length for any given subject was 141 seconds. The effects of positive acceleration on tracking performance are much more severe at lower acceleration levels than are the effects of transverse acceleration. The results also demonstrated that the subjects could perform the task significantly better with a right-hand control stick than with a conventional center control stick.

Using recently developed pilot support equipment developed by the NASA Ames Research Center, Chambers and Smedal found that a pilot was able to perform satisfactorily on a three-dimensional tracking task at a steady-state G level as high as $+7\ G_z$ for as long as 90 seconds, without encountering major physiological after-effects.

Low-frequency, high-amplitude vibrations (or oscillations) present an interesting environment for the human operator. The problem is especially acute in the case of high-speed, low-altitude aircraft, certain types of space vehicles, helicopters, and some surface carriers, such as jeeps and tanks. Most ground vehicles typically possess frequencies of from 1 to 7 cps with amplitudes yielding peak acceleration intensities up to 0.50 G.

The planes of vibration may be conveniently defined with reference to the human body in terms of vertical (up-down) vibrations, transverse (side-to-side) vibrations, and longitudinal (fore-aft) vibrations. The situation is complicated in many types of vehicles in that the occupants experience whole-body vibration in all directions. There are several excellent review articles on vibration: Dickerman (1958); Goldman and von Gierke (1960); Ashe (1960); Hornick (1961); Dennis and Elwood (1958); Guignard and Irving (1960); Riopelle and Hines (1958); Schmitz, *et al.* (1960), as well as Nadel's chapter later in this volume.

Man's tolerance to withstand vertical vibration is lowest in the range of 4 to 7 cps. Transverse and longitudinal vibrations have been less extensively studied, but they are objectionable at low-frequency values also. A need exists for data on the effects of horizontal vibration on performance of man. Recent studies have shown that the relatively low accelerations produced by low-frequency, high-amplitude vibrations produce significant decrements in tracking performance.

Hornick, *et al.* (1961), conducted two experiments to determine the effects of vibrations upon the tracking performance of seated subjects. Side-to-side vibrations of 1.5, 2.5, 3.5, 4.5, and 5.5 cps, with intensities of 0.15, 0.25, and 0.35 G were used. The longitudinal (fore-aft) vibration experiment utilized the same frequencies with intensities of 0.15, 0.25, and 0.30 G. They found that both side-to-side and longitudinal, whole-body vibration produced a decrement in tracking ability. Measures were taken during a previbration period, during the first 15 minutes of vibration, during the final 15 minutes of vibration, and during a post-vibration period.

Fraser (1961) found that subjects engaged in a tracking task during vibration showed highly significant decrements during transverse and vertical planes of vibration. Frequencies ranged between 2 and 12 cycles per second and the maixmum peak acceleration to which the subjects were disposed was 3.63 G. He concluded that exposure to harmonic sinusoidal vibration produces a decrement in tracking performance which is related primarily to the amplitude of vibration, although the function is also related to frequency and plane of vibration.

The Boeing Wichita Human Vibration Facility was used to provide vertical vibrations while performance of men during exposure to 10 experimental vibration conditions were produced by means of varying the frequency of vibration, the amplitudes of random and sinusoidal waves, and the power spectrum density of random vibrations. Subjects in an aircraft seat, mounted within a vibration facility, were tested on a vertically and horizontally moving tracking task. It was found that tracking performance was differentially affected on the vertically moving task according to the type of vibration conditions presented to the subjects. No significant effect was found on the performance of the horizontal moving task during vertical vibration exposures. Gorill and Snyder (1957) exposed subjects to vertical vibrations in a B-47 upward ejection seat and found a decrement in the performance of tracking tasks. Of the ranges used, the greatest decrement occurred at 30 cycles per second and 1.54 G. Schmitz, using a different apparatus, found similar results. However, Mozell and White (1958) found significant effects on visual performance, but not on tracking behavior, for frequencies from 5 to 8 cps. They suggest that significant effects may have been obtained had their tracking task been more difficult.

In a compensatory tracking task, Schmitz and Simons (1960) found that intensity had a significant effect on tracking proficiency. The intensity levels were 0.15, 0.18, 0.30, and 0.35 G. Significant effects were also found on a visual acuity task and on a constant foot-pressure task. It was concluded that types of psychomotor performance affected appear to be those which involve vision and muscular coordination.

Both vertical vibrations and side-to-side vibrations have significant decremental effects on compensatory tracking behavior (Hornick, *et al.*, 1961). Decrements were related to intensity increments within any given frequency range. The greatest decrements were found for the lower frequencies. Within a frequency, increments in intensity resulted in greater decrements. A trend was shown for tracking error to increase as time of exposure increased. Finally, there was evidence of some residual after effects of the vibration experience. Tracking tests conducted during a 15-minute post vibration exposure period indicated that complete recovery had not occurred.

To date, there is no evidence of any after-effects resulting from tolerable transverse accelerations. In a test using a simulated aircraft catapulting environment that extended up to 12 transverse G, exposing the pilots to transverse G accelerations while performing complex tracking tasks and compensate for vehicle stability disturbances, no post-acceleration decrements were noted (Brown, 1958a).

Similarly, Chambers and Lathrop (1961) tested three Mercury astronauts who were exposed to a series of acceleration tests in a centrifuge, during which time they continuously performed a tracking task presented on an oscilloscope. Their performance was carefully recorded before, during, and after exposures to $+11.4$ G_x and no post-accelerative effects were obtained.

Kaehler (1961) has studied tracking performance of 35 male subjects in situations in which the amplitudes of transverse G_x profiles and the potential time-lag constant characteristics of the task were varied. Acceleration loads of 0 G_x, and 3 G_x, and 6 G_x were used. A two dimensional compensatory tracking task was used which required the subject to hold the display at zero degrees in pitch and roll. The stimulus was a complex wave form representative of an aircraft flying in turbulent conditions. An analog computer was used to generate exponential time-lag constants of 0.1, 1.0, and 2.0 seconds in task characteristics. The results showed that compensatory tracking error was differentially affected by the increased exponential time lag-constants, and that the amount of compensatory tracking error increased significantly as the transverse accelerations increased. The results of this study showed that both the mean pitch error and mean roll integrated error increased as a function of increased transverse acceleration load and decreased time-lag constant.

In unpublished work by Chambers and Lathrop, tracking performance was studied in conditions in which both the amplitude of transverse acceleration and target velocity were varied. A two-dimensional tracking task was used that permitted target velocities of 1 V, 3 V, and 5 V. The human centrifuge at the U.S. Naval Air Development Center was used, and runs were $+0$ G_x, $+4$ G_x, and $+8$ G_x, with 2 minutes per run at peak G. The error increment was highly significant for both G and target velocity levels. The amount of error increased as a function of both the amplitude of transverse acceleration and the target velocity characteristic.

Neither of the two Mercury astronauts who have made suborbital Redstone flights into space have indicated that there was any marked impairment in their performance during either launch or re-entry G (Shepard, 1961; Grissom, 1961). It is important to note, however, that their vehicles were automatically controlled during re-entry, and consequently only limited tests of performance during the space flight induced accelerations were performed. Shepard (1961), for example, in recounting his experiences during re-entry accelerations, indicated that during the approximate 11 G_x re-entry, he was able to maintain his ability to observe, move, and communicate.

In a report concerning the seven Mercury astronauts during training exercises on the AMAL centrifuge, Voas (1960) reported that performance of the reentry rate damping task was characterized by more error under conditions of 11.4 re-entry centrifuge simulations than during static simulations of the same problem. For the pressure-suit-soft condition, the error index was 2.2 times as large as for the runs as compared with the static runs. When the pressure suits were inflated, the error index for the dynamic condition was nearly 3.3 times as great as it was for the static condition. Even during the relatively complex retrofire task at approximately 1.2 G_x, the error index was nearly twice as large for the acceleration condition as it was for the static condition.

B. EFFECTS OF CLOSED-LOOP INTERACTIONS BETWEEN ACCELERATION AND PERFORMANCE

When the responses of the subject are included within the driving mechanism of the acceleration device so that the accelerations he receives from moment to moment vary as a function of his behavior, an interesting type of interaction effect occurs between the subject and his acceleration environment.

The only known laboratory device capable of enabling studies of this interaction effect is the AMAL Human Centrifuge and its associated analog computer system. The pilot, placed within the gondola of the centrifuge, is provided with an instrument display panel, a control device, rudder pedals, and other piloting equipment as may be required. The pilot operates his control devices in response to information presented on the instrument panel and cues which he receives during the acceleration. The analog computer is used to close the loop between the pilot, his displays, his controls, and the centrifuge accelerations. Thus, the control movements which the pilot makes are converted into electrical signals and fed into the analog computer, which continuously generates the flight problem and provides solutions which result in output signals. Some of the signal outputs are converted by a coordinate conversion system into appropriate centrifuge control signals which regulate the power voltages to the arm and gimbal system of the gondola. Simultaneously, other signal outputs are fed to the pilot's instrument display panel. Thus the accelerations which the subject receives in the gondola of the centrifuge are a result of his own responses and of the problem dynamics stored in the analog computer.

The outputs of the conversion system drive the centrifuge to provide acceleration quantities which are related to the pilot's immediately preceding control manipulations according to some mathematical function. The inclusion of the instrument panel in the system is not necessarily used in all studies, since its function is to provide visual information in addition to the acceleration cues which the pilot receives from the behavior of the centrifuge gondola. The pilot-centrifuge-computer system described above consists basically of two closed-loop systems, one connecting the pilot's control responses with the driving system of the centrifuge, and one connecting the pilot's control responses with the driving mechanisms of the indicators on the pilot's instrument panel. In experiments, an investigator may use either or both closed-loop systems, depending upon the nature of his research problem.

In most flight simulation projects in which the behavior of the pilot with respect to both his flight information and his acceleration experience is being studied, both closed-loop systems are usually used. However, in projects in which one wants to study the effects of the acceleration experience on behavior, only the pilot's G control responses and the centrifuge may be in the loop. In other studies, in which the pilot's ability to use the instrument display within certain specific acceleration loads is being studied, it is frequently convenient to operate the display instruments closed-loop and the centrifuge open-loop by cams or by punched tape. Procedures for accomplishing studies of pilot-acceleration interactions have been summarized in the published literature (Brown and Collins, 1958; Fischer and Nicholson, 1959; Hardy and Clark, 1959; Chambers and Doerfel, 1959; Chambers, 1962b). Among the earlier studies utilizing this approach was a series of simulation experiments in which the ability of test pilots to control some of the acceleration aspects of the proposed X-15 rocket aircraft was evaluated, the most important of which were the re-entry accelerations and related fluctuating accelerations, the high-G accelerations, and accelerations resulting from various simulated aborts and system failures (Clark and Woodling, 1959).

Brown, *et al.* (1960) conducted piloting performance studies on a moving and a fixed simulator to determine the effects of motion cues on pilot's ability to execute control. The motion cues were vertical motion and pitching rotations, and an attempt was made to determine whether these affected the pilot's ability to perform a precise formation flying task. It was found that pilots could perform tracking tasks better in a moving cockpit than they could in a fixed cockpit. The ability of the pilots to perform this task was further enhanced by the inclusion of high-stick-force gradients. It was found that the effects of motions were most beneficial at zero-stick force gradient. The pilots always preferred to be supplied with motion cues. In the absence of control feel forces, some confusion was shown as to the proper direction of stick movement.

Work at AMAL on closed-loop tracking studies have shown that for unpracticed subjects, performance statically $(+1\ G)$ is better than performance under moderate acceleration. However, for practiced subjects and for most pilots, performance is better under moderate acceleration than under static conditions $(+1\ G)$. Pilots use motion cues (Brown, *et al.*, 1960). Also, for some types of tasks, the damping, stability, control loading, or other task characteristics may be designed so as to make performance easier under acceleration than under static conditions.

At high G, performance proficiency deteriorates markedly. This deterioration generally reflects impairment of vision, an inability to breathe, straining, or physiological difficulties which are regarded as *indirect* effects on complex task performance *per se*. At moderately prolonged high G endurance runs, performance deterioration occurs more slowly, and in these cases, it is usually attributed to fatigue.

The effects of closed-loop interactions between the pilot and his interactions have been extensively studied by Brown, *et al.* (1960). They compared the ability of six men to perform a tracking task in four experimental situations: in a TV-2 aircraft, in a static simulation of the aircraft, and in each of two centrifuge modes of simulations. One of the most interesting results from this study was that tracking performance on the centrifuge was inferior to performance accomplished under static conditions, and, for most subjects, inferior also to that accomplished in the TV-2 aircraft. Performance in the centrifuge appeared to be more difficult than it was under the static and aircraft conditions. Rapid transitions from one G level to another were especially disrupting to tracking performance.

There are some types of simulations in which the pilots find more difficulty in operating the centrifuge simulations than do nonpilots, apparently because of the presence of angular accelerations and other artifacts that may be unrealistic to the flight production, although the linear accelerations are realistic (Brown, 1957b). These anomolous angular accelerations may cause the pilots considerable difficulty when evaluated in terms of prior aircraft experience. The study by Brown (1960) and Kuehnel, *et al.* (1960), demonstrated that centrifuge-experienced nonpilots performed most proficiently on a centrifuge simulation of an aircraft, but poorest in the real aircraft, whereas the pilots did well in the aircraft, but poorer on the centrifuge. Brown (1960) points out that pilots do not find anomolous angular accelerations as disturbing when linear accelerations are high (4 G or more) as when they are low (1–3 G). Chambers has observed that at high transverse G accelerations, the angular accelerations are not readily perceptible. Gray and Crosbie (1958) have provided some more quantitative evidence on this in terms of the oculogyral illusion, which is a response to angular acceleration. By increasing linear accelerations in steps as angular accelerations were held constant, they found that the duration of the oculogyral illusion decreased as the linear acceleration increased.

One of the most interesting results from these studies is that when accelerations were not excessively high, some aspects of piloting performance are better than under static (1 G) conditions. For example, the ability to damp out unwanted oscillations and hold acceleration to a minimum was better during exposure to moderate acceleration loads. It has been suggested that actual exposure to acceleration provides useful information to the pilot and that the information provided about the vehicles' conditions, as perceived via the various sensory channels, as well as the additional motivation of being exposed to this type of flight condition, resulted in superior performance. The acceleration forces are believed to aid in providing smoothness and coordination in making piloting maneuvers. Results similar to these have been observed in later experiments by Chambers and Doerfel (1959), in which pilots flew a variety of complex control operations in closed-loop simulations of three types of proposed space vehicles.

The extent to which vibrations superimposed over the primary accelerations may influence complex psychomotor performance poses important problems. These problems have been considered by Gettine (1955), Jacobs (1961), Hornick, *et al.* (1961). To date, however, little specific quantitative data are available. There is major concern about possible pilot performance problems which may be encountered when sinusoidal oscillations of low frequency, high amplitude are superimposed on re-entry accelerations, as simulated on the human centrifuge. Except in the most practiced subjects, the tracking problem is lost and the simulation is aborted when closed-loop simulations are presented in this fashion.

In other studies (Eggleston and Cheatham, 1959; Chambers and Eggleston, 1959) it was also found that during closed-loop centrifuge accelerations, pilots generally did better on moderately high G than they did under static conditions, even though they were straining and undergoing some loss of peripheral vision. The pilots reported that this produced an incentive for performing better during the dynamic runs, as compared with the static runs. The pilot appeared to expect the acceleration cues to be of help to him in performing his piloting task, and the data indicated that the accelerations were of assistance to the pilot. However, at the upper end of the acceleration tolerance range (6 to 8 G_z), the dynamic runs were clearly the most difficult and were sometimes accompanied by abortions or excessive oscillations due to poor performance. At these G levels, it was frequently observed that the pilot did better on his primary piloting tasks, but that the performance impairment was greatest on his secondary piloting task. The conclusion from this work was that whereas performance on the primary command task may be as good or better for dynamic runs than for static runs at the higher G levels, performance on the secondary piloting task may be better on the static run than on the dynamic runs. Of the 360 runs in the experiment, there were 23 pairs of runs in which the pilot was able to fly the static simulations, but when the acceleration components were added, the pilot could not make successful re-entries. These were aborted runs, and were attributed to the acceleration components primarily. These aborts were due to (1) excessive oscillations; (2) pilot exceeding safety limits; (3) difficulties encountered by the pilot regarding his flight gear; (4) difficulties in operating controls; (5) inadequate head support; (6) eye difficulties or peculiar sensations; and (7) accidental stoppage by the pilot.

To study the effects of acceleration on the ability of pilots to perform control tasks while being subjected to the boost accelerations simulated on the AMAL Centrifuge, Chambers exposed pilots to staging acceleration profiled at levels of 3, 6, 9, 12, and 15 G_x. The analog computer facility generated the vehicle dynamics, the display and control problem for the pilot, and the commands for driving the centrifuge. A total of 201 dynamic runs and 160 static runs were made. The longitudinal control mode required almost continuous control, whereas the lateral-directional control task required only monitoring and correcting for disturbances. Few effects of the acceleration on performance of the pilots were shown up to 9 G_x, but above this level, performance deteriorated rapidly in the primary control quantities (longitudinal controls). Less deterioration was shown in the lateral-directional (secondary) control quantities. The pilots indicated that they were unable to concentrate on more than one or two things at a time at high G, thus some parts of the four-dimensional task shown here had to be neglected by the pilots.

Subjective ratings made by the pilots showed that at low accelerations, only nominal physical effort was required to perform the launch control task. However, at the highest accelerations tested, $15G_x$, nearly 100 per cent effort was required.

The ability of the pilots to perform 4 stage launch simulations was studied by Holleman, *et al.* (1960). The computer presented the vehicle aerodynamics and the vehicle inertia characteristics. The pilot's task was to complete an injection into orbit condition. At the acceleration levels studied (below 7 G_x) there appeared to be little effect on the ability to manage the primary control variables (altitude, velocity, and flight path). In one phase of this study, the performance of pilots on open and closed-loop centrifuge control modes were compared. No significant quantitative differences were found between the pilot's performance, although the pilots agree that the closed-loop launch simulations appeared to be much more realistic.

To date, there have been relatively few studies which have attempted to isolate the direct effects of acceleration experience on complex psycho-motor performance, when the conditions were such that the acceleration exposures which the pilot received were the immediate and complete results of his own performance. Due to the safety hazards, there have always been requirements for mechanical limits to be placed upon the centrifuge system in order to protect the pilot from excessive physical harm which may occur either through accident or through poor performance. Also, in most studies, it has been necessary to include in the computer system certain limiting controls over the possible ranges, amplitudes, directions of G, and rates of onset of accelerations to which the pilot could expose himself. Finally, due to the fact that the vast majority of closed-loop studies have involved simulations of aircraft and space craft dynamics, the effects of the pilot's performance have usually been programmed so as to produce effects that would be produced in an aircraft having the aerodynamic characteristics during specific flight maneuvers. These factors have tended to limit greatly the generalizations which may be derived from the experiments reported in the scientific literature. Also, it should be pointed out that major individual differences exist among pilots in their ability to perform closed-loop piloting tasks on the human centrifuge. Some of the primary ways in which pilots differ appear to be in terms of their piloting techniques, their methods of fighting G, their breathing and straining techniques, their eye-scan patterns and ability to use displayed information, their ability to tolerate pain, their motivation and interest in riding the centrifuge, and in their prior experience on acceleration devices.

C. EFFECTS OF CONTROLS, DISPLAYS, AND RESTRAINTS ON
PERFORMANCE DURING G

In addition to the direct effects of acceleration on human performance, there is a growing body of information pertaining to the effects of
other conditions on pilot performance during exposure to acceleration
(Chambers and Nelson, 1961). Important examples are the type of control device the subject is using, the characteristics of the task which he is
performing, the type of display panel he is using, and the restraint
system in which he is positioned. The characteristics of these conditions
are usually studied in human engineering experiments in which pilot
performance under acceleration is used as one of the primary criteria
against which the design and effectiveness of controls, displays, and
restraints are evaluated. Such studies help in providing the human pilot
with optimum performance capabilities during exposure to acceleration
environments.

The type of control device which the pilot uses has a major influence
on his performance under G, whereas statically, this may be of only
minor importance. Control devices have many characteristics that may
influence performance under acceleration conditions. Some of the major
characteristics are: (a) axes of motion with respect to the acceleration
vectors and the pilot's hand; (b) the number of axes of motion; (c) the
stick force gradients along each mode of control; (d) centering characteristics along each mode of control; (e) breakout force; (f) control
friction; (g) damping characteristics; (h) control throw; (i) control
response time (j) control harmony; (k) cross-coupling; (l) amount of
kinesthetic feedback provided by the controller; (m) shape and size;
(n) dynamic and static balancing; and (o) control sensitivity. The combinations and interactions of these characteristics are very complex. In
the present chapter the major ones are reviewed.

Involuntary control inputs due to acceleration forces can occur while
using either the side or center control stick. Similarly, if the control has
too large a "breakout force," over-control may occur. If the restoring
forces on the control are not strong enough, information as to the magnitude of the control input cannot come from hand pressure "feedback"
but must come from proprioceptive sensations or by looking at the
controller by looking at the response of the aircraft. If the stick is not
perfectly balanced, hand pressure responses as to the magnitude of G
increases may mislead the pilot.

In early versions of proposed space vehicles, various types of right-
hand side-arm controllers were tested: three-axis controllers, two-axis
controllers with toe pedals; two-axis digital controllers with toe-pedals,

and force-stick controllers. Figure 16 presents a diagram of four of these controllers: a three-axis, balanced controller, having all three axes intersecting at a point, Type I; a three-axis controller, unbalanced, having none of the three axes intersecting at a point, Type II; a two-axis fingertip controller, having two axes intersecting at a point, with yaw operated via toe pedals, Type III; and a two-axis controller whose axes do not intersect at a point, and which is accompanied by toe pedals for yaw

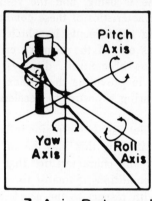

3-Axis, Balanced Controller

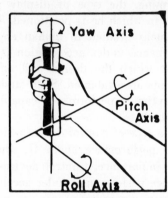

3-Axis, Unbalanced Controller

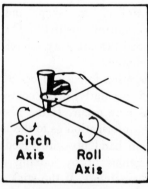

2-Axis, finger tip Controller

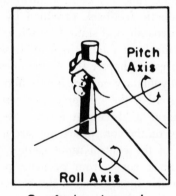

2-Axis, hand Controller

Figure 16. Four types of right-hand side-arm controllers used in high-G studies on the AMAL centrifuge. (Official photograph U.S. Navy.)

control, Type IV. The effects of two specific acceleration fields on the error performance in the pitch and roll of a tracking task for each of the four types of controllers were studied. When the pilots performed in the $+6\ G_x$ by $0\ G_z$ field, pitch error performance on all four controllers was essentially the same; however, when these same pilots flew the same problem in the $-2\ G_x$ by $+4\ G_z$ field, pitch error performance on Type II controller greatly increased, whereas performance on the other three controllers remained essentially unchanged. For roll error, a change in G fields resulted in an increment in error for Types II and III controllers and a reduction in error for Types I and IV, resulting in a shift in the rank order of the controllers.

Control loadings are important under acceleration fields (Brown, 1959). Compatability between control loadings, shape, position, and acceleration is very important in control design. In recent simulations at the AMAL, it has been found that modifications in the control loadings are very important in determining the success with which a pilot can fly a mission. However, a controller that has "perfect" control loadings during static tests does not necessarily have satisfactory control loadings under high G, or under fluctuating G fields.

The operation of controls within a high G acceleration field is influenced by the shape of the controls and the position of the body with respect to the primary G vector (Clark, *et al.*, 1945; Lambert, *et al.*, 1945; Buhrlen, 1937; Collins, *et al.*, 1958; Code, *et al.*, 1947; Kaehler, 1959). It also varies according to the particular limbs and muscle groups which are required in making the control operations. For example, at the AMAL, it was demonstrated that a small right-hand pencil-shaped signaling device could be operated by a human subject during a record-breaking run which rose to $+25\ G_x$ and back in 40 seconds. The subject was positioned in a contour couch at a back angle of eight degrees from supine. The controller was pivoted parallel to the $+G_x$ vector, and the subject pushed the stick slightly in response to a random sequence of lights.

Collins, *et al.* (1958) demonstrated that a human subject in a form-fitted couch could go as high as $+20\ G_x$ and that he could perform a small right-hand pencil stick control in response to flashing lights throughout a 48 second profile. Total time at peak G was 5 seconds. They also demonstrated that a thumb-operated switch could be operated effectively at this level. A subject immersed in water within a metallic G capsule protection device demonstrated that he could withstand $-31\ G_x$ and operate small buttons in response to signal lights.

In recent studies at the Aviation Medical Acceleration Laboratory (Chambers, 1961), it has been demonstrated that 3-dimensional side-

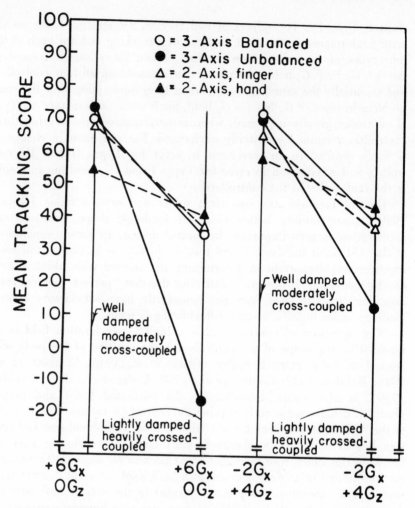

Figure 17. Mean tracking efficiency scores for test pilots who performed the same tracking task with each of four different types of side-arm controllers within given acceleration fields. (Official photograph U.S. Navy.)

arm controllers can be used through 15 G transverse (Chambers, 1961). Here the design of the controller and its position was important, since there are some center stick controllers which cannot be operated above 6 G effectively.

The differential effect of acceleration performance of pilots on different types of controllers is shown in Figure 17. Here, the mean tracking efficiency scores for test pilots who performed the same tracking task with each of four different types of side-arm controllers within given acceleration fields and with varying amounts of cross-coupling and damping are shown. The graph shows not only the effects of using different controllers within specific G fields or a particular tracking task, but it also illustrates the effects of damping and cross-coupling when acceleration is held constant.

During all types of high accelerations, the human subject experiences visual disturbances. Task performance proficiency may deteriorate under acceleration conditions if the subject cannot maintain good visual contact with the display information. There are several display characteristics which are of major importance in order to minimize the acceleration effects on performance. Since central vision is maintained longer than peripheral vision during acceleration stress, the display should be positioned so that the human eyes may maintain visual contact with it throughout the acceleration exposure. Since more illumination is required at higher G, adequate lighting must be provided for the peak G exposure.

Since the minimum size for the numbers and indicators on dials is larger under G than statically, the quantities to be displayed under G must be large enough to be continuously perceptible at higher G. Since the eye muscular responses are impaired by high accelerations, the indicators to be viewed should be located so as to require minimum instrument scanning and eye movements. The amount of pilot concentration is greater at high G than at low G, and consequently the flight instruments should be arranged so as to minimize effort in concentration, time sharing, and scanning. During the occurrence of all types of high accelerations, vision is one of the primary limiting factors for maintaining task performance proficiency.

In studying the effects of acceleration, one must consider the complexity of the task to be performed by the pilot, since task complexity is magnified under G (Brown, 1961). The measurement of the effects of high G on complex task performance is frequently complicated by task difficulty variables. Aerodynamic stability and damping, frequency, time constants and other vehicle response characteristics may make the performance of the piloting task in high G more or less difficult. If the simulated vehicle is stable, well damped, and within desirable frequency ranges, the pilot may find performance at high G to be relatively easy. However, the same piloting task may be entirely impossible at the same G level if the simulated vehicle has unacceptable aerodynamic characteristics. By varying the damping ratio conditions, the ease with which a task may be performed may be made progressively more difficult.

The type of restraint system which is used may be one of the most important variables in influencing how well the pilot is able to perform under acceleration conditions. To a large extent, his performance tolerance limits may be defined by the effectiveness of his restraint system. For example, it was found in one study that accelerations of $-3.5\ G_x$ or $+6\ G_x$ made it difficult, if not impossible, for pilots to meet the performance criterion satisfactorily. However, using a different type of restraint system, it was found that pilots could perform the same piloting tasks satisfactorily at $-6\ G_x$ or at $+12\ G_x$. The different type of restraint system nearly doubled the acceleration limits within which pilots could perform satisfactorily.

Figure 18 has been prepared to show the approximate performance time tolerances for experienced pilots for performing piloting tasks satisfactorily when immersed in acceleration fields during centrifuge simulations of several types of space vehicles. This figure shows only the

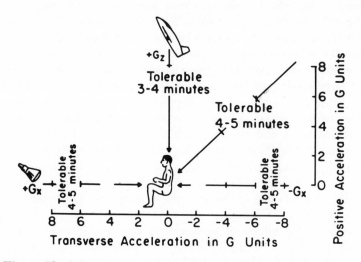

Figure 18. Approximate performance time-tolerances for pilots in advanced restraint system including individually fitted contour couches and associated chest, leg, arm, and head restraints. The figure shows approximate limits beyond which performance would be unsatisfactory. These approximations are based on data obtained at AMAL during centrifuge simulations of proposed space vehicles. (Official photograph U.S. Navy.)

tolerable times and G levels beyond which performance would be unsatisfactory.

Advanced restraint systems have enabled pilots to perform better at higher acceleration levels. These include individually molded form-fitted couches, extensive chest, leg, arm, and helmet supports, and face supports, and supports for the interior surface of the body.

More advanced restraint systems have been designed and tested, and it is expected that these will result in increased capabilities of human performance during exposure to acceleration forces of increased magnitude and duration (Clark and Gray, 1959; Smedal, *et al.*, 1961).

V. Higher Mental Abilities

This section is concerned with the effects of acceleration stress on higher mental abilities, such as are involved in making decisions, remembering events and information and solving problems. These are of special importance since during acceleration phases of space flight, astronauts may be required to monitor flight instruments, make scientific observations, process information, identify equipment malfunctions, initiate corrective action, make computations and make important decisions. This section attempts to present the results of some of the experiments on this problem.

A. PROBLEMS IN MEASURING HIGHER MENTAL ABILITIES

There is a serious lack of reliable, valid, and sensitive tests of higher mental abilities which can be administered within the physically restrictive and time-limited conditions encountered in centrifuges, simulators, and space capsules. Especially acute is the need for tests which may be used to monitor the intellectual functioning of the human subject while he is being exposed to stresses which approach his physiological tolerance limits. There is also a critical need for an adequate taxonomy that describes higher mental abilities as they may function during high G, prolonged G, or impact. Even under static conditions it is not possible to obtain psychological measures which are sensitive and reliable enough to measure subtle types of intellectual damage.

Most of the available information regarding higher mental abilities has been based on subjective opinions expressed by experimental subjects and observers during the exposures, or delayed post-flight debriefings and neurological examinations, or measures of piloting performance which require the use of generally unidentified but assumed psychological abilities. For the most part, these measures have not provided the degree of precision required in the measurement of subtle higher mental functioning, nor has it been possible in most situations to administer the available measuring devices during ideal times under ideal test conditions (Chambers and Smith, 1959).

Galambos (1961) has presented an excellent review of the problems involved in the psychological testing of subjects who are undergoing acceleration stress. Although a large number of men have been exposed frequently to severe cerebral anoxia and other physiological trauma resulting from acceleration, there are no reports of any severe behavioral pathology as a direct consequence of acceleration exposures. Galambos (1961) proposes a series of tests, principles, conditions, and recommendations to be used at all acceleration facility installations, and concludes by urging immediate research and development to devise a rational practical test battery for performance testing during acceleration stress.

Often peak G can be maintained for only a few seconds, making it impossible to use standardized psychological tests. The effects of G on mechanical and electronic apparatus also pose potential problems. Furthermore, in some situations, the difficulties subjects experience in moving, breathing, speaking, and sometimes enduring pain, make test administration by standard paper-pencil, interview, or apparatus test procedures impossible. However, it is possible to monitor the subject continuously with biomedical and performance instrumentation in order to sample at least some attributes of higher mental functioning.

B. CONFUSION, UNCONSCIOUSNESS, DISORIENTATION, AND VERTIGO

Exposure to high or prolonged acceleration may produce confusion, unconsciousness, disorientation, memory lapses, loss of control of voluntary movements, or prolonged vertigo. Although, in specific cases the symptoms may be regarded as medical indicators of intellectual impairment, it is difficult to arrive at any general conclusions concerning the nature of the intellectual impairment itself.

Kerr and Russell (1944) suggest that there may be brain damage and other impairment of cerebral function associated with the grayout, blackout, and unconsciousness induced by positive acceleration. In their study, the average threshold of unconsciousness was $+5\ G_z$. The mean duration of unconsciousness was 12 seconds, ranging from 3 to 60 seconds, and convulsive episodes occurred in 40 per cent of their cases. Hallenbeck (1946) found similar results. Periods of confusion and disorientation followed unconsciousness resulting from centrifugation. Numerous investigators since have cautioned that damage to the central nervous system and the intellectual abilities may be produced by high, prolonged, or frequent acceleration stress.

A report by Wood, *et al.* (1947) reviewed the research conducted on four subjects who were repeatedly exposed to acceleration stresses up to +6 G_z. Repeated losses of peripheral vision, periods of anoxia characteristic of blackout, and related physiological trauma, did not result in any measurable permanent residual dysfunction. Galambos (1961) tabulated results of questionnaires from nine acceleration research facilities and was unable to find any instances of neurological or other disorders which were clearly attributable to acceleration experience as such. Over a period of four years, a subject at the human centrifuge at the Pensacola Naval Air Station who had been exposed to over 379 episodes of grayout or worse and 15 exposures which resulted in unconsciousness. No permanent intellectual impairment was observed. An extreme case, perhaps, occurred at the human centrifuge at Wright-Patterson Air Force Base in which a human subject received six blackouts and 26 grayouts during 40 runs in a single day. Although fifteen years have elapsed during which he has received many additional high G exposures which resulted in grayout, blackout, and unconsciousness, there appears to be no indications of any impairment of higher mental functioning.

Similarly, at the AMAL, there have been many exposures of human subjects to blackout and unconsciousness. There are no recordings of impairment in any of the higher mental abilities. However, as has been the case at other centrifuge installations, there have not been extensive psychological testing projects designed to measure extremely subtle effects which may have occurred and which could not have been observed by standard clinical means. Unpublished work has indicated some temporary after-effects on speech and on ability to concentrate. One test pilot from Ames Research Center who took a series of prolonged transverse acceleration exposures reported vertigo with change of head position for 90 days following his last exposure, and several of the personnel at the AMAL have reported persistent vertigo following prolonged exposure to acceleration. However, these findings would appear to suggest peripheral vestibular damage rather than damage to the central nervous system.

Galambos (1961) reviewed reports concerning impact accelerations involving 18 subjects who experienced 90 impacts which extended to a magnitude of +55 G_x for a duration up to 0.12 seconds, and there were no observable signs of neurological damage. Other work is reviewed from deceleration studies in which definite signs of shock, retinal hemorrhage, frontal headaches, and other symptoms were encountered, and in no cases were there reports of intellectual damage.

The possibility exists that exposure to some of these acceleration stresses may cause acute and/or chronic intellectual impairment and related psychological abnormalities. Theoretically, at least, the repeated anoxia, mechanical trauma, hemorrhage, edema, nausea, vertigo, and behavioral impairment which occur as symptoms of the acceleration experience, for example, could possibly result in irreversible intellectual impairment. At our centrifuge facility, and at various other acceleration facilities, human subjects are frequently, and sometimes routinely, exposed to these conditions. Although we have been unable to find any cases from our laboratory or from reports of other research centers in which irreversible intellectual impairment has been reported, the possibility exists that damage may be so subtle, diffuse, or transitory, that it may not be observable in the usual neurological and psychological examinations (Chambers and Lathrop, 1961). Galambos (1961) has pointed out that since a human subject may be pushed easily to complete insensibility by applying sufficiently high G stress, and consequently his performance would also decline, the problem is to find a battery of tests of such sensitivity that impaired performance will be reflected long before black-out or unconsciousness occurs. Since there are relatively few such tests available, he thus proposed the development of certain tests designed to have sensitivity measure sensory functions, perception, vigilance, storage and retrieval of information, and cognitive operations. Brown (1961) has emphasized the lack of data in the scientific literature concerning the effects of acceleration on mental function.

C. DISCRIMINATING AND RESPONDING APPROPRIATELY AND QUICKLY

Some of the earliest quantitative approaches to the problem of measuring the effects of acceleration on higher mental functioning were to study the ability of subjects to discriminate and respond appropriately and quickly. Discrimination reaction time, perceptual speed, response time, and recognition time under acceleration stress seem to be useful indicators. Effects of positive acceleration on reaction time have been reported by some investigators (Burmeister, 1939; Warrick and Lund, 1946; Canfield, Comrey, and Wilson, 1948b, 1949; Brown and Burke, 1958). It is not known whether the results reported were due to central nervous system impairments, or to peripheral sensory difficulties in perceiving the stimulus, or to the major components of the response, or to the apparatus itself. In addition, these studies have been complicated by possible indirect psychological effects, such as higher motivation, excitement, emotional involvement, and attitudes.

The effects of transverse acceleration on discrimination reaction time has also been studied. In a study conducted at this laboratory, a complex discrimination reaction time apparatus was devised which presented four lights on a small display and four buttons on a small right-hand control stick. As each light came on, the subject was required to press one of the four corresponding buttons mounted in his right-hand stick. Both the initial programming of the response lights and the subject's responses were fed through connecting lines to an analog computer where partial datum reduction was accomplished. During pre-acceleration tests, each of the subjects responded to an 8 block series of 25 correct responses, then, during exposure to six transverse G for five minutes, each subject responded to twelve blocks of 25 correct responses. And during a post acceleration test (in the centrifuge, statically), each subject responded to 8 blocks of 25 correct responses, for 4 successive trials. Some of the subjects gained speed at the expense of accuracy, whereas others gained accuracy at the expense of speed.

In order to account for both types of possible decrement, reaction time and errors were normalized and then added. A repeatable pattern of performance was obtained in this manner. Using the one-tailed t test, it was shown that performance was significantly impaired under G. It is very striking that the decrement persisted after the acceleration tests were completed.

In a series of experiments on piloting performance during complex closed-loop centrifuge simmulations, the author used a battery of six paper-and-pencil perceptual-motor tests and one autokinetic movement test in examining test pilots who performed the flight simulation maneuvers. Only two tests in the battery showed any significant effects when administered twenty minutes after completion of the runs; the autokinetic movement test and the discrimination reaction time test. When seated in total darkness, subjects reported a motionless spot of light as revolving in the direction opposite to the direction of their centrifuge experience. When tested with the paper-pencil form of a discrimination reaction time test, these subjects performed more slowly and made more errors than they had made during pre-centrifuge testing sessions.

Time required to make simple motor responses, to perform discrimination reactions, and to perform mental arithmetic, was investigated by Weiss, et al (1954) on subjects who were exposed to simple tumblings of approximately 125 rpm rotation about an axis through the body and perpendicular to the long axis of the body. No significant decrement in performance on any of the tasks was observed. Similarly, no decrement in performance was found for subjects exposed to $+3G_z$ to perform arithmetic problems, rank numbers, name colors, and perform a word-separation task.

It has been demonstrated that reading speed is significantly impaired by 3 positive G, as compared with 1G (Frankenhaeuser, 1958). Color naming was also significantly impaired at $+G_z$. The following intellectual skills are significantly impaired by positive 3 G accelerations at peaks ranging from 2 to 10 minutes: the ability to count backwards from 100, subtracting 3 each time; the ability to multiply one and two digit numbers; the ability to judge the passage of time; and the ability to identify test figures which are identical to the stimulus figure and report its number verbally.

A task which required the subject to add random numbers in series of twos (which were presented via earphones) was administered to subjects who rode a centrifuge statically and at $+4.6\ G_z$ for three minutes each run (Cope and Jensen, 1961). Responses made by the subjects suggested that time and error increased during grayout and blackout, and the steepness of the response signal appeared to indicate a decrement which was related to EEG changes. The steepness of the slope provides a convenient means of continuously monitoring the amount of impairment in performing the addition task. The method of scoring and the use of an auditory stimulus has the advantage of giving an indication of mental function which is independent of changes in vision which may occur during grayout. The system also requires only a minimum amount of motor response.

Many of the ideal design and monitoring conditions have been taken into account by Miller, *et al.* (1960) in the construction of a device for measuring intellectual functions during acceleration. The device is capable of presenting three test batteries of 14 one-minute tests to evaluate reasoning, mathematical, verbal, and perceptual abilities. The device can be operated up to 14 G, and it features automatic scoring, tabulation of responses, and automatic pacing of stimulus presentations.

Cope and Chambers (1961) have also developed a device which is designed to provide a continuous record of the subject's mental functioning during the course of a centrifuge exposure. A punched tape programmer presents a random sequence of lights, to which the subject discriminates and reacts by pressing small buttons. A diode logic network insures that the subject is scored correctly, and that appropriate voltages are presented to an integrator circuit. The integrator output is recorded continuously as the run proceeds in terms of small steps, each of which is proportional to the reaction time for the corresponding

stimulus. Thus, the performance is integrated and observed simultaneously as the subject is exposed to the acceleration stress.

D. CONCENTRATION AND PERFORMANCE MAINTENANCE

Subjects tested at the Aviation Medical Acceleration Laboratory have reported difficulty in concentration and in the performance of time-sharing tasks during exposure to accelerations between 9 and 15 G_x. Holleman, Armstrong, and Andrews (1960) have made note of this, and a relatively large number of subjective reports have been taken by observers at the Aviation Medical Acceleration Laboratory regarding the problem of piloting concentration at high G. These deficiencies appear to be temporary, and they have occurred in a relatively few number of subjects, and conclusions concerning them are not yet definite.

Fluctuating accelerations appear to pose problems involving higher mental functioning and concentration, especially when the accelerations vary continuously in direction, rate of onset, or intensity (Gerathewohl, 1956; von Beckh, 1954). In a study cited earlier (Snyder, 1961) involving a series of 12 types of complex spin simulations, the pilots reported difficulty in thinking and reacting clearly, at relatively low $-G_x$ levels. In unpublished work by Chambers, pilots have reported confusion and difficulties in concentration when exposed to complex flight problems at levels of $+6\ G_z$, $-5\ G_x$, and $+12\ G_x$, during simulation of glide, drag, and low-lift space vehicles. The condition of acceleration involving alternating G stress may pose special problems and create confusion for the astronaut who attempts to control his own vehicle during the critical phases of insertion into orbit following boost accelerations, or during the reentry acceleration stress following long-term exposure to weightlessness. The best available data on this problem is reported by von Beckh (1959) who studied 11 subjects in more than 200 weightlessness and acceleration patterns produced by airplanes flying three types of profiles: (1) pre-weightlessness acceleration profiles, (2) post-weightlessness acceleration profiles, and (3) control flights, consisting of acceleration without following or preceding weightlessness. Defects in judgment, some disorientation, and associated reductions in efficiency occurred. The degree to which these were related to the somewhat severe physiological defects is unknown. In this study, by von Beckh, weightlessness could be maintained only for periods up to 45 seconds.

Extensive research, however, on human subjects during Keplerian trajectory flights in airplanes have revealed no intellectual impairment to date (Ballinger, 1952; von Beckh, 1954; Gerathewohl, 1956, 1958;

von Beckh, 1959). Similarly, on the sub-orbital Redstone-Mercury flights of Astronauts Alan B. Shepard and Virgil I. Grissom, no indications have been reported suggesting any intellectual impairment which may have occurred during or after exposure to the accelerations involved in those flights (Augerson and Laughlin, 1961; Jackson, *et al.*, 1961; Rubacky, 1961; Shepard, 1961; Voas, *et al.*, 1961; Voas, *et al.*, 1962b; Loftus, 1961; Grissom, 1961; Laughlin and Augerson, 1961; Douglas, *et al.*, 1961).

An attempt has been made to use time estimation tasks as an indicator of the effects of G on higher mental functioning. Continuous time estimation activities require concentration and attention, and are believed to show promise as measuring procedures. Among the most important studies are those of Frankenhaeuser (1957a, 1957b, 1958), in which impairment of several higher mental functions were reported after the relatively low accelerations of only 3 positive G for four minutes duration. Chambers and Eggleston (1959), have also obtained some data suggesting an impairment in the ability of test pilots to judge accurately the passage of short intervals of time under conditions of acceleration. There were also reports of difficulty in ability to concentrate. Chambers, however, was unable to find any effects at all in a related similar study in which time estimation measurements were taken before and after record-making runs of 23 and 25 transverse G.

During prolonged exposure to acceleration, continuous concentration and performance maintenance is difficult. For example, during a record breaking 2 G centrifuge run which lasted 24 hours, the subject started out with a somewhat detailed set of procedures to follow in making medical observations of himself, recording comments, writing and typing (Clark and Gray, 1959; Clark and Hardy, 1959). The subject soon found, however, that he took naps and listened to the radio, and suffered primarily from boredom and fatigue. Areas of contact with the chair were the greatest sources of localized discomfort. At 16 hours a mild anesthesia of the fourth and fifth fingers and outer third of the palm of the left hand developed (this remained for approximately 2 months after the experiment). The subject found it impossible to maintain his originally prescribed maintenance schedule and procedures for making observations.

In a shorter study ($+2$ G_x for 4 hours), a subject was secured in a contour couch and required to perform a two-channel matching memory task every 10 minutes. The subject was able to perform this task throughout the entire period with only very minor effects on the task. Task performance during the 4-hour exposure was not significantly different from performance before or after the exposure. Throughout the test period, performance was highly correlated with subjective estimations of performance proficiency on each of the two channels.

E. EFFECTS OF ACCELERATION ON IMMEDIATE MEMORY AND THE PROCESSING OF INFORMATION

The effects of acceleration on immediate memory has been of interest, since an astronaut or scientific observer during a launch, re-entry, or other space maneuver, may be required to perform tasks such as monitoring, reporting, and guidance, all of which require immediate memory and the processing of information.

Experiments concerning the effects of acceleration on immediate memory are not conclusive. In a recent experiment by Ross and Chambers conducted on the Human Centrifuge at the Aviation Medical Acceleration Laboratory, a running matching memory testing apparatus was developed which could be used under both static and acceleration conditions. This test required the memorization of a portion of a sequence of random symbols. As one symbol occurred, the subject was required to match it in memory with one that had been presented either three or four symbols previously and new symbols kept appearing continuously, so that the subject had to continuously forget earlier symbols as he added the new ones.

No significant differences in the percentage of correct memory matches were found between static and acceleration conditions. However, of the 27 subjects tested, only 24 were able to complete the series of four 5 G runs of four minutes each, and over half of these remaining subjects suffered physiological aftereffects which persisted for some time after the exposure. The incidental findings do, however, seem to be of some importance. First, an increase in the latency between presentation and time of response was noted. Secondly, the subjective comments concerning performance on this task did not correlate well with the actual quantitative measures. Subjects reported that their performances had deteriorated under acceleration, and that they regarded this acceleration exposure as an extremely stressful experience. There were also subjective reports of time compression while under acceleration.

In a more recent experiment, an attempt was made to determine the effects of transverse accelerations of $+1\ G_x$, $+3\ G_x$, $+5\ G_x$, $+7\ G_x$, and $+9\ G_x$ on the ability of subjects to continuously perform a two-channel matching task during exposures of 140 seconds at peak G. Although major individual differences were shown, most of the subjects began to show only slight decrement at the $+7\ G_x$ level, suggesting that performance tolerance limits for this task exist at some level above $+9\ G_x$.

F. ERROR CHARACTERISTICS OF PERFORMANCE IMPAIRMENT UNDER ACCELERATION STRESS

Chambers and Lathrop (1961) have proposed that in situations where a large number of acceleration exposures are involved, such as in the training of astronauts, an indication of the subject's intellectual functioning during acceleration stress may be obtained by studying the recordings of his performance on piloting tasks during the period of his exposure, and comparing these with similar recordings taken during prior and post runs in which the same piloting tasks were performed. The piloting tasks themselves then serve the function of being tests of higher mental functioning.

Tracking behavior, for example, requires not only the motor response of pushing the control stick, but also higher mental processes, such as predicting the input stimulus sequences, perception of the display elements and the interrelations, careful attention and concentration, practice and learning, adaptability on the part of the man to changing task requirements, time-sharing, recognition and discrimination behavior, perceptual anticipation, judgment, evaluation and decision-making. Other piloting tasks involving monitoring displays, communicating, navigating and flying complex flight maneuvers may also involve many of the same higher mental abilities which are usually measured by standard intelligence tests. Consequently, in addition to attempts to study higher mental abilities *per se* at our laboratory, we have also attempted to utilize the performance of the piloting tasks themselves as measures of intellectual functioning under stress.

These recordings, and various numerical quantities derived from these recordings, contain vital information concerning the underlying processes which control his behavior. During the hundreds of acceleration tests conducted on astronauts, test pilots and other volunteer subjects, certain aspects of piloting performance have been observed which evolved as characteristic of performance impairment. These are all quantitative measures recorded in terms of amplitude, frequency, or duration parameters which are meaningful expressions of accuracy, speed, and consistency behavior. They do not appear to be characteristic of any particular piloting task, but rather, they appear to be common to a large variety of piloting tasks. These are:

a. Increase in error amplitude.

b. Lapses, or increasing unevenness and irregularity of performing the task.

c. Oscillations.

d. Falling off in proficiency on some parts of a task while maintaining proficiency on other parts.

e. Changes in phasing and/or timing task components.

f. Reduction or cessation in performance output of some task components.

g. Inadvertent control inputs.

h. Failure to detect and respond to changes in the stimulus field.

i. Errors in retrieving, integrating, storing and processing information.

j. Changes in the rate of performance, such as sudden initiation of performance nonessential to the task.

Error amplitude is used most frequently as an indicant of performance. The vast majority of research on human behavior under acceleration has been done on tracking error amplitude scores. These scores are concerned with the difference between the obtained response and the desired response. Assuming that the subject can perform the task satisfactorily during static tests, any obtained large error quantities during acceleration may be attributed to the stress.

From time to time, the subject's performance may falter or may even stop temporarily. The subject is unable to maintain his performance at a consistently high level of proficiency. These may be called lapses, or expressions of increasing irregularity, and they usually increase in frequency and duration as the adversity of the acceleration stress is increased. They are useful indications that the stress is approaching tolerance limits. An example of lapses is shown in Figure 19. Presented here are records of errors made in a compensatory tracking task while under accelerative stresses. This particular problem was presented by randomly varying the position of a target on the face of an oscilloscope by means of analog computer control. The subject's task was to correct for this movement by operation of a sidearm controller, similar to that used in the current Mercury capsule, in the two axes of pitch and roll to overcome scope disturbances in the vertical and horizontal axes.

In the upper chart, the most noticeable performance impairment is that the roll axis is allowed to degrade and primary attention is focused on the elimination of errors in pitch. In this respect, we also have an example of the previously listed reduction in performance output on one of the task components. Lapses and irregularity in performing the task in the preferred pitch mode may be observed. This particular subject functions at a very high level with almost perfect tracking for a period of time and then lapses into relatively large errors. Following this brief lapse, performance again returns to normal, only to be followed by another lapse.

The lower portion of Figure 19, illustrates one other type of error commonly found in performance records. A phasing or cyclical type of error is shown very clearly in roll error, and to some extent also in pitch

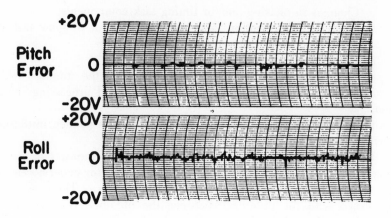

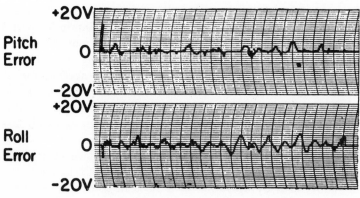

Figure 19. Example of performance errors in pitch and roll during exposure to $+6G_x$. (Official photograph U.S. Navy.)

error. Here the small random errors in tracking seem to be superimposed on a relatively low frequency sinusoidal type of error.

Another error characteristic which has been observed is that of performance oscillations. An example of this is shown in Figure 20. Note that the roll, pitch, and yaw performance lines show some small oscillations as G rises. However, at peak G, and right after peak G, note the marked increase in the amplitude of these oscillations. It is these oscillations which frequently typify the period of marked straining, or during the period of recovery from straining. Whereas the lapses dealt with in the previous paragraph concerned a performance of irregularity, these oscillations are quite regular, but they increase in amplitude during

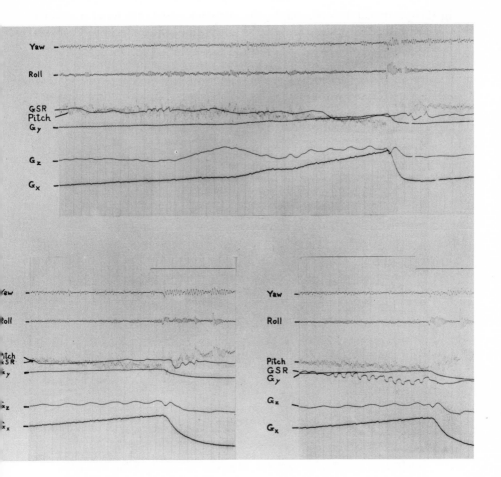

Figure 20. Examples of performance oscillations in pitch, roll, and yaw. Examples of oscillations in the GSR (galvanic skin response) are also shown. (Official photograph U.S. Navy.)

the period of straining and in recovery immediately after peak G. Oscillations of this type have been observed in many different types of acceleration runs. (These behavior ocsillations should not be confused with the engineering oscillations frequently observed in unstable vehicles.) However, it would be possible to support the argument that the amount of behavioral oscillation which one encounters may be greatly influenced by vehicle instability.

Another example of performance oscillations is shown in Figure 21.

In this particular record sample, the astronaut was performing a manual re-entry task, closed loop, using a three-axis side-arm controller. Attention is called to the recordings for pitch, roll and yaw. Excessive oscillations are shown building up for pitch and for yaw during the approach to the 15 G peak. These deflections are now shown for roll. This is one kind of piloting performance which may have major significance during exposure

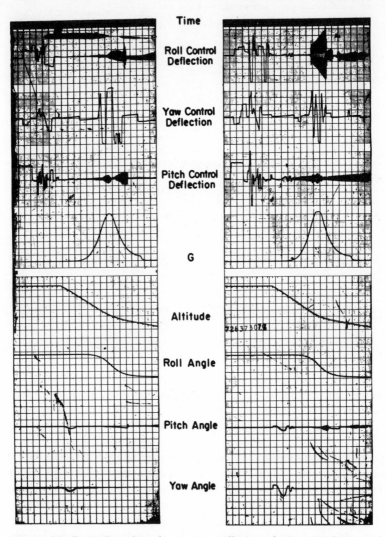

Figure 21. Examples of performance oscillations during simulations of a reentry task on the AMAL human centrifuge. (Official photograph U.S. Navy.)

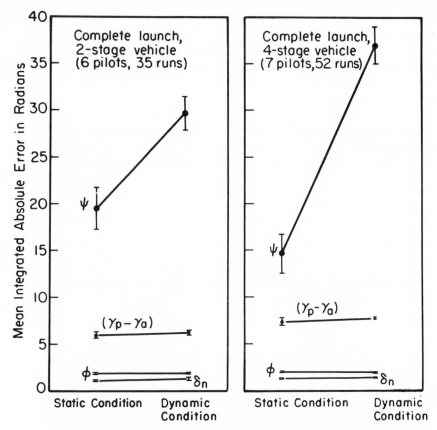

Figure 22. Performance of pilots on a 4-stage launch simulation under static and dynamic conditions. (Official photograph U.S. Navy.)

to extremely stressful centrifuge tests, or extremely difficult performance tasks.

A partial decrease in performance proficiency may be an indication that the subject is reaching his performance limits, or that he is unable to cope with the problem during the stress. Figure 22 presents an example of this kind if situation. This study of the ability of 7 pilots to fly complete launch simulations of 2-stage vehicles and of 4-stage vehicles demonstrated that in both cases one aspect of the task (yaw) suffered major impairment under the acceleration stress, whereas other aspects (angle of attack, roll and nozzle angle) did not. This illustration indicates that in studying performance, all components of the task must be examined. This same principle also holds for the simultaneous performance of different tasks during acceleration.

Inadvertent control inputs may also indicate the severity of the stress. The subject may exhibit behavior that is not planned or directed, and does not assist him in performing his mission or task. An example of this is shown in Figure 23, which shows roll, pitch, and yaw control move-

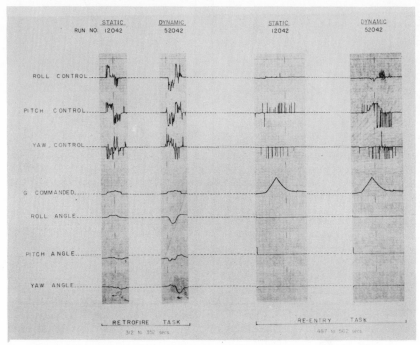

Figure 23. Examples of inadvertent control inputs which occurred during dynamic simulations but not during static simulations of the Mercury Redstone vehicle on the human centrifuge. (Official photograph U.S. Navy.)

ments during the re-entry portion of a simulated Mercury-Redstone vehicle. The static run shows a very few of these inputs; however, during the dynamic run, major additional and unnecessary inputs were demonstrated for pitch and yaw. It is interesting to note that these occurred immediately following peak G, and disappeared when the subject returned to the static condition.

In addition to these types of errors, other discrete types of performance changes are often immediately noticeable. One of the most striking is the failure to detect and respond to changes in the stimulus field. This frequently occurs when the G force is from head-to-foot and blackout or grayout results. In such cases, peripheral vision fails, and responses to peripheral stimuli also fails. This same failure to note changes in the visual field also becomes a leading factor when an array of dials and meters (containing both primary and secondary instruments) faces the subject. Under acceleration, attention tends to be focused on the primary instruments, and changes in secondary instruments may not be detected.

Equally as striking are the changes in the rate of performance under acceleration. In one particular example, subjects were required to press a button at least once per second while performing a tracking task under acceleration reaching 10 G_x. One subject's rate of pressing tended to increase with acceleration until a final upper limit of nearly 250 responses per minute was reached. This contrasted sharply with certain other subjects who tended to hold the response button in the depressed position.

A somewhat different type of error is concerned with the retrieving, integrating, storing, and processing of information. During, or after, acceleration stress the subject may be required to perform maneuvers which serve as a test of his ability to retrieve, store, or process information. At the monitoring station, it is possible to view all of the events as they occur, and determine the extent to which the subject is able to cope with the task requirements, some of which may be based on prior events which occurred during earlier parts of the acceleration exposure.

VI. Personality, Emotional Behavior, and Motivation

The effects of acceleration on personality, emotional behavior, and motivation cannot be measured as precisely as the more quantitative performance aspects which have been presented in earlier sections of this chapter. Most of the observations to date are based on the verbal comments of men during acceleration exposures and debriefing sessions, films, television, the results of interviews and questionnaires, and physiological measures taken during the acceleration stress. Although there seems to be general agreement that acceleration stress influences these aspects of human behavior and also that these aspects influence how a person performs during acceleration stress, there are relatively few publications in which quantitative information is published (Brown and Lechner, 1955; Brown, 1960, 1961; Chambers, 1962b).

Large individual differences have been observed, ranging from euphoria to fear and fright, extreme apprehension, tension, and nausea. There are some persons who seem to take great pleasure in being exposed to accelerations while others may be very fearful, or regard the accelerations, especially high G, as a highly competitive courageous activity. It is difficult to separate or define the personality, emotional, and motivational aspects, because of (1) the large individual differences which exist among subjects; (2) the lack of quantitative measuring devices which may be administered during the progress of the run; and (3) the necessary priority which physical welfare and safety demand, making the administration of any of the currently available psychological instruments impossible.

Brown (1960), in writing that the anticipation of acceleration forces contributes to anxiety, concludes that the prospect of a centrifuge ride may be an effective anxiety inducer. This assumes that an elevated heart rate, for example, may be an index of anxiety, if the increase occurs in situations in which there is no change in the amount of physical stress, as when the subject is waiting for a centrifuge exposure to occur. As far back as 1946, Hallenbeck, Wood, Lambert, and Allen found that pulse rates were approximately 10 beats faster per minute during the interval prior to G than during the G itself. The increase in pre-acceleration pulse rate is probably a psychological effect. Brown, Ellis, Webb, and Gray (1957) have also demonstrated that the pulse rates of the subjects immediately prior to exposure to acceleration ware faster than during the acceleration run itself. In the case of subjects who had had some prior experience on the centrifuge, the pulse rate varied according to the G level which was anticipated. One of the most consistent effects of acceleration itself is an increase in pulse rate, and there seems to be some suggestion that the increment may have been due to conditioning rather than to anxiety.

Studies using the galvanic skin response as an indicator of autonomic arousal have shown significant changes in some subjects prior to the onset of acceleration. Two studies at the AMAL have suggested that the direction of change was not consistent. Schock (1960) reported that human subjects exposed to pre-weightlessness accelerations and weightlessness in the F94C aircraft showed marked changes in the galvanic skin response and in heart rate. He concluded that these changes were due to emotional factors rather than to weightlessness or to the positive G per se. Earlier, Schock (1958) suggested that during long-term weightless periods, it is likely that anxiety, apprehensions, and emotional disturbances may occur. These emotional disturbances may limit ability to perform satisfactorily during re-entry accelerations when ability to perform with maximum emotional control is necessary.

Evidence indicates that acceleration tolerance is influenced by the psychological aspects of the situation in which the tests are made (Kerr and Russell, 1944; Lambert, 1950; Brown and Lechner, 1955; Brown,

1961). Tolerance in aircraft, for example, is usually higher than that on the centrifuge, and at least some of this has been attributed to the "excitement of flying." In laboratory studies at the AMAL it has been a frequent observation that subjects have higher positive G tolerances when they are excited and tense than they do when they are relaxed. The subject's attitude, interest motivations, and willingness to undergo the exposure to G, are commonly observed as exerting a major influence on the way in which the subject sustains the G and performs his task. Laboratory experience indicates that naive subjects undergo significant changes in pulse rate, blood pressure, and GSR in anticipation of the start of a high G exposure. However, these changes become minimized following repeated exposures to acceleration.

Some subjective observations have been made on subjects who have been exposed to prolonged centrifuge runs. For example, Clark, who rode the centrifuge at 2 G for 24 hours (Clark and Hardy, 1959), indicated that he lost interest in the various activities which he had planned for himself during his 24 hour ride (medical observations, writing, and typing) and spent most of his time listening to the radio and napping. In a recently completed investigation, conducted by Chambers and Ross, a subject was exposed for 4 hours to 2 G in the centrifuge. This subject was required to perform a complex two-channel running matching memory task every 10 minutes. Data from this preliminary study indicated that the subject was able to maintain maximum performance throughout the four-hour period. However, it took great effort on the part of the subject during the last portion to continue to perform to criterion.

At AMAL, the Mercury astronauts and other volunteer subjects have been exposed to as much as 8 hours' confinement in the Human Centrifuge, under conditions in which various acceleration stresses were imposed. In these studies, the astronauts were strapped in their contour couches, confined within their pressure suits, placed within the gondola of the centrifuge, and presented with realistic preflight tasks, monitoring requirements, and communications. After one to two hours prelaunch wait, they went through accelerations expected on the Atlas rocket, and spent approximately 4½ hours in simulated orbit. This was followed by re-entry accelerations and egress. In some of these studies, the launch and re-entry acceleration profiles were simulated successively within a single all day session. Whereas extensive personality, biochemical, performance, and physiological tests have been conducted, the results have not shown any significant long-term personality or emotional effects. In most instances, it was not possible to make quantitative measures of personality, emotional behavior, or motivation immediately before, during, or after these centrifuge exposures, because of the extensive number of other engineering and physiological tests which were required.

Pilots and astronauts, however, have frequently reported that variables other than the acceleration itself were more stressing. Pressure points, muscle cramps and pains due to the pilot's restraint system, uncomfortable temperature, failure of the urinary bag, or discomfort due to the biomedical sensors or special flight gear, or long-term delay in planned testing due to equipment malfunction, have created extremely aggravating and sometimes emotionally disturbing conditions. All available data seem to indicate that nearly all of the emotional, personality, and motivational aspects are susceptible to training and experience. It appears that the experienced subject can overcome any psychological problems which he may encounter before, during, or following high-G acceleration exposures.

VII. Space Flight Simulation

A. DYNAMIC FLIGHT SIMULATION USING THE AVIATION MEDICAL ACCELERATION LABORATORY CENTRIFUGE

Many of the physiological, psychomotor, cognitive, and emotional problems expected to be encountered in aerospace flight are studied by means of simulation techniques. By using centrifuge rocket tracks, and other acceleration devices, it is possible to produce the acceleration condition of real flight. The human centrifuge at the AMAL is one device used for research and training in these types of simulations. On this device, the effects of a large number of acceleration profiles have been studied on the ability of human subjects to perform perceptual and motor tasks. Most of these studied have been concerned with skill performance within three general types of proposed space vehicle configurations, as illustrated in Figure 24. At the bottom left of the figure is shown a high drag, variable lift winged vehicle (Type I). During re-entry in this vehicle, the pilot performs while sitting in a normal flying position and receives acceleration forces which are primarily head-to-foot with respect to his body ($+G_z$). At the top of the figure is shown the high drag capsule (Type II), in which the pilot performs while sitting facing backwards with respect to his velocity, and in which he received acceleration forces which are primarily chest-to-back ($+G_x$). To the right is shown a sketch of a glide capsule (Type III) in which the pilot performs while facing forward in his vehicle, and in which he receives G forces which

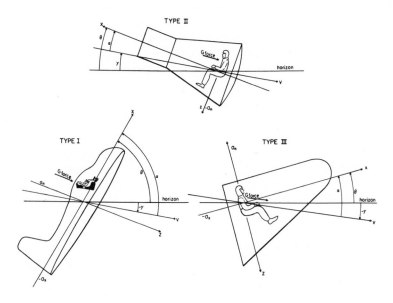

Figure 24. Three basic types of proposed space vehicles whose acceleration profiles have been extensively studied and simulated on the AMAL human centrifuge. (Official photograph U.S. Navy.)

are resultants of back-to-chest $(-G_x)$, and head-to-foot components $(+G_z)$. During re-entry, the pilot in the high-drag, variable lift winged vehicle is pressed down into his seat; the pilot in the high-drag capsule is pressed against the back of his seat; and in the glide vehicle, the pilot is pressed against his shoulder straps. Simulations in the first vehicle type have gone to as high as $+10 \ G_z$; simulations in the second vehicle have gone as high as $+21 \ G_x$; and simulations in the third vehicle have gone as high as a resultant G of 14.

The subject in the gondola of the centrifuge is conceived as having essentially these forces acting upon him during various phases of his simulation. Within the gondola of the centrifuge is an instrument panel and an associated pilot control system. A continuous real-time solution to any particular flight problem is generated by the computer. The subject manipulates his controls in response to display information on the panel programmed by the computer. His control responses result in changes in electrical signals which are transmitted to the analog computor system containing aerodynamic equations and motion constants. The output signals which represent vehicle accelerations are converted by a coordinate conversion system into appropriate centrifuge control signals for the arm and gimbal motions. The outputs of the conversion system control the centrifuge such that the accelerations to which the pilot is exposed at any given moment are appropriate for the immediately preceding control manipulations which the pilot performed. Simultaneously, pilot performance and vehicle recordings made on paper charts, tape, movies, and closed circuit television assist in the study of the subject's behavior. The centrifuge is capable of attaining 40 G in seven seconds, and its two-gimbal system at the end of the 50-foot arm presents a wide variety of acceleration patterns to which the subject may expose himself. To date human performance studies have been conducted on vehicle simulations of the X-15 Research Aircraft, the Mercury Capsule, the Dyna-Soar, the Apollo, a number of proposed space vehicles, and several airplanes. A typical centrifuge simulation problem is illustrated in Figure 25.

By presenting a variety of piloting tasks to test pilots under conditions of various simulated vehicle and flight conditions, it has been possible to study the piloting skills of human subjects under a wide distribution

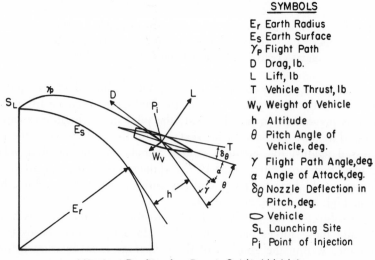

Mission Profile for Boost-Orbital Vehicle

Figure 25. A typical centrifuge simulation problem. The dynamics of a proposed boost-orbital vehicle were programmed by an analog computer to the pilot's display panel, controller, and driving mechanism of the centrifuge. The pilot's task was to "fly" the vehicle from launch to insertion into orbit, using the flight quantities provided and undergoing the acceleration stresses associated with the various phases of the flight.

(Official photograph U.S. Navy.)

of acceleration profiles. Examples are as follows: maintain a constant angle of attack; maintain a constant rate of descent; perform certain step changes in angle of attack at certain times; change the rate of descent from its initial value to some prescribed value and hold it; allow G to build up but not to exceed a certain value and hold it; allow G to build up but not to exceed a certain value and hold it there as long as possible; level off at a certain G value; control angular motions only; damp out oscillations; fire retro-rockets; re-enter as fast as you can; attain re-entry attitude; attain orbital attitude; recover from spin; track while performing flight coordination maneuvers; and perform complete launch, orbit, and re-entry mission, using manual side-arm controller and certain instruments on the display panel.

Closed-loop centrifuge simulations of each of the three types of vehicles have been completed in situations which offer a wide variety of piloting problems. The capabilities of the human pilot for performing launches and re-entries when he is given certain flight control quantities, certain types of piloting equipment and control, and restraint equipment have been studied (Clark and Woodling, 1959; Chambers and Doerfel, 1959; Hardy, *et al.*, 1959; Hardy and Clark, 1959). In addition, experiments have been conducted to determine the degree to which the human pilot may perform secondary monitoring, troubleshooting, and communication tasks which were incidental to the primary flight mission. In general, the attempt in these centrifuge simulations has been to determine the performance tolerance limits within the physiological tolerance limits which a human pilot may withstand (Clark and Woodling, 1959; Chambers and Doerfel, 1959; Chambers and Nelson, 1961a). There have been many experiments which have attempted to study the effects of acceleration on perceptual and motor skills using various types of acceleration devices. The scientific literature cantains a number of review articles summarizing these findings (Brown and Lechner, 1956; White, 1958a; Clarke, *et al.*, 1959; Chambers and Eggleston, 1959; Brown, *et al.*, 1961; and Smedal, *et al.*, 1961).

Extensive psychological instrumentation is necessary in order to observe human behavior during these simulations. At the AMAL, a multi-channel recorder and closed-loop television system are available to monitor the performance of the subject within the centrifuge. At a remote location, there is a performance monitoring system which provides in-line data recording and data processing. The responses are processed by a small analog computer system which provides individual means and standard deviations of the subject's performance on several dimensions. Also, associated with the in-line data processing system is a 14-channel magnetic tape recorder for permanent data recording and later data processing, if needed. At an even more remote location, a larger computer system records other performance quantities and their derivatives. Here, these are converted to digital form, taped and eventually reduced to IBM cards for processing by a high-speed digital computer system for statistical analysis.

B. UTILIZATION AND QUANTIFICATION OF ERROR CHARACTERISTICS

When there is insufficient knowledge about the reliability, validity, and sensitivity of response indicants, or when the psychologist or medical monitor is uncertain as to just what aspects of performance should be observed in order to monitor the subject's intellectual functioning, it is useful to obtain a relatively complete and continuous record of the subject's behavior at several levels of response complexity. The performance of several selected task components and their combination may be selected for continuous observation before, during, and after the acceleration stress. The errors listed above may occur simultaneously, independently, or in various combinations.

Thus, in most flight simulation and astronaut training programs, it is necessary to have both provision for monitoring one or more medical quantities, and one or more performance quantities.

When graphical records are obtained, they will include EKG, pulse wave, respiration, blood pressure, transverse acceleration, positive acceleration, tracking efficiency, pitch error, heading error, and control motion in roll, pitch, and yaw recorded simultaneously throughout the period of exposure to the acceleration stress. Certain parameters may deviate considerably from desirable or safe limits. These recordings serve a very useful and somewhat meaningful purpose for monitoring, since they show a descriptive and continuous picture of the subject's functioning. The run may be stopped at any point in the event any of these deflections suggest stress beyond the tolerable limits of the subjects.

Thus, whereas the graphic recordings of spatial-temporal patterns of stimuli and responses are very useful for monitoring the behavioral functioning of a subject during exposure to acceleration stress, and also during early phases of investigation prior to the selection of a final series of performance indicants, the use of a computer and automatic data readout system is required in order to accumulate generalizable and meaningful information concerning performance decrement.

Some of the performance impairment indicants are relatively easy to quantify. For example, Figure 26 shows one method by which absolute errors in performance may be processed. Here, the task to be performed was compensatory tracking in pitch and roll of a target moving in a

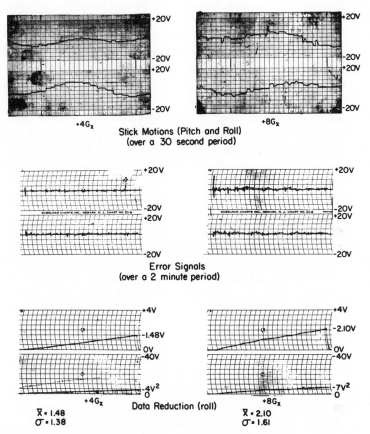

Figure 26. In-line performance recording and data processing during exposure to +4 G_x and +8 G_x. (Official photograph U.S. Navy.)

random pattern on the face of an oscilloscope. The records shown here are from one subject who performed the task for two minutes under both +4 G_x and +8 G_x accelerations.

The uppermost pair of graphs are the control stick motions that were made under these two stress conditions. It is immediately apparent that the subject is doing a better job of tracking under the 4 G condition than under the 8 G condition. This record was used by the medical officer to monitor the subject's physical well-being.

The central portion of Figure 26 shows the first step in processing the information given in the upper records. Here, the stick motions were subtracted from a theoretically perfect performance, and errors of performance were recorded. A comparison of these two records shows that the performance at 8 G was indeed less perfect than the performance at 4 G.

The final step in quantification of these increases in error is shown in the lower two graphs. Only the computations for roll error are shown here, although a similar analysis was conducted for pitch error also. The input error signals were changed to absolute errors and then fed to analog computer integrators for computation of the average error, shown in the uppermost lines of these two graphs. The same signals were also sent to squaring units and then to integrators for computation of a statistic relative to the variability of these errors. Finally, two sets of numbers that represent a quantified estimate of the subject's performance are obtained. As can be seen in this figure, the performance at $+4$ G_x is clearly superior to that at $+8$ G_x with respect to both average error and variability of error.

In some of the other indicants of performance impairment, quantification may be handled by means of advanced statistical techniques. For example, oscillations may be quantified by means of computing spectral density functions and determining the parameters of frequency, period, and delay time. Changes in phasing or timing of the task component might possibly be studied by means of variable time delays and specification of an autocorrelation function.

In general, these error signals may be specified by means of two fundamental distributions, an *amplitude distribution* and a *frequency distribution*. Each of these distributions has statistical indicants or scores of performance which may be interpreted as estimates of one or more parameters of these basic distributions, such as the *mean, average deviation, integrated absolute error, standard deviation, root mean square, and range*. It is also possible to determine the proportion of the distribution lying between any two designated limits, and specify whether the distribution is normal, skewed, leptokurtic, or multimodal. If one wishes, the scores may be converted into scores by using tables of normal probability in order to facilitate comparisons of large numbers of subjects.

The amplitude distribution of tracking error scores, for example, is composed of continuous error signals sampled periodically, so as to yield a series of discrete error magnitudes. The frequency of each amplitude category may be determined, and the data plotted as an error-amplitude distribution. From this distribution, one can derive any of the statistics normally used to describe any population sample.

The frequency distribution is best discussed in terms of the power density spectrum and its transform, the autocorrelation function. A series of error records may have similar amplitude distributions but may differ with respect to the frequency with which the error fluctuates. One may record slow, smooth motions under static conditions, while under acceleration conditions, the recordings of the same person may show quick, corrective motions, characterized by an attempt to merely "stay with the target" as opposed to the smoother relaxed attempts to predict the position of the target. A series of these error records may be analyzed in terms of component frequencies. The resulting power density spectrum shows a plot of the mean squared amplitudes against frequency and is used to specify the time characteristics of a signal that may contain all frequencies within a particular band width.

The frequency characteristics may be expressed also by an autocorrelational function. This autocorrelational function may be used to identify periodicities in a time-varying series. It indicates the correlation of the series with itself at later times. Similarly, the cross correlation function may be used, but in a slightly different way. It is most useful in comparing two sets of values which are derived from different time series. For example, one may determine whether roll and yaw error signals are related to pitch error signals. This is of great value in indicating how fluctuations in one dimension of control are related to fluctuations in other dimensions.

It is in the area of utilization of the quantified scores discussed above, that additional research is needed. If, for example, we have complete error histories on personnel riding the centrifuge, then any cumulative effects of repeated exposures can be recognized. In records of raw or unprocessed data, it would be difficult, if not impossible, to ascertain whether or not any differences exhibited were significant. With suitable quantification and statistical analysis, the significance of small changes in performance would become readily apparent. Such techniques would allow the assessment of the degree to which the independently variable quantities of time at peak G, rate of onset of G, magnitude of peak G and others contribute to impairment.

C. PSYCHOLOGICAL VARIABLES CONCERNING PERFORMANCE IN CENTRIFUGE SIMULATIONS OF SPACE FLIGHT

Below are several psychological factors which influence pilot performance during simulated boost, orbit, and re-entry rocket flight trajectories. These factors are based on observations of 63 men who collectively received over 3300 centrifuge exposures to simulations of several basic types of proposed space vehicle designs on the centrifuge at AMAL (Chambers and Nelson, 1961b).

Factor No. 1. Performance Tolerance Limits. In addition to the *physiological tolerance limits* which define the end points for reliable functioning of any particular physiological system during exposure to acceleration stress, there are also *performance tolerance limits* which define the end points for reliable functioning of any particular performance ability system under these same conditions of acceleration. The physiological and performance tolerances may be functionally related, but need not be the same, since both are dependent upon the criteria which are accepted. It is these performance tolerance limits which have major psychological implications for manned space flight during launch and re-entry.

Factor No. 2. Practice Effects. Major increments in performance proficiency in high G environments occur as a function of practice. Practice results in physiological adaptation and conditioning, as well as learning to make performance compensations for the acceleration disturbances. The pilot improves his performance by: (1) accommodating to the sensations induced by G; (2) learning to resist the effects of G through the use of proper straining and breathing techniques; (3) learning or relearning the task in the context of changed muscular and sensory capacities induced by the acceleration; and (4) learning to execute the physiological and performance aspects of the task simultaneously.

Factor No. 3. Restraint Systems. The type of restraint system which is used for G protection has an important influence on ability to perform within high acceleration fields. As far as the pilot is concerned, high G may become low G if the appropriate restraint system is used.

Factor No. 4. Individual Differences. Individual differences exist among pilots in their ability to perform psychological tasks at high G. These differences are due to variations in piloting techniques, methods of fighting G, and ability to tolerate pain and to accommodate to any particular type of restraint system. Susceptibility to motion sickness, and also interest in the performance task, are additional variables which contribute to the pilot's ability to perform during high G stress.

Factor No. 5. Control Device. In certain types of acceleration environments, the pilot's performance proficiency varies as a function of the characteristics of the control device that the pilot uses in performing his flight task. In attempts to investigate the effects of acceleration forces on the ability of the pilot in high G environments, several different types of side-arm controllers have been used. The pilot must become adapted to the type of control device he is using. A number of controller characteristics have been studied at various centrifuge laboratories, and in various aircraft and spacecraft. All characteristics are important, especially the following: number of axes of motion, location of the axes of motion with respect to the G and to the pilot's hand; stick force gradients along each mode of control; centering characteristics along each mode of control;

dead band zone; breakout force; control friction; dynamic and static balance; damping characteristics; control throw; response time of control; control harmony; cross coupling; amount of kinesthetic feedback; shape and size; dynamic and static balance; and control sensitivity.

Factor No. 6. Display Characteristics. The instrument display characteristics of the piloting task influence performance capabilities during launch and re-entry accelerations. During the occurrence of all types of high acceleration, the human pilot experiences visual disturbances. These disturbances result from shifts in the availability of arterial blood to the retina; mechanical pressure on the eyes, such as "eyeballs in," "eyeballs out," "eyeballs up," and "eyeballs down"; mechanical forces acting on the eye musculature, eyelids and associated structures; distortions of the eye anatomy; and accumulation of tears. Considering these symptoms, it is possible to list a number of important display characteristics: (a) the position of the display instrument with reference to the subject's visual field; (b) the degree of interpretation which is required of the pilot; (c) the accuracy of the instrument itself when exposed to high G; (d) the illumination; (e) the physical form in which the display information is presented; and (f) the amount of instrument scanning that is required at high G.

Factor 7. Control Feedback Sensitivity. Acceleration impairs the ability of the pilot to sense changes in control characteristics which may occur as a function of specific acceleration vectors. There may be direct results of the acceleration forces on the receptors; there may be an effect on the central or autonomic nervous system; or there may be an effect on circulatory and other physiological systems which indirectly affect the ability of the subject to sense changes in his hand or fingers.

Factor 8. Task Difficulty Level. Changes in task characteristics which have little effect upon static performance may seriously impair performance under high G. Aerodynamic stability and damping, frequency, and other vehicle response characteristics may make the performance of the piloting task at high G more or less difficult. If the simulated vehicle is stable, well-damped, and within desirable frequency ranges, the pilot may be able to perform very well at high G. However, if the task is made more difficult, his piloting efficiency may drop severely due to the same acceleration level.

Factor 9. Higher Mental Processes. Intellectual skills, decision making, judgment, prediction, memory and related cognitive processes may be modified under acceleration and these changes obviously affect perceptual and motor skill performance.

Factor 10. Emotional Processes, Fear, and Anxiety. Anticipation of the effects of acceleration may produce emotional reactions, fear, and anxiety which are greater in terms of physiological response than the direct effects of acceleration themselves.

VIII. Acceleration Training

As high performance aircraft and manned space systems become more complex, acceleration training procedures also become more complex. In anticipating some of these problems, it has been pointed out that there are many areas in training itself which require very close attention. Some of these are: (1) improved techniques for developing and maintaining highly reliable human performance in complex systems; (2) improved techniques for fostering long-term retention of knowledge and skills; (3) improved techniques for developing skills under completely simulated conditions; (4) techniques for providing automatic adaptive training within space-craft while in long-term flight; (5) improved techniques for indoctrination and orientation types of training; and (6) techniques for accommodation to interactions between physiologically stressful environments and psychologically stressful tasks.

In the case of acceleration training and physiological conditioning for space flight, Chambers (1959b) has further emphasized the lack of a criterion around which to build and evaluate simulators and training programs. There is a severe need for (1) more devices and techniques for simulating space flight conditions; (2) basic research on the effects of G on control-display relationships and the human transfer function; and (3) basic research on the psychological capabilities of man in space. Fleishman (1959) has emphasized the need for *ability definitions* and an adequate *taxonomy* with which tasks and human abilities required to perform them in some environments may be studied. The problem of breaking away from traditional ways of thinking in the planning and development of training programs for unusual environments poses a problem. Standard, time-tested methods of training may not be appropriate for some of the new problems to be encountered by the astronaut in his hostile environments, such as the unpredictable conditions which may occur during emergency, abort, or escape. In a recent review of the problems and approaches to be recommended in the training of astronauts (see Publication No. 873, AF-NRC Committee on Bioastronautics, 1961). The importance of acceleration training was emphasized not only in the preparation of pilots who have flown X-15 and Mercury missions, but also for pilots who may be expected to fly the Dyna-Soar, Gemini, Apollo, and other aerospace vehicles of the future. Some of the evaluations of various acceleration training programs and space flight simulation procedures have been reported by astronauts and scientists concerned with training effectiveness (Shepard, 1961; Grissom, 1961; Slayton, 1961; Voas, 1961; and Chambers, 1962b).

A. EFFECTS OF PRACTICE

Practice results in physiological adaptation and conditioning, as well as aiding the pilot in learning to make performance compensations for acceleration disturbances. The pilot improves his performance by: (1) accommodating to the sensations induced by G; (2) learning to resist the effects of G through the use of the proper straining and breathing techniques; (3) learning or relearning the task in the context of changed muscular and sensory capacities induced by the acceleration; and (4) learning to execute the physiological and performance aspects of the task simultaneously. As an example of such learning see Figure 27. Group I had no prior centrifuge experience on the Johnsville centrifuge; Group II had prior centrifuge experience on other programs. Successive pairs indicate the first through eighth static-dynamic pair of runs which each pilot experienced. Each point is the mean difference between static and dynamic runs. Positive scores indicate that the pilot made more errors on the static runs; negative scores indicate that the pilot made more errors on the dynamic runs. The figure shows that it required several trials for Group I to do as well on its dynamic runs as on its static runs, while Group II performance shows no systematic change with practice. In higher G environments much greater increments in performance proficiency occur as a function of practice. The increment in proficiency is very rapid for subjects who have not had prior acceleration experience. However, even in the most experienced subjects, increments in performance proficiency may be expected in situations in which the task itself is difficult.

Improvement as a function of practice has been demonstrated in a number of experiments, the most notable of which are those by Fletcher, Collins, and Brown (1958), and Brown (1960). These subjects, however, all performed under conditions of relative low G stress. A remarkable performance record on a compensatory pursuit tracking task was shown by three of the Mercury astronauts recently at the AMAL (see Figure 28). The mean error performance for these astronauts is plotted as a function of integrated error during successive minutes throughout launch and re-entry, part of which took the astronauts through a $11.4G_x$.

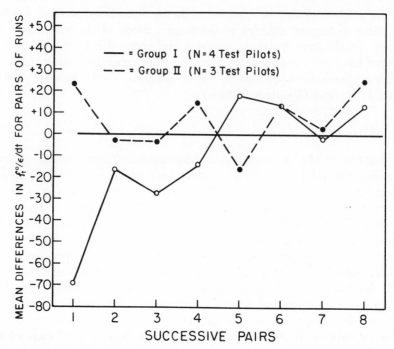

Figure 27. Comparison of performance curves for two groups of pilots who differed in terms of prior centrifuge experience. The scores are based on pairs of static and dynamic runs for each pilot tested under identical conditions, except for the presence or absence of acceleration stress. (Official photograph U.S. Navy.)

No significant effects on their performance were found at the times these records were taken. The performance shown here had been preceded by extensive practice.

It is interesting to note, however, that as far back as 1942, it was reported that repeated daily runs did increase a person's tolerance to positive acceleration (Rose, 1942). In fact, as later studies have shown, repeated exposure of human subjects to acceleration frequently results in a lowering of acceleration tolerance. However, this is not always the case, since several studies have suggested many subjectively beneficial effects resulting from transverse acceleration practice. It seems impossible to reach any definite conclusion on this point, due to the absence of control groups in most of the studies reported to date. However, Frazer and Reeves (1958) report that over a period of 6 weeks rats were preconditioned by exposure to $+2\ G_z$, and $+12\ G_z$. Then all rats, including control rats, were exposed to $+20\ G_z$. Mean survival times

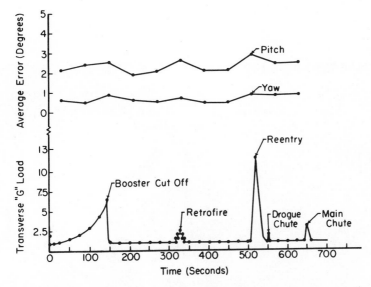

Figure 28. Mean performance scores for three astronauts who performed a tracking task before, during, and after a centrifuge simulated Redstone sub-orbital flight. (Official photograph U.S. Navy.)

for the controls was 1281 seconds whereas mean survival time for the $+2\ G_z$ conditioned group was 969 seconds, and the mean survival time for the $+12\ G_z$ preconditioned group was 2011 seconds.

B. ACCELERATION TRAINING FOR PILOTS AND ASTRONAUTS

One of the most valuable acceleration training devices for the Mercury suborbital and orbital flights is the AMAL Human Centrifuge (Slayton, 1961; Grissom, 1961; Voas, 1961). The two-gimbal gondola mounted at the end of the centrifuge arm contained an instrument panel and active flight instruments, a piloting flight control device, and a complete environmental control system similar to the Mercury spacecraft. A large analog computer associated with the panel, controller, and driving mechanism of the centrifuge permitted extensive training on a wide variety of piloting tasks and emergency conditions during exposure to the various acceleration profiles of the Redstone and the Atlas rockets. A complete environmental control system, pressure-suit, contour couch restraint system, 100 per cent oxygen system, and biosensors were provided, and when the gondola was sealed and depressurized to 5 pounds per square inch, the interactions of many different space-flight variables

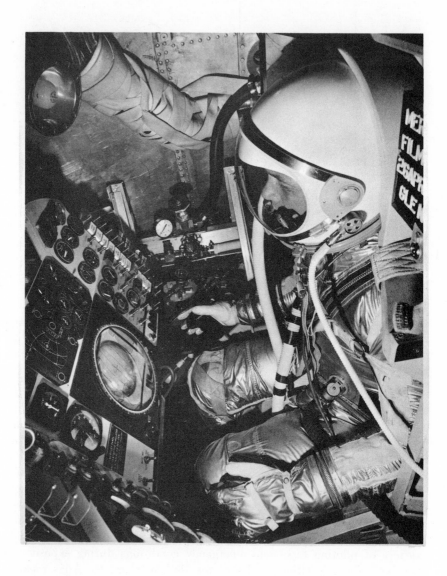

Figure 29. Mercury Astronaut in AMAL human centrifuge during training and simulation in preparation for Mercury Redstone and Mercury Atlas space flights. (Official photograph U.S. Navy.)

could be produced as in actual flight (Figure 29). During a course of 5 training programs on this facility, the astronauts received practice in straining in order to maintain good vision and physiological functioning under high G loads, and in developing breathing and speaking techniques during high G launch, re-entry, and abort stress. Experience in tumbling and oscillating during relatively high G exposures was also provided. The astronauts were given extensive practice in controlling their simulated vehicle during re-entry and during other phases of their simulated flights. They also became skilled in the operation of their environmental control systems and capsule communication procedures during acceleration exposure. Simultaneously, extensive physiological monitoring and performance measurement provided continuous information on astronaut endurance and piloting skill. Also, "complete mission simulations" were also presented, during which early morning suiting, testing, waiting in the gondola, launch, orbit, re-entry, recovery, escape, post-flight testing, and debriefing were provided on a real-time basis. This type of simulation presented physiological and psychological conditioning, testing, and evaluation along real-time scale profiles. An additional advantage of this type of training was that astronauts were able to experience the many subtle and elusive interactions which occur between the interactions of physiological, psychological, and engineering stress variables.

An acceleration training program is complex. In addition to the initial familiarization with the sensations, perceptions, and pain associated with various types of acceleration profiles, the astronaut must be thoroughly trained in appropriate physiological reaction to severe stresses. During early stages of training, these consist largely of learning how to strain, breathe, talk, and see while under G. Later, these become somewhat automatic, and the astronaut can concentrate on the performance tasks and acclimate himself to the environmental stress. The astronaut is strapped in a restraint system and confined within a pressure suit, and must remain immobile for long periods of time. For this reason, psychological aggravation and frustration are customarily associated with acceleration training. Also, there is considerable hazard during acceleration training programs, since the possibility always exists for harmful effects of the acceleration on the human body. Extensive physiological and medical monitoring is provided. To date, there has been extensive research on the effects of positive acceleration. However, there is still much research needed on transverse acceleration, lateral acceleration, tumbles, and impact accelerations. Much of the results of these studies are to be found in Brown and Lechner (1955); Brown (1961); and Chambers and Nelson (1961a, b).

An extensive amount of training is required for accomplishing high proficiency levels in performing complex tasks during exposure to acceleration stress. The success of any astronaut training program can be evaluated only in terms of actual space flight. The validity of the devices and procedures used for training will remain unknown until more space flights are accomplished. Ideally, the training should provide the astronaut with complete knowledge, skill, and confidence in all aspects of the space flight, prior to his attempting the flight. Mercury astronaut Alan B. Shepard, in reviewing the results of his suborbital flight in the Freedom VIII capsule, wrote:

"The re-entry and its attendant acceleration pulse of 11 G was not unduly difficult. The functions of observation, motion, and reporting were maintained, and no respiration difficulties were encountered. Here again, the centrifuge training had provided good reference. I noticed no loss of peripheral vision, which is the first indication of 'gray-out' " (Shepard, 1961, page 73).

Mercury astronaut Donald K. Slayton (1961) has emphasized the basic philosophy that every training device or method which has even remote possibilities of being of value should be utilized. In informal interviews and debriefings, the seven Mercury astronauts have emphasized the importance of experiencing all of the environments expected to be encountered in space, and in "building confidence." This confidence appears to be a kind of psychological conditioning which results from the astronaut's repeated success in enduring and performing selected aspects of simulated space flight stresses. To date, the seven Mercury astronauts have received familiarization and training on at least 20 different training devices (Slayton, 1961; Voas, 1961; Voas, *et al.*, 1961; Grissom, 1961). These are listed below under the categories (a) Static Training Devices; (b) Dynamic Training Devices; and (c) Airplanes. The list does not include all devices, since new devices are being continuously developed and tested as astronaut training proceeds.

Devices Used in Mercury Astronaut Training for Space Flight

A. Static Training Devices—Fixed Base Trainers
    Analog Flight Simulator No. 1 (LEAC Simulator)
    Analog Flight Simulator No. 2 (MB-3 Simulator)
    Flight Instrumentation Display Mock-Up
    Mercury McDonnell Procedures Trainer
    Ground Recognition Trainer
    Link Trainer in Planetarium
    Environmental Control System Simulator
    High Temperature Chamber
    Carbon Dioxide Chamber
    Low Pressure Chamber

B. Dynamic Training Devices–Moving Base Trainers
  AMAL Human Centrifuge (Johnsville AMAL Centrifuge)
  Air-lubricated Free Attitude Simulator (ALFA)
  Multi-axis Spin Test Inertial Facility (MASTIF)
  Equilibrium Chair
  Revolving Room
  SCUBA Training Equipment
  Mercury Egress Trainer in Hydrodynamic Tank
  Mercury Egress Trainer in Ocean

C. Aircraft
  C-131 Airplane
  KC-135 Airplane
  F-100 Jet Airplane
  F-102 Jet Airplane
  F-106 Jet Airplane

Whereas some manned space systems may provide automatic control of vehicle attitude and flight path, the astronaut must be provided with adequate training in manual control in the event manual back-up is required during re-entry deceleration. The current Mercury capsule, for example, provides several alternatives for attitude control (Voas, 1960, 1961; Voas, *et al.*, 1961). Space craft of the future will require the astronaut to maneuver the vehicle. In these crafts, thorough training in control of vehicle attitude and flight path will be necessary for launch, insertion into orbit, interplanetary travel, control of attitude during retro-fire, rate damping during re-entry, and landing. It may be anticipated that a typical flight mission may involve automatic control of attitude control meneuvers during some portions of the flight, and manual control during other portions.

For the seven Mercury Astronauts, several fixed base and moving base simulators have been the primary devices used for attitude control training (Voas, 1960, 1961; Voas, *et al.*, 1961; Senders, 1960; and Rubacky, 1961). The fixed base trainers provided for a cockpit, flight instruments, side-arm controller, and miscellaneous equipment, associated with an electronic computer system. The moving base simulators were similar to these, except that the astronaut and all of his attitude flight control equipment were placed on devices which provided motion sensations to the astronaut. These were the centrifuge, the Air-Lubricated Free Attitude Trainer, or the three-gimballed tumbling simulator, "MASTIF" (Voas, 1960; 1961; Voas, *et al.*, 1961). Pitch, roll, yaw, or rotation motion cues, tumbling, and acceleration were associated with the astronaut's performance on the attitude control tasks.

In training the Mercury Astronauts, the C-131 and KC-135 and F-100 aircraft provided training and orientation during weightlessness. The centrifuge provided training in orientation with respect to shifts of primary G vectors and associated instrument indications. The multiaxis spin test inertial facility (MASTIF) provided practice and familiarization in rotation in three axes simultaneously; the Rotation Room provided familiarization with coriolis effects; and the Air Lubricated Free Attitude Trainer provided practice in maintaining stability and controlling about all three axes on an essentially frictionless platform when various visual cues were prenoted. There are, however, many other possible devices which may be of use for this type of training, and these have been excellently summarized by Guedry and Graybiel (1961).

Experience has emphasized the importance of routine procedures training accompanied by trouble-shooting, and emergency training. For the most part, this must be accompanied by a thorough series of practice tests simulating all of the possible situations. The astronaut must learn to cope with every possible emergency that may occur, and develop skills in trouble-shooting as well as in making appropriate decisions and taking appropriate actions.

Navigation and orientation training during exposure to acceleration is important. Motion cues and small angular accelerations and their associated illusions are some of the environmental factors which make training in orientation and in navigation essential. Misleading perception of the duration, direction, and plane of whole-body movements may likely provide severe problems in orientation and navigation. Consequently, much training must be provided, especially as space stations and extended space flight missions become a reality.

The astronaut's world will be a three dimensional world rather than the two-dimensional world to which he has been accustomed. Previously, it was structured with respect to a vertical direction; now he will be free to move up and down as readily as he moves parallel or sideward with respect to the earth's surface. He will be weightless and somewhat spatially disoriented. Training programs will be necessary to thoroughly acclimate the subject to these conditions, in order that he may truly achieve a genuine three-dimensional space locomotion and may perform his tasks reliably.

The psychological aspects of survival training are of major importance, since following abort or mission completion, survival may depend largely upon the ability of the astronaut to remain emotionally calm and self-controlled. It is likely that the requirements for training programs designed to build confidence will increase as man requires prolonged exposure to linear and angular accelerations which may be involved in space platforms and in interplanetary travel.

The Mercury astronauts have emphasized that building confidence is a very essential part of their training. Confidence in their ability to sustain high or prolonged G, heat, or other stress, has been found to be an essential training factor. A major psychological aspect of all training programs during the next few years may well be that of building up the astronaut's confidence regarding his ability to perform the space flight mission successfully.

There is an obvious need for much research on the problems of learning and conditioning during acceleration stress. The Working Group on Training of Astronauts (Report No. 873, 1961) has explored many of these problems. Training and training equipment should be emphasized early in the development of any satisfactory space-crew training program. Also, there should be feedback from current space-flight programs to the training programs of future space systems. Similarly, research should be undertaken to determine the extent to which training in unusual environmental conditions such as vibration and acceleration should be incorporated into training equipment so as to maximize transfer of training. Also, the committee recommends experiments to identify the conditions which evoke emotional responses, and to determine techniques for habituating or reducing anxiety-provoking situations. Finally, the committee emphasizes the need for additional acceleration training facilities, and the development of new measures of human performance which may be used to evaluate the more subtle aspects of human behavior during acceleration training.

C. BASIC TYPES OF PERFORMANCE ERRORS

A review of the technical literature on perceptual, motor, and cognitive performance indicates that there are several characteristic degradations which may occur for any given skill during acceleration stress. These may be regarded as psychological mechanisms of degradation of performance, or they may be merely descriptive of the types of errors which reflect the effects of the acceleration. They describe a series of potential degradations which may occur to skill proficiency, and are summarized below.

a. Increases in error amplitude.

b. Lapses. The psychomotor response appears to phase on and off target, showing a very irregular rate of response. A marked variability in performance is shown.

c. Performance oscillations.

d. Falling off in proficiency on some parts of a task while maintaining proficiency on other parts. Reduction or cessation in performance output of some task components.

e. Changes in phasing and/or timing task components.

f. Inadvertent control inputs.

g. Failure to detect and respond to changes in the stimulus field.

h. Errors in returning, integrating, steering, and processing information.

i. Sudden changes in rate or frequency of performance, such as sudden initiation of performance nonessential to the task.

j. Response lags. Increases in latency of response to discrimination stimuli. Also, there may be large changes in timing of component response sequences, or gross misjudgments on the passage of time.

k. Overcontrolling or undercontrolling, as during a transition phase.

l. Perceived disintegration of the perceptual field or display.

m. Disassociation of corrective response from appropriate control unit.

n. Loss of proficiency due to fixation-block-confusion; narrowed attention associated with the excessive concentration on one portion of the task to the extent that the pilot fails to respond to clearly defined stimuli regarding the situation as a whole.

o. Omission of portions of simple tasks, or of parts of complex perceptual-motor tasks. These occur especially during overload when the subject may not process all of the stimulus information, such as the inputs necessary to perform the secondary parts of the task at the originally achieved level of proficiency.

p. Approximations. The subject's behavior becomes less accurate, although the task does not increase in difficulty level. His responses become less precise, but minimally adequate to meet the required criterion of proficiency.

q. Queuing. A kind of delaying of the response during peak loads, and then catching up on the skill during lulls.

r. Error and/or escape from the performance task. The subject's error amplitude and error frequency distributions increase rapidly, and, in some situations, the subject may stop responding altogether, as through drowsiness or refusal to continue performing the task.

s. Stereotyping of responses and movements, regardless of the stimulus situation. All of the stimuli appear to have an apparent equivalence to the subject during prolonged confinement, if there is excessive redundancy. There is a loss of flexibility of set, and a dysjunction of discrimination and response.

t. Filtering. A systematic filtering or omission of certain categories of stimulation and responding, according to some subjective priority scheme. Frequently, this appears to occur when there is a marked increase in stresses which are incidental to the primary purpose of the confinement.

All of the above error performances are highly variable, very difficult to measure, and extremely sensitive to subtle changes in the environment. If recorded during repeated trials, they are useful in evaluating the effectiveness of acceleration training procedures.

IX. Summary

This chapter has reviewed research findings on the effects of acceleration stress on human performance. Research findings are summarized on the effects of G on vestibular, kinesthetic, proprioceptive vision, hearing, and orientation senses. Then research on the ability of human subjects and pilots to perform simple and complex psychomotor tasks while immersed in various acceleration environments is reviewed, and the problems of measuring interactions between acceleration environments and human behavior are evaluated. Some of the major problems in measuring higher mental functioning during exposure to acceleration stress are reviewed, as are the results of preliminary experiments in this area. Attempts to measure the effects of acceleration stress on personality, emotional behavior, and motivation are summarized. Error characteristics of performance impairment, and the utilization and quantification of these error characteristics are reported. Recent work using various acceleration facilities to simulate space flight conditions are reviewed, and an attempt is made to formulate some general psychological principles concerning man's performance in acceleration environments during interactions with displays, control, and restraints. Finally, some of the applications of the results of acceleration research to training and conditioning of human subjects, and to design equipment for use within these environments, is reviewed. The conclusion is reached that much more data are needed concerning the accelerations which the human pilot may endure physiologically and still perform various control functions. A series of performance tolerance maps along various dimensions of human ability would be invaluable in the design of space vehicles and the allocation of manned machine functions for proposed space vehicles. A series of performance tolerance maps would also greatly aid in the development of a theory concerning the effects of the many variables which interact with acceleration to produce changes in the ability of the pilot to perform certain control functions.

References

Armstrong, H. G. "Neuropsychic Examination," in H. G. Armstrong (ed.), *Aerospace Medicine*, Baltimore: Williams and Wilkins, 1961, pp. 66–73.

Ashe, W. F. *Physiological and Pathological Effects of Mechanical Vibration on Animals and Man*, Progress Report No. 3, NIH RF Project 862, Bethesda, Md., September, 1960.

Augerson, W. S., and Laughlin, C. P: "Physiological Responses of the Astronaut in the MR-3 Flight," in *Proceedings of a Conference on Results of the First U.S. Manned Suborbital Space Flight*, Washington, D.C.: U.S. Government Printing Office, June 6, 1961, pp. 45–51.

Bairstow, L. *Applied Aerodynamics*, London: Longmans, Green, 1920.

Ballinger, E. R. "Human Experiments in Subgravity and Prolonged Acceleration," *J. Aviation Med.*, 23:319, 1952.

Bates, G. "A Bibliographic Index for Cataloging the Acceleration Literature," in *Human Acceleration Studies*, Publication No. 913, by Panel on Acceleration Stress for the Armed Forces–NRC Committee on Bio-Astronautics, Washington, D.C.: National Academy of Sciences–NRC, 1961, pp. 1–6.

Beckman, E. L., Coburn, K. R., Chambers, R. M., DeForest, R. E., Augerson, W. S., and Benson, V. G. "Physiologic Changes Observed in Human Subjects during Zero G Simulation by Immersion in Water up to Neck Level," *Aerospace Med.*, 32:1031–1041, 1961.

————, Duane, T. D., and Coburn, K. R. *Limitation of Ocular Motility and Pupillary Dilation in Humans Due to Positive Acceleration*, U.S. Naval Air Development Center, AMAL, Report No. NADC-MA-6140, Johnsville, Pa., December 12, 1961.

————, ————, Ziegler, J. E., and Hunter, H. N. "Some Obervations on Human Tolerance to Accelerative Stress. IV. Human Tolerance to High Positive G Applied at a Rate of 5 to 10 G per Second," *J. Aviation Med.*, 25:50–66, 1954.

Beeding, E. L., and Hessberg, R. R. *Daisy Track Tests, 4 Feb.–19 May, 1958*, Runs No. 271-337, Test Rep. No. 8, AFMDC, Holloman AFB, N.M., November, 1958.

————, ————. *Daisy Track Tests, 22 May 58–9 July, 1959*, Test Rep. No. 59-14, Test Nos. 338-519, AFMDC, Holloman AFB, N.M., December, 1959.

————, and Mosley, J. D. *Human Deceleration Tests*, AFMDC, TN, 60-2, January, 1960.

Benson, V. G., Beckman, E. L., Coburn, K. R., and Chambers, R. M. *Effects of Weightlessness as Simulated by Total Body Immersion upon Human Response to Positive Acceleration*, U.S. Naval Air Development Center, AMAL, Report No. NADC-MA-6132, Johnsville, Pa., June 26, 1961.

Bondurant, S. "Transverse G. Prolonged Forward, Backward, and Lateral Accelleration," in O. H. Gauer, and G. D. Zuidema (eds.), *Gravitational Stress in Aerospace Medicine*, Boston: Little, Brown, 1961, pp. 150–159.

————, Blanchard, W. G., Clarke, N. P., and Moore, F. "Effect of Water Immersion on Human Tolerance to Forward and Backward Acceleration," *J. Aviation Med., 29* (12) : 872–878, 1958.

————, Clarke, N. P., Blanchard, W. G., Miller, H., Hessberg, R. R., and Hiatt, E. P. *Human Tolerance to Some Accelerations Anticipated in Space Flight*, WADC Tech. Rep. 58-156, Wright Air Dev. Center, USAF, April, 1958.

Brown, B. P., Johnson, H. I., and Mungall, R. G. *Simulator Motion Effects on a Pilot's Ability to Perform a Precise Longitudinal Flying Task*, NASA TN D-367, Washington, D.C.: NASA, 1960.

Brown, C. W. *Speed and Accuracy of Reaching for Controls in Different Areas from the Prone Position*, USAF, Wright-Patterson AFB, Dayton, Ohio, Report No. MCREXD-674-4H, January, 1948, 34 pp.

Brown, J. L. *Human Performance Limitations in Aircraft Catapulting and Arresting* (letter report concerning), TED ADC AE-1407 (NM 1102 12.2), September 26, 1957a.

————. *Subjective Preference among Different Modes of Closed-Loop Operation of the Centrifuge for Flight Simulation*, Report No. LR-35 U.S. Naval Air Development Center, Johnsville, Pa., December, 1957b.

————. *The Study of Human Performance Limitations in Aircraft Catapulting with a Linear Track* (letter report on proposed experimental program), AMAL, Naval Air Development Center, Johnsville, Pa., TED ADC AE-1407 (NM 02 12.2) August 13, 1958a.

————. *Tracking Performance during Simulated Exit and Re-entry Flights of the X-15 Research Aircraft*, NADC-MA-5801, AMAL, Naval Air Development Center, Johnsville, Pa., January 15, 1958b.

————. *Chance Vought Project for the Study of Pilot Performance during Centrifuge Simulation of the Boost Accelerations of the Dyna-Soar Orbital Vehicle Exit Flight*, Letter Report TED ADC RS-7019, AMAL, U.S. Naval Air Development Center, Johnsville, Pa., April 22, 1959.

————. "Acceleration and Motor Performance," *Human Factors, 2*(4) :175–185, 1960.

————. "The physiology of Acceleration Performance," in O. H. Gauer and G. D. Zuidema (eds.), *Gravitational Stress in Aerospace Medicine*, Boston: Little, Brown, 1961, pp. 90–114.

————, Bevan, W., Senders, J., and Trumbull, R. *Report of the Working Group on Sensory and Perceptual Problems Related to Space Flight*, Publication No. 872, Nat. Acad. Sci.–Nat. Res. Coun., Washington, D.C., 1961, 51 pp.

————, and Burke, R. E. *The Effect of Positive Acceleration on Visual Reaction*

Time, NADC-MA-5712, U.S. Naval Air Development Center, Johnsville, Pa., August 12, 1957.

—— and ——. "The Effect of Positive Acceleration on Visual Reaction Time," *J. Aviation Med., 29*:48–59, 1958.

—— and Collins, C. C. "Air to Air Tracking during Closed Loop Centrifuge Operation," *J. Aviation Med., 29* (11) :794–804, 1958.

——, Ellis, W. H. B., Webb, M. G., and Gray, R. F. *The Effect of Simulated Catapult Launching on Pilot Performance,* Report No. NADC-MA-5719, AMAL, U.S. Naval Air Development Center, Johnsville, Pa., December 31, 1957.

—— and Lechner, M. *Acceleration and Human Performance: A Survey of Research,* Report No. NADC-MA-5503, AMAL, U.S. Naval Air Development Center, Johnsville, Pa., March 22, 1955.

Brown, J. L., Woodward, L. K., and Pidcock, G. B. *Optical Sighting: The Effect of Positive Acceleration on Pilot's Head Position,* Report No. NADC-MA-5509, AMAL, U.S. Naval Air Development Center, Johnsville, Pa., August 30, 1955.

Bryan, G. L., Wilson, R. C., Willmorth, N. E., Svenson, D. W., Green, G. A., and Warren, N. D. *The Effects of Increased Positive Radial Acceleration on Reaching and Manipulating Toggle Switches,* Contract N6-ori-77, Task Order 3, Dept. of Psychology, University of Southern California, Los Angeles, June, 1951, 20 pp.

Buhrlen, L. "Versuche über die Bedeutung der Richtug beim Einiwirken von fliehraften auf den menschlichen Körper," *Luftfahrtmedizin, 1*:307–325, 1937.

Burmeister, H. "Measurement of Optical Reaction Time in Both Positive and Transverse G," *Luftfahrtmedizin, 3*:277–284, 1939.

Burns, N. M., and Gifford, E. C. *Human Engineering Investigations of Aircraft Cockpit Visual Displays. Part 1: Time Estimation and Anxiety,* Report No. TED NM AV-43001, U.S. Naval Air Material Center, Philadelphia, January 29, 1960.

Canfield, A. A. "The Influence of Positive G on Reaction Time," *Amer. Psychol., 5*:362, 1950a.

——. "The Effect of Positive G on the Speed and Accuracy of Reaching Movements," *Amer. Psychol., 5*:482, 1950b.

——, Comrey, A. L., and Wilson, R. C. *An Investigation of the Maximum Forces Which Can Be Exerted on Aircraft Elevator and Aileron Controls, USN,* Psychology Dept., University of Southern Calif., Los Angeles, Report to ONR, Contract N6ori77, September, 1948a.

——, ——, and ——. *The Effect of Increased Positive Radial Acceleration upon Human Abilities (Part II: Perceptual Speed Ability).* Psychology Department, University of Southern California, Los Angeles, Report No. R. R. 4, September, 1948b.

——, ——, and ——. "Study of Reaction Time to Light and Sound as Related to Increased Positive Radial Acceleration," *J. Aviation Med., 20*:350–355, 1949.

————, ————, and ————. "The Influence of Increased Positive G on Reaching Movements," *J. Appl. Psychol.*, 37:230–235, 1953.

————, ————, ————, and Zimmerman, W. S. "The effects of Increased Positive Radial Acceleration upon Discrimination Reaction Time," *J. Exp. Psychol.*, 40:733–737, 1950.

Chaffee, J. W. *The Effect of Acceleration on Human Centers of Gravity*, General Dynamics, Report FZY-013, Fort Worth, Texas, December 26, 1961, 96 pp.

Chambers, R. M. "Changes in Time Perception Following Stimulus and Response Variations," *Amer. Psychol.*, 13:395, 1958a.

————. "Task-Component Training Principles for Modifying Component and Total Task Criterion Performance," in G. Finch and F. Cameron (eds.), *Air Force Human Engineering, Personnel and Training Research*, Washington, D.C.: Publication No. 516, Nat. Acad. Sci.–Res. Coun., 1958b.

————. *Transfer of Training among Components within a Complex Psychomotor Task*, Report No. NADC-MA-5920, AMAL, U.S. Naval Air Development Center, Johnsville, Pa., December 28, 1959a.

————. "Dynamic Simulation for Space Flight," in R. M. Chambers, and B. J. Smith, *What Needs Doing about Man in Space?*—a discussion at the 1959 APA convention (48 pp.). Philadelphia: General Electric, 1959b, pp. 6–8.

————. *Effects of G Environments on Psychomotor Abilities*, Report No. NADC-MA-6121, AMAL, U.S. Naval Air Development Center, Johnsville, Pa., 1960a, p. 80.

————. "Human Learning and Performance during Closed-Loop Centrifuge Simulation of Proposed Space Vehicles," *Amer. Psychol.*, 15:473, 1960b.

————. *Control Performance under Acceleration with Side-Arm Attitude Controllers*, Report NADC-MA-6110, AMAL, U.S. Naval Air Development Center, Johnsville, Pa., November 27, 1961.

————. *Problems and Research in Space Psychology*, Report No. NADC-MA-6145, AMAL, U.S. Naval Air Development Center, Johnsville, Pa., 1962a.

————. "Psychological Aspects of Space Flight," in J. H. U. Brown (ed.), *The Physiology of Space Flight*, New York: Academic Press, 1962b.

————, Augerson, W. S., Kerr, R., and Morway, D. "Effects of Positive Pressure Breathing on Performance and Physiology during Acceleration," *Aerospace Med.*, 33:331, 1962.

———— and Doerfel, H. V. *Closed-Loop Centrifuge Simulation of Space Vehicle Performance*, Preprint No. 807-59, New York: American Rocket Society, 1959.

———— and Eggleston, J. M. *Pilot Performance during Centrifuge Simulated Boost and Reentry of Proposed Space Vehicles*, paper read at fourteenth meeting of the Flight Test and Aeromedical Panels, NATO-AGARD, Athens, Greece, May 12, 1959.

———— and Lathrop, R. G. *Considerations in Testing for Intellectual Impairment due to Acceleration*, paper read at AMA, New York, June, 1961.

————, Morway, D. A., Beckman, E. L., and Coburn, K. R. *Effects of Water Immersion on Performance Proficiency*, Report No. NADC-MA-6133, AMAL, U.S. Naval Air Development Center, Johnsville, Pa., 1961.

——— and Nelson, J. G. "Pilot Performance Capabilities during Centrifuge Simulations of Boost and Reentry," *Amer. Rocket Soc. J., 31* (11):1534–1541, 1961a.

——— and ———. *Principles Concerning Pilot Performance in Centrifuge Simulations of Space Vehicles,* Report NADC-MA-6143, AMAL, U.S. Naval Air Development Center, Johnsville, Pa., December 22, 1961b, 25 pp.

——— and Smith, B. J. *What Needs Doing about Man in Space?* Philadelphia: General Electric, December, 1959c.

Christensen, K. K., and Johnson, L. *A Study to Determine Methods of Simulating Effects,* WADC Technical Note 58-314, ASTIA Document No. AD 211849, Armour Research Foundation of Illinois Institute of Technology, October, 1959, p. 302.

Clark, B., and Graybiel, A. "Human Performance during Adaptation to Stress in the Pensacola Slow Rotating Room," *Aerospace Med., 32* (2):93–106, 1961.

———, ———, and MacCorquodale, K. "Illusory Rotation of Target during Turns in Aircraft," *Amer. J. Psychol., 61*:50–58, 1948.

Clark, C. C. *Acceleration and Body Distortion,* Report No. ER 12138, Life Sciences Dept., Martin Co., Baltimore, November, 1961a.

———. *Some Body Displacements and Medical Effects of Lateral Accelerations during Navy Centrifuge Simulation of Ejection Capabilities from the Army AO Aircraft,* Report NADC-MA-6044, U.S. Naval Air Development Center, Johnsville, Pa., April 11, 1961b, 21 pp.

——— and Faubert, D. *A Chronological Bibliography on the Biological Effects of Impact,* Report No. ER 11953, Life Sciences Dept., Martin Co., Baltimore, September 27, 1961.

——— and Gray, R. F. *A Discussion of Restraint and Protection of the Human Experiencing the Smooth and Oscillating Accelerations of Proposed Space Vehicles,* Report NADC-MA-5914, U.S. Naval Air Development Center, Johnsville, Pa., October, 1959, 50 pp.

——— and Hardy, J. D. "Preparing Man for Space Flight," *Astronautics,* February, 1959, pp. 18–21, 88–90.

——— and ———. *Gravity Problems in Manned Space Stations,* Report NADC-MA-6033, U.S. Naval Air Development Center, Johnsville, Pa., March 29, 1961, 30 pp.

———, ———, and Crosbie, R. J. *A Proposed Physiological Acceleration Terminology with an Historical Review,* Publication 913, Human Acceleration Studies, Nat. Acad. Sci.–Nat. Res. Coun., Washington, D.C., 1961, pp. 7–65.

——— and Woodling, C. H. *Centrifuge Simulation of the X-15 Research Aircraft.* Report NADC-MA-5916, AMAL, U.S. Naval Air Development Center, Johnsville, Pa., December 10, 1959, 35 pp.

Clark, W. G., Henry, J. P., Greely, P. O., and Drury, D. R. *Studies on Flying in the Prone Position* (Interim Report), OSRD, Report No. CAM 466, Nat. Res. Coun., Comm. on Aviat. Med., August 20, 1945.

Clarke, N. P., Hyde, A. S., Cherniack, N. S., *et al. A Preliminary Report of Human Response to Rearward Facing Reentry Acceleration,* Report No.

WADC TN 59-109, Wright Air Development Center, Wright-Patterson Air Force Base, Ohio, July, 1959, 14 pp.

Cochran, L. B. "Studies on the Ease with Which Pilots Can Grasp and Pull the Ejection Seat Face Curtain Handles," *J. Aviation Med.*, 24:23–28, 1953.

——, Gard, P. W., and Norsworthy, M. E. *Variation in Human G Tolerance to Positive Acceleration*, Report No. 001059.02.10., U.S. Naval School of Aviat. Med., Pensacola, Fla., August, 1954.

Code, C. F., Wood, E. H., and Lambert, E. H. "The Limiting Effect of Centripetal Acceleration on Man's Ability to Move," *J. Aero Sci.*, 14:117–123, 1947.

Collins, C. C., Crosbie, R. J., and Gray, R. F. *Pilot Performance and Tolerance Studies of Orbital Reentry Acceleration*, letter report TED ADC AE 1412, AMAL, U.S. Naval Air Development Center, Johnsville, Pa., September 19, 1958.

—— and Gray, R. F. *Pilot Performance and Tolerance Studies of Orbital Reentry Acceleration*, letter report No. 11 Serial 7390 TED ADC AE 1412, AMAL, U.S. Naval Air Development Center, Johnsville, Pa., September 16, 1959.

Cope, F. W., and Chambers, R. M. *A System for Continuous Integrated Recording of Reaction Time for a 4 Light Discrimination Task*, Report NADC-MA-6114, AMAL, U.S. Naval Air Development Center, Johnsville, Pa., December 29, 1961, 7 pp.

—— and Jensen, R. *Preliminary Report on an Automated System for the Study of Higher Mental Function in the Human Subjected to Acceleration Stress.* Research Report No. NADC-MA-6113, AMAL, U.S. Naval Air Development Center, Johnsville, Pa., September 8, 1961.

Creer, B. Y., Smedal, H. A., and Wingrove, R. C. *Centrifuge Study of Pilot Tolerance to Acceleration and the Effects of Acceleration on Pilot Performance.* NASA Technical Note D-337, National Aeronautics and Space Administration, Washington, D.C., November, 1960, 35 pp.

Day, R. E. "Training Aspects of the X-15 Program," in *The Training of Astronauts*, Publication 873, Nat. Acad. of Sci.–Nat. Res. Coun., Washington, D.C., 1961, pp. 5–14.

Dennis, J. P., and Elwood, M. A. *The Effects of Vibration Experienced in Different Seating Positions*, Ministry of Supply, Directorate of Physiological and Biological Research, Clothing and Stores Experimental Eestablishment, No. 78, 1958.

Dews, P. B., and Morse, W. H. "Some Observations on an Operant in Human Subjects and Its Modification by Dextro Amphetamine," *J, Exper. Anal. Behav.*, 1:359–364, 1958.

Dickermann, D. "A Study of the Influence of Vibration on Man," *Ergonomics, 1*, No. 4, 1958.

Dixon, F., and Patterson, J. L., Jr. *Determination of Acceleration Forces Acting on Man in Flight and in the Human Centrifuge*, U.S. Naval School of Aviation Medicine, Pensacola, Fla., Project No. NM001 059.04.01, July 1, 1953.

—— and ——. "Determination of Accelerative Forces Acting on Man in Flight and in the Human Centrifuge," in O. H. Gauer and G. D. Zuidema (eds.), *Gravitational Stress in Aerospace Medicine,* Boston: Little, Brown, 1961, pp. 243–256.

Douglas, W. K., Carmault, R. J., Jr., Graybiel, A., Knoblock, E. C., Augerson, W. S., and Laughlin, C. P. "Results of the MR-4 Preflight and Postflight Medical Examination Conducted on Astronaut Virgil I. Grissom," in *Results of the Second U.S. Manned Suborbital Space Flight,* Washington, D.C., U.S. Government Printing Office, July 21, 1961, pp. 9–15.

Duane, T. D. "Observations on the Fundus Oculi During Blackout," *AMA Arch. Opth., 51:*343–355, 1954.

——, Beckman, E. L., Ziegler, J. E., and Hunter, H. N. *Some Observations on Human Tolerance to Exposures of 15 Transverse G,* Report No. NADC-MA-5305, AMAL, U.S. Naval Air Development Center, Johnsville, Pa., July 30, 1953.

Edelberg, R., Henry, J. P., Maciolek, J. A., Salzman, E. W., and Zuidema, G. D. "Comparison of Human Tolerance to Acceleration of Slow and Rapid Onset," *J. Aviation Med., 27:*482–489, 1956.

Eggleston, J. M., and Cheatham, D. C. "Piloted Entries into the Earth's Atmosphere," Preprint No. 59–98, *Inst. Aero. Sci.,* June, 1959.

Eiband, A. M. *Human Tolerance to Rapidly Applied Accelerations: A Summary of the Literature,* NASA Memorandum 5-19-59E, National Aeronautics and Space Administration, Washington, D.C., June, 1959.

Enoch, J. M. "Amblyopia and the Stiles-Crawford Effect," *Amer. J. Opt. and Arch. Amer. Acad. Opt., 34:*298–309, 1957.

Fischer, C. F., and Nicholson, F. T. *Acceleration Simulations on the Human Centrifuge,* symposium on Space Medicine Electronics, The Franklin Institute, May 23, 1959.

Fleishman, E. A. "Primary Abilities in the Space Environment," in R. M. Chambers and B. J. Smith, *What Needs Doing about Man in Space?*—a discussion at the 1959 APA convention (48 pp.). Philadelphia: General Electric, 1959, pp. 16–18.

Fletcher, D. E., Collins, C. C., and Brown, J. L. "Effects of Positive Acceleration upon the Performance of an Air-to-Air Tracking Task," *J. Aviation Med., 29:*891–897, 1958.

Frankenhaeuser, Marianne. *Effekter av radialacceleration pa psykiska funktioner,* I. Meddleanden fran Flyg- och navalmedicinska namnden, *6:*20–33, 1956.

——. *Effects of Prolonged Radial Acceleration on Performance,* reports from the Psychological Laboratory, University of Stockholm, No. 48 (110 pp.), August, 1957a, pp. 1–10.

——. *Effects of Gravitational Stress on Time Perception, ibid.,* No. 52, 1957b.

——. "Effects of Prolonged Gravitational Stress on Performance," *Acta Psychologica, 14:*92–108, 1958 (also *Nordisk Psykologi, 10:*48–64, 1958.

Fraser, T. M., Hoover, G. N., and Ashe, W. F. "Tracking Performance during Low Frequency Vibration," *Aerospace Med., 32*:829–835, 1961.

Frazer, J. W., and Reeves, Elizabeth. *Adaptation to Positive Acceleration,* Report NADC-MA-5818, AMAL, U.S. Naval Air Development Center, Johnsville, Pa., December, 1958, 14 pp.

Galambos, R. "Psychological Testing of Subjects Undergoing Acceleration Stress," in *Reports on Human Acceleration,* Nat. Acad. Sci.–Nat. Res. Coun., Publication 901, Washington, D.C., 1961, pp. 13–54.

Gauer, O. H. "The physiological effects of prolonged acceleration," in *German Aviation Medicine—World War II,* Washington, D.C.: Dept. of the Air Force, 1950, pp. 554–583.

———. "Definitions: Magnitude, Direction, and Time Course of Accelerative Forces," In O. H. Gauer and G. D. Zuidema (eds.), *Gravitational Stress in Aerospace Medicine,* Boston: Little, Brown, 1961a, pp. 10–15.

———. "The Physiology of Negative Acceleration," *ibid.,* pp. 134–139 (1961b).

——— *and Haber, H.* "Man under Gravity-Free Conditions," *German Aviation Medicine, World War II,* Vol. I, Dept. of the Air Force, Washington, D.C.: U.S. Govt. Printing Office, 1950.

——— and Henry, J. P. *Physiology of Flight.* Air Force Manual 160-30, Washington, D.C.: U.S. Govt. Printing Office, July, 1953.

——— and Ruff, S. "Die Ertraglichkeitsgrenzen für Fliehkrafte in Richtung Rücken-brust," *Luftfahrtmedizin, 3*:225–230, 1939.

——— and Zuidema, G. D. (eds.). *Gravitational Stress in Aerospace Medicine,* Boston: Little, Brown, 1961a.

——— and ———. "The Physiology of Positive Acceleration," *ibid.,* pp. 115–135 (1961b).

Geldard, F. A. "Labyrinthine Sensitivity," in F. A. Geldard (ed.), *The Human Senses,* New York: John Wiley, 1953, pp. 249–269.

Gettine, G. L. "Vibration Tolerance Levels in Military Aircraft," *Supplement to Shock and Vibration Bulletin, 22*:24–27, 1955.

Gerathewohl, S. J. "Personal Experiences during Short Periods of Weightlessness Reported by Sixteen Subjects," *Astronautica Acta, 2*:203–217, 1956.

———. "Weightlessness: The Problem and the Air Force Research Program," *Air Univ. Quart. Review, 10*:121–141, 1958.

Goldman, D. E., and von Gierke, H. E. "The Effects of Shock and Vibration on Man," *NMRI Lecture and Review Series,* No. 60–3, 1960.

Goldstone, S., Boardman, W. K., and Lhamon, W. J. "Effect of Quinal Barbitone, Dextroamphetamine and Placebo on Apparent Time," *Brit. J. Psychol., 29*: 324–328, 1958.

Gorill, R. B., and Snyder, F. W. *"Preliminary Study of Aircrew Tolerance to Low Frequency Vertical Vibration,"* Boeing Aircraft Co. Document No. D-3-1189, 1957.

Gray, R. F. *Relationships between Oculogyral Illusions and Nystagmus,* Report No. NADC-MA-5609, AMAL, U.S. Naval Air Development Center, Johnsville, Pa., August 24, 1956.

———. "Functional Relationships between Semicircular Canals and Otolith Organs," *Aerospace Med., 31* (5) :413–418, 1960.

——— and Crosbie, R. J. *Variation in Duration of Oculogyral Illusion as a Function of the Radius of Turn,* Report No. NADC-MA-5806, AMAL, U.S. Naval Air Development Center, Johnsville, Pa., May 22, 1958.

———, ———, Hall, R. A., Weaver, J. A., and Clark, C. C. *The Presence or Absence of Visual Coriolis Illusions at Various Combined Angular Velocities,* Report NADC-MA-6131, AMAL, U.S. Naval Air Development Center, Johnsville, Pa., June 29, 1961, 14 pp.

——— and Webb, M. G. *High G Protection,* Report NADC-MA-5910, AMAL, U.S. Naval Air Development Center, Johnsville, Pa., February, 1960, 18 pp.

Graybiel, A. "Oculogravic Illusion," *AMA Arch. Ophthal., 48*:605–615, 1952.

———, Clark, B., and Zarriello, J. J. *Observations on Human Subjects Living in a "Slow Rotation Room" for Periods of Two Days: Canal Sickness,* Research Project MR005.13-6001 (formerly NM 170111), Subtask 1, Report No. 49, Naval School of Aviation Medicine, Pensacola, Fla., October 15, 1959.

———, Guedry, F. E., Johnson, W., and Kennedy, R. "Adaptation to Bizarre Stimulation of the Semicircular Canals as Indicated by the Oculogyral Illusion," *Aerospace Med., 32* (4) :321–327, 1961.

——— and Hupp, D. I. "The Oculogyral Illusion: A Form of Apparent Motion Which May Be Observed Following Stimulation of the Semicircular Canals," *J. Aviation Med., 17*:3–27, 1946.

——— and Patterson, J. L. *Thresholds of Stimulation of the Otolith Organs as Indicated by the Oculogravic Illusion,* Report No. NM 001 059.01.38, U.S. Naval Aviat. Med. Lab., Pensacola, Fla., July, 1954.

Grissom, V. I. "Pilot's Flight Report," in *NASA Results of the Second U.S. Manned Suborbital Space Flight,* Washington, D.C.: U.S. Govt. Printing Office, July 21, 1961, pp. 47–58.

Guedry, F. E., Jr., and Ceran, S. J. "Derivation of 'Subjective Velocity' from Angular Displacement Estimates Made during Prolonged Angular Accelerations: Adaptation Effects," Report No. 376 ii, *USA Med. Res. Lab. Rep.,* 1959, 21 pp.

———, Cramer, R. L., and Koella, W. P. *Experiments on the Rate of Development and Rate of Recovery of Apparent Adaptation Effects in the Vestibular System,* USAMRL Proj. 6 95 20 001, Rep. 338, USA Medical Research Lab., Fort Knox, Ky., June, 1958.

——— and Graybiel, A. *Rotation Devices Other than Centrifuges and Motion Simulators,* Publication 902, Nat. Acad. of Sci.–Nat. Res. Coun., Washington, D.C., 1961.

——— and Montague, E. K. "Quantitative Evaluation of the Vestibular Coriolis Reaction, *Aerospace Med., 32* (6) :487–500, 1961.

Guignard, J. C., and Irving, A. "Effects of Low-Frequency Vibration on Man," *British Assoc. of Cardiff,* September, 1960.

Hallenbeck, G. A. *Design and Use of Anti-G Suits and Their Values in World War II*, Report No. 5433, USAF Wright-Patterson AFB, Ohio, March 6, 1946, 151 pp.

———, Wood, E. H., Lambert, E. H., and Allen, S. C. "Comparison of Effects of Positive G on Subjects Studied at Both the Mayo and Air Technical Service Command Centrifuges," *Fed. Proc., 5*:40–41, 1946 (abstract).

Ham, G. C. "Effects of Centrifuge Acceleration on Living Organisms," *War Med., 3*:30–56, 1943.

Hanna, T. D., and Gaito, J. "Performance and Habitability Aspects of Extended Confinement in Sealed Cabins," *Aerospace Med., 31* (5):399–406, 1960.

Hardy, J. D., and Clark, C. C. "The Development of Dynamic Flight Simulation, *Aero/Space Engineering, 18* (6):48–52, 1959.

———, Clark, C. C., and Gray, R. F. *Acceleration Problems in Space Flight*, Report NADC-MA-5909, AMAL, U.S. Naval Air Development Center, Johnsville, Pa., October, 1959, 34 pp.

Headley, R. N., Brinkley, J. W., Lokatos, G., and Managan, R. F. *Human Factors Responses during Ground Impact*, WADC TR 60-590, Aerospace Med. Div., Wright Air Development Center, Dayton, Ohio, November, 1960.

Henry, J. P. *Studies of the Physiology of Negative Acceleration*, AF Technical Report 5953, Air Matériel Command, Wright-Patterson AFB, Ohio, 1950.

Hessberg, R. R., Jr. "Acceleration Environments Pertinent to Aerospace Medical Research," in *Human Acceleration Studies*, Publication No. 913, Panel on Acceleration Stress for the Armed Forces–NRC Committee on Bio-Astronautics, Nat. Acad. Sci–Nat. Res. Coun., Washington, D.C., 1961a, pp. 66–71.

———. "Escape from High Performance Aircraft," in O. H. Gauer, and G. D. Zuidema (eds.), *Gravitational Stress in Aerospace Medicine*, Boston: Little, Brown, 1961b.

Hill, J. H. *Pilot's Ability to Activate Cockpit Controls under G Conditions*. Letter Report TED ADC AE-6303.1, AMAL, U.S. Naval Air Development Center, Johnsville, Pa., April, 1957.

———. *Evaluation of the Torso-Head Restraint System and the Integrated Harness Restraint System under Conditions of Acceleration*, Letter Report TED ADC AE-5209, AMAL, U.S. Naval Air Development Center, Johnsville, Pa., April 2, 1959.

——— and Brown, J. L. *Comparative Evaluation of a Standard Face Curtain and an Experimental D-ring Located on the Seat Front as Modes of Actuating Ejection during Exposure to Acceleration*, Report TED ADC AE-5205, MA-3, 3585, AMAL, U.S. Naval Air Development Center, Johnsville, Pa., May 5, 1958.

———, ———, and Peck, L. H. *Pilot's Ability to Actuate Cockpit Controls under G Conditions*, Letter Report TED ADC AE-6303.1, AMAL, U.S. Naval Air Development Center, Johnsville, Pa., April 1, 1957.

——— and Webb, M. G. *Pilot's Ability to Actuate Ejection Controls: Final*

Report Concerning, Letter Report TED ADC AE-5205, AMAL, U.S. Naval Air Development Center, Johnsville, Pa., February 5, 1959.

Holleman, E. C., Armstrong, N. A., and Andrews, W. H. *Utilization of the Pilot in the Launch and Injection of a Multistage Orbital Vehicle*, I.A.S. Paper No. 60-16, NASA Flight Research Center, Edwards, Calif., January 27, 1960, 42 pp.

Hornick, R. J. "Human Exposure to Helicopter Vibration" (a literature review), BRL Report No. 133, February, 1961.

———, Boettcher, C. A., and Simons, A. K. *The Effect of Low Frequency, High Amplitude, Whole Body, Longitudinal and Transverse Vibration upon Human Performance*, Final Report, Contract No. DA-11-022-509-ORD-3300, Ordnance Project No. TEI-1000, Bostrom Res. Lab., Milwaukee, 1961.

Howard, P., and Byford, G. H. *Threshold Determination Techniques on the Human Centrifuge*, FPRC Memo 75, RAF Institute of Aviation Medicine, Farnborough, England, September, 1956.

Hunter, H. N., and Weiss, H. S. *Pilot's Ability to Simulate an Emergency Escape with Various Types of Ejection Seats While Subjected to a Fluctuating Acceleration*, Letter Report TED ADC AE-6303.3, AMAL, U.S. Naval Air Development Center, Johnsville, Pa., November 3, 1953.

Jackson, C. B., Jr., Douglas, W. K., Culver, J. F., Ruff, G., Knoblock, E. C., and Graybiel, A. "Results of Preflight and Postflight Medical Examinations," in *Proceedings of a Conference on Results of the First U.S. Manned Suborbital Space Flight* (76 pp.), Washington, D.C.: U.S. Government Printing Office, June 6, 1961, pp. 31–36.

Jacobs, H. I. "A Review of Available Information on the Acoustical and Vibrational Aspects of Manned Space Flight," *Aerospace Med.*, *31*:468–477, 1961.

Johnson, W. H. "Head Movements in Relation to Spatial Disorientation and Vestibular Stimulation," *J. Aviation Med.*, 27:148, 1956.

———, Smith, J. B., and Sullivan, J. A. "Acceleration as a Means of Determining the Sensitivity of the Components of Non-auditory Membranous Labyrinth," *Ann. Otol.*, *69*:610, 1960.

Jones, E. R. "Man's Integration into the Mercury Capsule," in *The Training of Astronauts*, Publication No. 873, Nat. Acad. of Sci.–Nat. Res. Coun., Washington, D.C., 1961, pp. 15–21.

Kaehler, R. D. "Human Psychomotor Performance under Varied Transverse Accelerations," *J. Aviation Med.*, *30*(3):189, 1959.

———. *The Effects of Tranverse Accelerations and Exponential Time-Lag Constants on Compensatory Tracking Performance*, ASD TR 61-457, School of Medicine, University of Southern California, Los Angeles, September, 1961, 42 pp.

——— and Meehan, J. P. *Human Psychomotor Performance under Varied Transverse Accelerations*. WADD TR 60-621, School of Medicine, University of Southern California, Los Angeles, August, 1960, 56 pp.

Keighley, G., Clark, W. G., and Drury, D. R. "Flicker Fusion Frequency Measurements on Man Subjected to Positive Acceleration on a Human Centrifuge," *J. Appl. Physiol.*, 4:57–62, 1951.

Kennedy, W. A., Kerr, W. K., Russell, W. A. M., and Franks, W. R. *Influence of Accelerations Produced in the Centrifuge on Reaction Time*, Report No. 11, Nat. Res. Coun., Canada, April 10, 1944.

Kerr, W. K., and Russell, W. A. M. *Effects of Positive Acceleration in the Centrifuge and in Aircraft on Functions of the Central Nervous System*, Report No. C2719, Nat. Res. Coun., Canada, April 15, 1944.

King, B. C., Morrow, D. J., and Vollmer, E. P. *Cockpit Studies—The Boundaries of the Maximum Area for the Operation of Manual Controls*, Project X-651, Medical Research Inst., Bethesda, Md., July, 1947.

Kornhauser, M. "Theoretical Prediction of the Effect of Rate-of-Onset on Man's G-Tolerance," *Aerospace Med.*, 32(5):412–421, 1961.

Kuehnel, H., Nicholson, F. T., and Futterweit, A. *Comparison of Tracking Performance in the TV-2 Aircraft and the ACL Computer/AMAL Human Centrifuge Simulation of This Aircraft*. Report NADC-MA-6016/NADC-AC-6008, U.S. Naval Air Development Center, Johnsville, Pa., November 7, 1960, 47 pp.

Kydd, G. H., Fenichel, R. L., and Crosbie, R. J. *Observations on the Relationships between Human Acceleration End Points and the Centrifuge Acceleration Pattern*, Report NADC-MA-6146, AMAL, U.S. Naval Air Development Center, Johnsville, Pa., February, 1962, 14 pp.

Lambert, E. H. "The Physiological Basis of 'Blackout' as It Occurs in Aviators," *Fed. Proc.*, 4:43, 1945.

————. "Effects of Positive Acceleration on Pilots in Flight with Comparison of Responses of Pilots and Passengers in an Airplane and Subjects on a Human Centrifuge, *J. Aviation Med.*, 21:195–220, 1950.

————, Wood, E. H., and Baldes, J. *Man's Ability to Withstand Transverse Acceleration When in the Sitting Position*, Nat. Res. Coun., Div. of Med. Sci., Comm. on Aviat. Med., Report No. CAM 418, March 7, 1945.

Lansberg, M. P. "On the Origin of the Unpleasant Sensations Elicited by Head Movements during and after Sensations," *Aeromed. Acta*, 4:67–72, 1955.

Laughlin, C. P., and Augerson, W. S. "Physiological Responses of the Astronaut in the MR-4 Space Flight, in *NASA Results of the Second U.S. Manned Suborbital Space Flight*, Washington, D.C.: U.S. Government Printing Office, July 21, 1961, pp. 15–23.

Leverett, S. D., Jr., Whitney, R. U., and Zuidema, G. D. "Protective Devices against Acceleration, in O. H. Gauer, and G. D. Zuidema (eds.), *Gravitational Stress in Aerospace Medicine*, Boston: Little, Brown, 1961, pp. 211–220.

———— and Zuidema, G. D. "Standardization of Human Centrifuge Techniques, *ibid.*, pp. 263–270.

Lewis, S. T., and Stapp, J. P. "Human Tolerance to Aircraft Seat Belt Restraint," *J. Aviation Med.*, 29:187–196, 1958.

Loftus, J. P. *Weightlessness and Performance: A Review of the Literature*, ASD

Technical Report 61-166, Aeronautical Systems Div., Wright-Patterson AFB, June, 1961, 34 pp.

Lombard, C. F., Canfield, A. A., Warren, N. D., and Drury, D. R. *The Influence of Positive (Head to Foot) Centrifugal Force upon Subject's (Pilot's) Ability to Exert Maximum Pull on an Aircraft Control Stick*, Report to ONR, Contract N6ori77, Dept. of Psychology, University of Southern Calif., Los Angeles, January, 1948.

McCormick, E. J. *Human Engineering*, New York: McGraw-Hill, 1957.

Martin, E. E., and Henry, J. P. *The Supine Position as a Means of Increasing Tolerance to Acceleration*, Technical Report No. 6025, AMC, Wright-Patterson AFB, Ohio, 1950.

Meehan, J. P., and Jacobs, H. I. *Relations of Several Physiological Parameters to Positive G Tolerance*. Report No. 58-665, WADC, Dayton, Ohio, 1958.

Miller, I., Simon, G. B., and Cohen, E. *A Device and Tests for Measuring Intellectual Functions during Acceleration*, WADD Tech. Rep. 60-366, WADC, Dayton, Ohio, May, 1960, 43 pp.

Mozell, M. M., and White, D. C. *Behavioral Effects of Whole Body Vibration*. Report No. NADC-MA-5802, AMAL, U.S. Naval Air Development Center, Johnsville, Pa., January, 1958.

Niven, J. I., and Hixon, W. C. *Frequency Response of the Human Semicircular Canals: I. Steady-State Ocular Nystagmus Response to High-Level Sinusoidal Angular Rotations*, Project MR005.13-6001, Report No. 58, U.S. Naval School of Aviation Medicine, Pensacola, Fla., 1961, 32 pp.

Preston, T. H., Edelberg, R., Henry, J. P., Miller, J., Salzman, E. W., and Zuidema, G. D. "Human Tolerance to Multistage Rocket Acceleration Curves," *J. Aviation Med.*, 26:390, 1955.

Riopelle, A. J., and Hines, M. *Effects of Intense Vibration*, Final Report, Contract No. DA-49-007-MD-535, US AMRL Report No. 358, Ft. Knox, Ky., 1958.

Rose, B. *Description of the Human Centrifuge*, Report No. C2145, Nat. Res. Coun., Canada, April 16, 1942.

Ross, M. D. "Reactions of a Balloon Crew in a Controlled Environment," *J. Aviation, Med.*, 30(5):326–333, 1959.

Rubacky, E. P. *Freedom 7*, Washington, D.C.: Educational Services, 1961.

Schafer, G. E. "Sensory Illusions in Flying," *J. Aviation Med.*, 22:207–211, 256, 1951.

Schmitz, M. A. *The Effect of Low Frequency, High Amplitude, Whole Body Vertical Vibration on Human Performance*, Progress Report No. 2, Bostrom Research Laboratory, Milwaukee, January, 1960.

—— and Simons, A. K. *Man's Response to Low-Frequency Vibration*. Preprint No. 59-A-200, New York: The American Society of Mechanical Engineers, 1960.

——, ——, and Boettcher, C. A. *The Effect of Low-Frequency High Amplitude, Whole-Body Vertical Vibration on Human Performance*, Final Report,

Contract No. DA-49-007-MD-797, BRL Report No. 130, Bostrom Research Laboratory, Milwaukee, 1960.

Schock, G. J. D. "Some Observations on Orientation and Illusions When Exposed to Sub and Zero-Gravity, *Dissert. Abst., 18*(5) :1832–1833, 1958.

———. "Airborne GSR Studies," *Aerospace Med., 31*(7) :543–546, 1960.

Schubert, G. "Coriolis-Nystagmus," *J. Aviation Med., 25* :257–259, 1954.

Senders, J. *Early Development of Space Vehicle Attitude Control and Display Philosophy*, Preprint No. 1400-60, paper presented at annual meeting of ARS, Washington, D.C., 1960.

Shepard, A. B., Jr. "Pilot's Flight Report, Including In-Flight Films," in *Proceedings of a Conference on Results of the First U.S. Manned Suborbital Space Flight* (76 pp.), Washington, D.C.: U.S. Government Printing Office, June 6, 1961, pp. 69–75.

Sieker, H. O. *Devices for Protection against Negative Acceleration. Part I. Centrifuge Studies*, WADC Technical Report 52-87, Wright-Patterson AFB, Ohio, 1952, 15 pp.

———. "Effect of Acceleration on the Heart," in O. H. Gauer, and G. D. Zuidema (eds.), *Gravitational Stress in Aerospace Medicine*, Boston: Little, Brown, 1961, pp. 52–60.

Simons, D. G. "Observations in High Altitude, Sealed-Cabin Balloon Flight," *Air University Quarterly Review, 10*(2) :65–88, 1958a.

———. "Pilot Reactions during 'Manhigh II' Balloon Flight," *J. Aviation Med., 29* (1) :1–14, 1958b.

Slayton, D. K. "Pilot Training and Preflight Preparation," in *Proceedings of a Conference on Results of the First U.S. Manned Suborbital Space Flight* (76 pp.), Washington, D.C.: U.S. Government Printing Office, 1961, pp. 53–60.

Smedal, H. A., Creer, B. Y., and Wingrove, R. C. *Physiological Effects of Acceleration Observed during a Centrifuge Study of Pilot Performance*, NASA TN D-345, Washington, D.C.: National Aeronautics and Space Administration, 1960.

Smedal, H. A., Stinnett, G. W., and Innis, R. C. *A Restraint System Enabling Pilot Control under Moderately High Acceleration in a Varied Acceleration Field*, NASA TN D-91, Washington, D.C.: National Aeronautics and Space Administration, 1960, 19 pp.

———, Vykukal, H. C., Gallant R. P., and Stinnett, G. W. "Crew Physical Support and Restraint in Advanced Manned Flight Systems, *Amer. Rocket Soc. J., 31*(11) :1544–1948, 1961.

Snyder, R. Z. *A3J1 Spin Simulation Program on the Navy Human Centrifuge*, Report NADC-MA-6104, AMAL, U.S. Naval Air Development Center, Johnsville, Pa., 1961, 14 pp.

Stapp, J. P. "Human Tolerance to Severe, Abrupt Acceleration," in O. H. Gauer, and G. D. Zuidema (eds.), *Gravitational Stress in Aerospace Medicine*, Boston: Little, Brown, 1961.

Stewart, W. K. "Some Observations on the Effect of Centrifugal Force in Man," *J. Neurol. Psychiat., 8* :24–33, 1945.

Stoll, Alice M. "Human Tolerance to Positive G as Determined by the Physiological End Points," *J. Aviation Med.*, 27:356–367, 1956.

Swearingen, J. J., McFadden, E. B., Garner, J. D., and Blethrow, J. G. "Human Voluntary Tolerance to Vertical Impact," *Aerospace Med.*, 31:989–998, 1960.

The Training of Astronauts, Panel of Psychology-Armed Forces-NRC Committee on Bio-Astronautics, Publication 873, Nat. Acad. Sci.–Nat. Res. Coun., Washington, D.C., 1961.

Vandenberg, J. D. *Performance Effectiveness of the Grumman Fingertip Three Axis Side Arm Controller*, Report No. ADR-09-01-61.3, New York: Grumman Aircraft Engineering Corp., 1961.

Voas, R. B. *Psychological Factors in the Manual Control of Attitude in the Mercury Vehicle*, Preprint No. 1402-60, paper presented at meeting of American Rocket Society, Washington, D.C., December 6, 1960.

———. "Project Mercury: Astronaut Training Program," in B. E. Flaherty (ed.), *Psychophysiological Aspects of Space Flight*, New York: Columbia University Press, 1961, 393 pp.

———, Van Bockel, J. J., Zedekar, R. G., and Backer, P. W. "Results of In-Flight Pilot Performance," in *Proceedings of a Conference on Results of the the First U.S. Manned Suborbital Space Flight* (76 pp.), Washington, D.C.: U.S. Government Printing Office, June 6, 1961, pp. 61–67.

von Beckh, H. J. "Experiments with Animals and Human Subjects under Sub- and Zero-Gravity Conditions during the Dive and Parabolic Flight," *J. Aviation Med.*, 25:235, 1954.

———. "Human Reactions during Flight to Acceleration Preceded by or Followed by Weightlessness," *Aerospace Med.*, 30(6):391–409, 1959.

Warrick, M. J., and Lund, D. W. *Effect of Moderate Positive Acceleration (G) on the Ability to Read Aircraft-Type Instrument Dials*, Memo Report TSEAA 694-10, Wright-Patterson AFB, Ohio, 1946.

Weaver, A. B., Rubenstein, M., Clark, C. C., and Gray, R. F. *Encapsulation of Humans in Rigid Polyurethane Foam for Use as a Restraint System in High Acceleration Environments*, Report No. NADC-MA-6147, U.S. Naval Air Development Center, Johnsville, Pa., 1961.

Weiss, H. S., Edelberg, K., Charland, P. V., and Rosenbaum, J. R. *The Physiology of Simple Tumbling. Part 2. Human Studies*, Report WADC-53-139, Wright-Patterson AFB, Ohio, 1954.

Weitz, J. *Effect of Shape of Handles and Position of Controls on Speed and Accuracy of Performance*. Project 266, Report No. 1, USAF School of Aviation Medicine, Randolph Field, Texas, 1944.

———. *Effect of Shape and Color Coding of Airplane Controls on Speed and Accuracy*, Report No. PR 336-1, USAF School of Aviation Medicine, Randolph Field, Texas, 1951.

Wells, J. G., and Morehouse, L. E., "Electromyographic Study of Effects of Various Headward Accelerative Forces upon Pilot's Ability to Perform Standardized Pulls on Aircraft Control Stick," *J. Aviation Med.*, 21:48–54, 1950.

Westheimer, G. "Mechanism of Sacadia Eye Movements," *A.M.A. Arch. Ophth.*, 52:710–724, 1954.

White, W. J. *Acceleration and Vision,* WADC Technical Report 58-333, Wright-Patterson AFB, Ohio, 1958a.

———. *Variations in Absolute Visual Thresholds during Accelerative Stress.* WADC Technical Report 58-334, Wright-Patterson AFB, Ohio, 1958b.

———. "Visual Performance under Gravitation Stress," in O. H. Gauer and G. D. Zuidema (eds.), *Gravitational Stress in Aerospace Medicine,* Boston: Little, Brown, 1961a.

———. *Acceleration (G) and Visual Performance,* Paper 352A, Society of Automotive Engineers-National Aeronautics Society, New York, 1961b.

——— and Jorve, W. R. *The Effects of Gravitational Stress upon Visual Acuity,* WADC-TR 56-247, Wright Air Development Center, Ohio, 1956.

——— and Riley, M. B. "The Effects of Positive Acceleration (G) on the Relation between Illumination and Dial Heading," in Finch, G., and Cameron, F. (eds.), *Symposium on Air Force Human Engineering, Personnel and Training Research,* Publication 455, Nat. Acad. of Sci.–Nat. Res. Coun., Washington, D.C., 1956.

Willmorth, N. E., and Green, G. A. "The Effect of Increased Positive Radial Acceleration on the Speed and Accuracy of Reaching Movements," *Amer. Psychol.,* 5:465, 1950.

Wilson, R. C., and Canfield, A. A. "The effects of increased positive radial acceleration upon pupillary response," in *Psychological Research on the Human Centrifuge: Final Report,* Tech. Report N6ori77, Dept. of Psychology, University of Southern California, Los Angeles, 1951.

Wood, E. H., Lambert, E. H., and Code, C. F. "Do Permanent Effects Result from Repeated Blackouts Caused by Positive Acceleration?" *J. Aviation Med.,* 18:471–482, 1947.

Zuidema, G. D., Cohen, S. I., Silverman, A. J., and Riley, M. B. "Human Tolerance to Prolonged Acceleration," *J. Aviation Med.,* 27(6):469–481, 1956.

8

TEMPERATURE EFFECTS ON OPERATOR PERFORMANCE

Edwin Hendler

Air Crew Equipment Laboratory
Naval Air Equipment Center
Philadelphia, Pennsylvania

MAN not only has the capability of performing complex psychomotor tasks that far exceed anything yet demonstrated by other kinds of animals, but he is also distinguished from all other organisms in having the most sensitive and efficient body-temperature regulating mechanism. It is man's brain, of course, that is largely responsible for his performance capability. In order to function properly, the brain requires an environment that is maintained in a state of dynamic equilibrium. An essential part of this environment, which must remain stable, is thermal. While the temperature of many of the more peripheral parts of the body can vary considerably from time to time and place to place, those of the inner "core," and especially that of the brain, are kept within narrow limits by a host of complex mechanisms. Small changes of the brain temperature, amounting to a few degrees in either direction, produce profound physiological alterations that result in a rapid deterioration of performance capability. In this chapter some of the more salient points relating to basic physical concepts of temperature, temperature regulation in man, and the effects of temperature on human performance are reviewed.

Physical Factors

It is necessary at the outset to differentiate three related terms: temperature, thermal energy, and heat. Temperature is a fundamental quantity in physics, just as length, mass, and time. Thermal energy and heat, on the other hand, are derived quantities and therefore can be defined only in terms of the fundamental quantities just mentioned. Thermal energy is identical to mechanical energy, except that it is associated with the random motion of atoms and molecules rather than the gross movements of macroscopic bodies. The kinetic energy of the molecules making up a substance is measured by the temperature of that substance. Thermal energy in the process of being transferred from one substance to another is heat. Since an isolated body in thermal equilibrium with its surroundings does not transfer heat, its heat content is undetermined. That substance which loses heat to another during a heat-transfer process is defined as being at a higher temperature than the substance that gains the heat. The latter is defined as having a lower temperature than the former. If no heat exchange occurs between two substances, these substances are defined as being at the same temperature. This last case does not necessarily imply that the thermal energy per unit of volume of each substance is equal; it merely means that, on the average, no energy is transferred from one to the other. Thermal equilibrium among various objects occurs when they all reach the same temperature.

Thermal energy can be added theoretically without limit to a substance, thereby increasing its temperature indefinitely. There is, however, a lower limit to temperature, called *absolute zero*, established experimentally to be about $-273°C$. At this temperature, a substance has given up all of the thermal energy it is capable of losing, thus becoming as cold as it can get.

Joseph Black has distinguished *calorimetry*, or the measurement of the amount of heat, from *thermometry*, the measurement of temperature, or the intensity of heat. While thermometers are used to measure temperature directly, there is no method for directly measuring heat. Thermal energy and its components, heat and work, are derived from measures of other properties of the system, such as temperature, pressure, volume, displacement, and force.

Since heat is an energy form intimately associated with movement from one substance to another, it is proper to inquire briefly into the methods of heat transfer. Three processes of heat transfer have been observed. The first of these, *conduction*, depends upon a molecular transfer of energy in any kind of medium, be it solid, liquid, or gas. The second, *convection*, depends upon the mass motion of molecules from one position to another and therefore occurs only in gaseous or liquid media. The third, *radiation*, is energy transmission by electromagnetic waves and therefore can occur in the absence of any material medium. In fact, as in the case of the most familiar portion of the electromagnetic spectrum, that of visible light, energy transfer by radiation is accomplished most efficiently in a vacuum. In the vacuum of space, radiative heat exchanges assume major importance. Under the usual environmental conditions compatible with human life, all three forms of heat transfer occur simultaneously, with one or the other assuming preeminence as the conditions change.

The rate at which heat flows through a substance is proportional to the temperature gradient within it. The proportionality constant is a characteristic of the particular material involved and is called its *thermal conductivity*. Silver has a thermal conductivity about 20,000 times greater than that of air, but the thermal conductivity of body tissues is only about 10 to 20 times greater than that of air. The effective conductivity of living tissues is largely dependent upon blood flow, and changes in blood flow through the skin can vary over a hundredfold from one set of environmental conditions to another. The reciprocal of thermal conductivity is *thermal insulation* (or, more rarely, *thermal resistance*) and is analogous to electrical resistance as stated in Ohm's Law. When nonevaporative heat flows from the body into the environment, it must pass through the thermal insulations represented by the tissues, by clothing, and by the air surrounding the body.

Insulation has been expressed in "clo" units, 1 clo being equal to $0.18°C/cal/hr/m^2$. Clothing having a thermal insulation value of 1 clo will keep a seated resting subject comfortable indefinitely at an ambient temperature of $21°C$, 50 per cent or less relative humidity, and an air movement of 20 ft/min. From this definition it can be inferred that a value of 1 clo unit is just about the thermal protection afforded by normal indoor clothing worn by men. Under very cold and windy conditions, considerable heat loss from the body can occur without passing through the clothing (such as that from the respiratory tract and exposed parts of the body), thereby preventing direct use of the clo unit to express over-all insulation. The insulative capacity required in clothing for protection against extreme environmental temperatures depends in large measure upon the heat produced by the wearer. Because, under most circumstances, the body is clothed in relatively good insulators, the amount of heat exchanged by conduction with the surroundings is relatively insignificant and therefore is included for analytical purposes with the heat exchange by convection.

In order for two bodies at different temperatures to exchange heat by convection, a fluid medium must be available to remove heat from the warmer body and carry it physically by streaming to the cooler body. Portions of fluids that are warmed become less dense and therefore tend to rise in relation to cooler, more dense portions. If heat is continually supplied to the cooler portions of a contained fluid and removed from the warmer portions, a cycle of convection currents is set up. The relative movements of portions having different densities depend upon gravity. Therefore, in the weightless state in space, convective heat exchange will occur only if a fan, or other equipment to produce pressure changes in the vehicle atmosphere, is provided.

Molecules above absolute zero in temperature are constantly radiating and absorbing energy. When the amounts of emitted and absorbed radiation are equal, a state of thermal equilibrium exists. The transfer of radiant energy depends upon the temperatures and the kinds of surfaces of the radiating bodies. The laws governing radiative heat transfer describe the shape of the curve relating the intensity of radiation to the wavelength for a theoretical "black body." Maximum radiation occurs at shorter wavelengths for bodies at higher temperature. Thus, the sun, with an absolute temperature of $6000°K$, radiates maximally at about 0.5 micron, while the human body, with an absolute temperature of about $300°K$, radiates maximally at about 9.5 micron. The net transfer of heat due to radiative heat exchange represents the difference between the amounts of radiation emitted and absorbed.

The theoretical "black body" absorbs all the incident radiation striking it without reflecting any. All real objects, however, reflect some of the radiant energy incident upon them. For certain radiation wavelengths, many objects are so close to "black" that for convenience they are considered as black bodies. Black bodies have an emissivity of 1 and an absorptance of 1. In the region of the electromagnetic spectrum where the skin emits radiation because of its temperature, its emissivity is so close to 1 (0.985) that it is generally considered to be a black body. This energy is confined to the infrared portion of the spectrum and is therefore not visible to the eye. Of course, in the visible portion of the spectrum, the skin reflects appreciable amounts of incident energy. Because of the essential "blackness" of all skins, regardless of color, in the infrared region, sensitive radiometers may be used to measure skin surface temperature after they are calibrated with experimental black bodies at known temperatures.

The human body, whether nude or clothed, is surrounded by a layer of still air about ½ to 1 cm in thickness. Convective heat losses of the body depend upon the heat conducted through this air layer. Because the amount of convective heat loss varies with specific environmental conditions, the position and movements of the subject and the nature and extent of the structures supporting him, convective heat loss is not usually measured directly. Instead, it is calculated as the difference between total heat loss and the portion due to radiation and evaporation. A probable error of less than 4 per cent of the metabolic rate was found when direct determinations of heat loss due to convection were compared to those obtained as the calculated difference just mentioned (Winslow, *et al.*, 1936).

In contrast to the natural convection just described, which is caused by the heating of the air layers next to the skin, forced convection occurs when there are bodily movements or outside pressure changes producing gusts and wind. Within certain limitations of air velocities, empirical formulas have been derived to relate convective heat loss from the body to the velocity of the surrounding air. At very high air velocities, the frictional forces in the air cause the surface of an object to heat up, even though the air is considerably cooler than the object itself. This causes the well-known heating effect produced on rocket nosecones returning to the earth through the atmospheric layers. The insulation of garments worn in very cold environments is considerably reduced by the convective air currents set up under clothing layers during exercise. Thus, an almost automatic compensation is provided to remove much of the increased bodily heat production resulting from the same exercise.

Moisture is evaporated almost continuously from the surfaces of the respiratory tract and the skin. The liquid that is evaporated first forms a vapor whose temperature is close to that of the skin. Following this change of state, the saturated vapor cools to ambient temperature and also expands. The total heat absorbed by one gram of evaporated liquid on the surface of the body varies with skin and air temperatures, and with the ambient relative humidity, but roughly approximates 600 cal. The area of skin covered with sweat can vary in extent to compensate for changes in the ambient vapor pressure, which therefore limits the effectiveness of physical analogs designed to simulate evaporative heat loss under various environmental conditions. The usual way to measure heat loss due to evaporation is by determining the amount of weight lost by the subject. Under controlled conditions, weight loss of the subject represents evaporation of liquid, except for a small correction factor due to the replacement of some of the inspired oxygen by expired carbon dioxide. Naturally, water that merely drips from the body without evaporating on its surface, is not effective in removing body heat, although it may result in considerable weight loss.

Unless the physical environment surrounding a man is relatively homogeneous with regard to temperature and emissivity, it becomes very difficult to directly measure radiant heat exchange. Various types of instruments have been constructed for the purpose of integrating the radiant heat exchange contributions made by the components of a complicated environment, such as an aircraft cockpit during flight. In general, however, these instruments are also affected by heat exchange due to other causes; and, therefore, what one usually obtains is an index which can then be correlated with comfort or physiological response. In addition to the environmental factors, radiant heat exchange with the human body is also dependent upon mean skin temperature and the amount of body surface participating in the exchange. Mean weighted skin temperature is usually obtained by measuring the temperature over several predetermined locations on the skin surface (using thermocouples, thermistors, or a radiometer), weighting these temperature readings according to the fraction of the total body area each represents, and then averaging the weighted readings. Of the total skin area, only a part is effective in radiant energy exchange with the environment. Surfaces like those between the fingers, between legs, under the arms, and under the chin are shielded from the environment and therefore decrease the active radiating area. Posture plays an important role here, and a change from a sitting to a spread-eagle position increases the effective radiating surface area from about 73 per cent to about 85 per cent of the total surface area.

A man can lose the equivalent of his basal metabolic heat production by radiation alone in an environment of 19°C and gain over twice this amount of heat production by radiation alone in an environment of 59°C (Winslow and Herrington, 1949). Normally, only about 20 kg/cal/hr/m² are lost from the body by its radiant heat exchange with the surroundings (Hardy and Du Bois, 1937). Therefore, man as a heat source produces only about 2.5 per cent of the radiant intensity that reaches the earth from the sun.

Physiological Factors

The topic of temperature regulation is an old established domain in physiology, the observed and substantiated facts of which have been discussed and interpreted for many years. Of the vast literature that exists on this much discussed subject, only the principal factors will be included in the following section.

The internal body temperature, or core temperature, is maintained at approximately 37°C in man by a combination of interacting mechanisms. Some of these mechanisms are physiological in nature, and as such are completely automatic, while the others require conscious behavioral activity. Examples of the latter include such practices as wearing clothing, heating and ventilating buildings, and sleeping under blankets. The mechanism of physiological temperature regulation form the basis of the following discussion.

By experimental methods such as tissue destruction, local electrical and thermal stimulation, and recording of bioelectric potentials, it has been established that some discrete regions in the brain act as "centers" in initiating, modifying, or arresting certain bodily functions usually associated with thermoregulation. The word "center" as used here to describe these neural areas of control is not meant to imply that some discrete, sharply defined area or group of neural elements is exclusively responsible for regulating the body temperature in homotherms. Although certain areas in and around the hypothalamus appear particularly sensitive to a variety of stimuli capable of eliciting physiological responses affecting thermoregulation, other parts of the central nervous system can influence thermoregulatory responses after the hypothalamus and large parts of the surrounding brain tissue have been removed (Thauer, 1935). Animals with lesions in the hypothalamus have shown alterations in response to heated and cooled environments, but the degree and nature of the impairments were not consistent (Keller, 1950). Of course, the precise areas of functional impairment in the brains of operated living animals are never certain; and deductions on this question can be arrived at only by examination of the fixed and stained tissues some time after the lesions have been made. In addition, the function of one part of the brain that is inactivated may be assumed partially or wholly by other parts, with the passage of time. In spite of difficulties like these, however, the general pattern of thermoregulatory mechanisms has become more apparent since the first experimental work in this area almost a century ago.

Information accumulated regarding the principles of regulating and control systems in general has been applied to analysis of the temperature control and regulating mechanism of warm-blooded animals. A recent analysis by Hardy (1961) led to the conclusion that functions such as on-off regulators, continuous proportional control, and rate control are found in the automatic temperature regulation of mechanisms of homotherms. Because, however, of the inability at the present time to identify the particular part of the body that is being thermoregulated, as well as the widespread thermal receptors responsible for sensing changes in temperature, a definitive physical and mathematical explanation of the physiological control system cannot now be given. According to Burton's concept (Burton and Edholm, 1955), central integration of afferent impulses from the temperature receptors is based upon a "normal" distribution of body temperature. When this "normal" distribution is upset, compensatory reactions occur. By this analysis, then, the regulated temperature encompasses much more that that of a group of cells in the hypothalamus or at any other particular location. It is known that changes in both skin and hypothalamic temperatures produce changes in metabolic heat production, vasomotor activity, and sweating, the latter three representing the usual physiological responses measured to assess thermoregulatory effectiveness.

The essence of a temperature regulating system lies in the fact that an element of the system is maintained at a controlled level of temperature in spite of demands tending to produce significant deviations from this level. In the body, the processes of heat loss must be balanced by heat production in order that "body" temperature be maintained. Body temperature is usually measured by summing weighted measurements of skin and rectal temperatures, the usual weighting factors being 30 per cent for skin temperature and 70 per cent for rectal (or core), temperature. The heat content of the body is the product of its mean body temperature, its mass, and the specific volumetric heat of its tissues. Under equilibrium conditions, when the heat content of the body does not change, the rate at which heat is produced by metabolic processes, exercise, or fever is equal to the rate of heat loss by radiation, convection, and evaporation. Each of these avenues of heat loss have been mentioned already.

To control body heat exchange and maintain a constant internal temperature, tissues of the periphery are allowed to cool or warm by changes in blood flow. Vasomotor activity not only controls the amount of blood flowing through the periphery, it also changes the flow from deeper to more superficial vessels, and vice versa. The principal thermal gradients in the limbs extend longitudinally, from the hands along the arms and/or from the feet along the legs to the trunk. The major thermal gradients in the trunk are transverse to the surface and usually much smaller in magnitude than are those in the limbs. Although the shapes of these gradients are complex and differ greatly under different environmental conditions, they tend to become flattened when the surface of the body is warmed and to become steep when the surface is cooled. By this mechanism, the heat content of the body, and therefore the core temperature, is kept relatively uniform in spite of variations in the environment.

The effective insulation of a given thickness of air around cylinders having small radii is less than the same thickness of the air layer around cylinders having larger radii. This relative loss of effective insulation is due to what is called the *curvature effect*. Because of their relatively small radii, the fingers act as effective heat exchange structures. Regulation of the amount of blood flowing through the fingers is an important method used in affecting the total amount of heat gained or lost without producing significant changes in average skin temperature (Burton and Edholm, 1955).

Over the limited ambient temperature range from 28 to 31°C, merely minimal changes in vasomotor tone are sufficient to maintain thermal balance in a resting human. Small, irregular fluctuations in skin temperature and slower, cyclic changes in rectal temperature occur under these circumstances. It has been postulated that temperature regulation in these conditions is primarily controlled by the cutaneous thermal receptors rather than by central hypothalamic activity (Hardy, 1961). Assuming a value for the thermal insulation of the tissues between 0.1 and 0.8 clo and a resting metabolic rate, it has been calculated that the skin temperature could change from a minimum of about 30°C to a maximum of about 36°C without producing a change in deep body temperature (Bazett, 1949).

Exposure of a normally clothed man to a cold environment (below about 15°C) produces a drop in skin temperature and stimulation of the peripheral cold receptors within a few minutes, as evidenced by distinct sensations of cold. In addition, the peripheral blood vessels constrict, while those in the core region dilate, thereby resulting in a shift of blood flow to the warmer regions of the body. Piloerection over the surface tends to increase the thickness and effectiveness of the insulating air covering the skin. Shift of the blood to the core is accompanied by an initial rise in rectal temperature, which gradually falls even below normal levels if the cold exposure is prolonged. By constriction of the superficial veins in the skin, cooled blood returning to the core travels along the deeper-lying arteries, thereby precooling the blood supply to the limbs.

Thus, a gradual cooling of the distal portions of the limbs occurs, reducing heat loss from these parts, to about one-sixth that measured when the blood vessels are dilated. Even under cold conditions, however, about two-thirds of the normal, resting heat loss due to evaporation of water from the skin and respiratory tract persists (Newburgh and Harris, 1945).

Supplementing the effects of vasoconstriction in the face of continuing heat loss, heat production increases. Heat production results from shivering, the specific dynamic action of foods, exercise, and secretion of hormones. Intermittent chills and shivering usually result in "bursts" of heat production that tend to restore lost body heat, although the loss generally exceeds replacement. Voluntary muscular exercise increases metabolic heat production and assumption of a curled-up position decreases the body area from which heat can be lost. The question of whether increased heat production in the cold is achieved without contractions of skeletal muscles is still not settled. The thyroid, adrenal, pituitary, and sympathetic nervous system have all been implicated in the increased metabolic response elicited by cold exposure. No consistent metabolic adaptive responses have been found in men living in cold climates, although this may merely reflect the fact that man has adopted a variety of behavioral responses to minimize his actual exposure to cold. In this respect, laboratory tests of nude or lightly clothed resting men in long exposures to cool environments may far exceed the demands encountered under usual living conditions in very cold climates.

One of the principal physiological responses upon exposure to a warm environment is the rapid onset of peripheral vasodilation. Since this response may occur while the internal temperature of the body is falling, it appears to be reflex in nature. Although heat application may have a direct dilating effect upon the skin blood vessels, the effect can also be elicited by blocking the action of sympathetic nerve fibers or by stimulation of vasodilator or pain fibers. The formation and release of bradykinin by active sweat glands also produces a periglandular vasodilatation (Fox and Hilton, 1958). Vasodilatation brings the more peripheral parts of the body, especially the hands and feet, which are initially below core temperature, to higher temperatures, thereby enabling the core to lose heat to the cooler periphery.

Heat is transported primarily by the convective action of the blood; the amount and distribution of blood flow determines the effectiveness of the vasomotor response. When the major portion of the blood flow to the limbs is confined to the deeper lying vessels, heat exchange takes place primarily between warmer and cooler blood flowing in adjacent vessels. On the other hand, blood flow through the dilated superficial vessels of the skin causes the temperature of the distal tissues to increase. Changes in tissue thermal conductance, which reflect changes in tissue blood flow, may increase by a factor of six, while concomitant blood flow changes themselves may be many times greater. Relatively small changes in skin temperature have been found to be sufficient for producing large changes in the cutaneous blood flow of the hand (Cooper, *et al.*, 1956). Depending upon the size and sensitivity of the body area heated or cooled, changes in blood flow through a distant local region of the skin may be induced. Thus, heating the face was found to be more effective in raising the skin temperature and blood flow of the hands in a cool environment than heating the chest or legs (Bader and Macht, 1948).

Water derived from the blood in cutaneous capillaries and tissue spaces diffuses through the epidermis and passes as vapor into the ambient atmosphere (regardless of its relative humidity) without causing a noticeable wetting of the skin surface. Together with vapor evaporating from the moist surfaces of the respiratory tract, almost one quarter of the total heat loss from the body is thus accounted for under usual conditions. This continuous "insensible" loss of water from the body may include the output of some intermittently active sweat glands.

When the ambient temperature exceeds approximately 29°C for clothed rested men (about 31°C for nude men), producing a skin temperature of 34.5°C, active sweating is necessary in order to achieve thermal balance. At ambient temperatures above that of the body, evaporation is the only mechanism by which heat loss can occur. This evaporation must not only compensate for the environmental heat load, but also for metabolic heat production caused by exercise. Vapor pressure of the atmosphere, air movement over the body, and wetted skin area are some of the other factors affecting evaporative heat loss. Although ineffective in removing body heat, dripping sweat may reduce salt accumulation on the skin and thus remove a substance that could interfere with evaporative cooling by lowering the vapor pressure (Macpherson and Newling, 1954).

Extremely hot conditions (38°C dry-bulb temperature, 34.8°C wet-bulb temperature) in which hard work is being done by acclimatized men can lead to sweating rates of about 4 liters per hour (Ladell, 1945). Loss of body fluid at this astounding rate can be supported for only a short period. Even at rates of about 1½ liters per hour, fatigue of the sweating mechanism occurs within hours and leads to high skin and rectal temperatures not unlike those occurring in heat stroke. Prolonged exposure to a hot climate may also result in fatigue of the sweating mechanism. Replacement of body water by voluntary drinking due to thirst sensations during periods of marked sweat loss is usually not sufficient to prevent dehydration, in spite of the fact that urine formation is also depressed. The latter occurs because of release of antidiuretic hormone from the pituitary. Once profuse sweating begins, the normal hemodilution observed in a warm environment is reversed, and hemoconcentration results (Adolph, 1947). The central nervous system must also contribute to the hemodilution reaction to heat, since cord transection or anesthesia minimizes or abolishes the reaction (Barbour and Tolstoi, 1924).

Heat acclimatization refers to the marked improvement in working ability, elimination of subjective discomfort, and reduction in the physiological cost of performance after prolonged exposure to a hot environment. The physiological changes include reduced cardiovascular strain, secretion of a more dilute sweat, and increased stability of body temperature. Salt retention in the acclimatized individual is in marked contrast to the 20g/day salt loss that may occur in unacclimatized persons working in the heat. Increased secretion of the hormone, aldosterone, by the adrenal cortex may be responsible for this salt retention. Another characteristic change seen in heat acclimatization is the increased capability of the sweat glands to produce sweat and the shortened latency between heat exposure and the start of sweating. Increases in metabolic rate commonly seen in acute heat exposure tend to return toward normal values after acclimatization has occurred, and this holds true for both the resting and working individual.

Eighty per cent of the energy expended in muscular exercise appears in the form of heat generated within the body. The internal thermal stress of exercise causes the body temperature to increase to a level that is essentially the same, regardless of environmental temperature. This body temperature increase depends primarily upon work rate, but may not begin, in a warm environment, before sweating occurs. The temperature of the skin overlying active muscles is increased, but once evaporation of sweat becomes effective, skin temperature falls and remains relatively low without evoking cold sensations. Depending upon the duration and severity of the exercise and the nature of the environmental conditions, heat-loss mechanisms continue to operate for some time after exercise stops. Panting is a response rarely seen in man, except when body temperature is increased by exercise or extreme environmental conditions. Increased respiratory ventilation not only increases oxygen uptake and removes large quantities of carbon dioxide produced in exercise, but also removes increased amounts of body heat by convection and evaporation. It is interesting to consider that the same body temperature changes that occur with moderate exercise are free of the concomitant performance decrement seen in subjects at rest in a hot environment.

Before leaving the discussion of physiological reactions relating to body temperature regulation, brief mention must be made of temperature sensation. The exact identification of the cutaneous temperature receptors has been a matter of controversy for many years. Application of modern techniques of fixing and staining tissues has, however, resulted in the observation of fine, naked axoplasmic filaments situated just below the stratum granulosum. Thus, except for its most superficial layer, the skin is plentifully supplied with nerve terminals potentially capable of giving rise to afferent impulses that may evoke temperature sensation. Stimulation of localized skin areas has shown that marked thermal sensitivity differences exist between one region and another, that spatial summation plays an important role in determining the intensity of sensation experienced, and that temperature sensation is related to the absolute temperature level of the skin and its rate of change of temperature. In connection with the last two phenomena, the former may be associated with the static impulse discharge of the thermal receptors while the latter may be produced by phastic, or transient, discharges.

Present indications are that only very small changes in the firing rate of any given receptor are necessary to evoke temperature sensations. It has been speculated that the intimate mechanism of fiber stimulation may be the reversible disruption of protein bonds in the fibril membrane, thereby causing permeability and electric potential changes (Hardy, 1961). From analyses of subcutaneous temperature changes after irradiation of the skin with pulsatile infrared and microwave stimuli, it has recently been proposed that the effective stimulus for threshold warmth sensation in the forehead is a temperature increase of about $0.02°C$ occurring between two subcutaneous layers. The more superficial layer is about 150–200 microns below the skin surface, while the deeper layer is about 1 mm below the surface (Hendler and Hardy, 1962). The relative importance of peripheral and central temperature receptors in the regulation of body temperature is still a matter of lively debate and is stimulating further investigations in this important area of interest.

Many of the factors discussed above were involved in the extensive training given to the Project Mercury astronauts. Control was exercised over the level and changes in temperature and flow rate of suit ventilation gases, of chamber wall and air temperatures, and of barometric pressure. In this way, the thermal and pressure conditions of prelaunch, orbit, reentry and post-landing phases of various orbital flight patterns could be simulated. By measuring weight changes of the subject and clothing, skin surface and rectal temperatures, and heart action (electrocardiograms), the physiological status of the subjects could be evaluated during extended test periods lasting almost 17 hours. The results of these experiments showed that the principal thermal stress occurred during the post-landing period (Hendler and Santa Maria, 1961), and this was also the actual experience of the astronaut who had completed the first U.S. orbital space flight (Glenn, 1962). Tests of this kind are not only useful for training purposes, but they also provide information for evaluating environmental and life support systems.

Performance Factors

It is obvious that performance and behavior of the individual as an operating entity depends upon the functional status of the parts that comprise the whole. As indicated previously, exposure of the individual to environmental temperature extremes can result in a wide variety of compensatory changes, the over-all effects of which can confidently be expected to result in performance decrement when the compensation is insufficient. Inasmuch as performance may involve little physical work but considerable mental effort of a sustained and intensive nature, it may be expected that the precise effects of temperature stress are difficult to ascertain quantitatively and reliably. Actually, a review of the work done in many laboratories in attempts to determine the effects of ambient environmental conditions on performance leads one to the general conclusion that in contrast to the more readily demonstrable decreases in capability to do physical work, the effects upon performance involving largely mental processes are more variable and unpredictable.

Reactions to muscular activity, even in moderate environmental temperature, depends upon such factors as the type of work to be done, and the age, sex, and nutritional and physical condition of the individual. Physiological criteria most commonly used in assessing the effects of muscular work usually include measures of heart rate, blood pressure, respiratory rate and volume, composition of expired respiratory gases, levels of blood lactate and glucose, body temperature, and rate of sweating. Measurements made while subjects are resting have little significance for determining the capacity of the individual to work efficiently, and one must therefore depend upon data collected during the periods of exercise and subsequent recovery. This task has been eased by recent advances in biomedical instrumentation miniaturization and telemetering techniques.

Of all the factors mentioned that influence the capacity of an individual to do muscular work, none has a greater effect than physical fitness. The physically fit individual is the one who performs the maximum amount of work for the minimum cost, where cost is measured as the total amount of energy required to perform the work done, including that expended during the recovery period. Perhaps the most convenient index of the physiological response of an individual to a given physical task is the measurement of heart rate. It is a measurement that can easily be obtained with present-day instrumentation without interfering with the subject's movements or adding to the difficulty of the task. It is also a fatithful mirror of the changes occurring among the other physiological factors mentioned previously. In addition, heart rate is one of the few measures that can detect difference between physically fit and unfit subjects while they are at rest, before exercise. In general, a slow heart rate when the subject is recumbent or erect, with only a small rate change accompanying these posture changes, is indicative of superior physical condition. It is common observation, however, that regardless of the physical fitness of the working individual, a stage is eventually reached where the level of performance begins to deteriorate and fatigue effects become subjectively and objectively obvious.

Maximum work rate depends upon the efficiency of supplying oxygen to the tissues for releasing the energy necessary for muscular contractions. Consumption of oxygen varies from ½ liter per minute during light work to over 2 liters per minute during heavy work. Insufficiency of oxygen can partly be compensated by the substitution of anerobic processes, but when these processes predominate, excessive amounts of lactic acid are accumulated, until performance stops. High blood levels of lactic acid decrease the alkali reserve and thus enhance the expulsion of carbon dioxide from the body. Based upon tolerance limits to accumulated lactic acid, it has been calculated that an individual can run at top speed without breathing for about 43 sec. After heavy exercise, blood levels of lactic acid may be 30 times greater than normal, and it may require an hour and a half for the excess acid to be reconverted to glycogen in the liver and excreted in the urine. Recovery after exercise involves utilization of oxygen to metabolize both the usual food materials for energy and excess lactic acid. Even though the "debt" of oxygen incurred during severe exercise is "repaid" during the post-exercise recovery process, a much longer period may be required for all physiological processes to return to their normal levels.

During hard work, heart rate can increase almost instantly and rise to 150 per cent of its resting level. A drop in pulse pressure (the difference between systolic and diastolic pressures) to about half of its maximum value, during exercise, is indicative of increasing fatigue. This decrease in pulse pressure may persist during the recovery period, particularly if the preceding exercise was severe. Blood pressure and heart rate usually resume resting, pre-exercise levels within ½ to 1 hour after exercise stops, although the surrounding conditions may modify these responses. Blood flow during exercise is diverted chiefly to the working muscles, although an increasing amount of blood is directed to the skin for cooling purposes and to the respiratory muscles. An increased amount of oxygen is extracted from blood hemoglobin as it passes through the working muscles.

In evaluating the physiological cost of heat stress and work, Brouha (1960) found that oxygen consumption alone was insufficient as a measure for this purpose and that cardiovascular function must also be taken into account. He showed that cardiovascular stress increased with high temperature and high humidity conditions and that heart rate during work and recovery varied with work load, environment, and sex, while pulmonary ventilation, oxygen consumption and oxygen debt were primarily dependent upon work load and only secondarily upon environment. Work consisted of pedaling a bicycle ergometer. Heart rates at rest and during work were found to increase linearly with ambient temperature; and an accumulated strain, as evidenced by increased heart rate, resulted from repeated work cycles, especially in severe environments.

Muscular exercise of the type described above is representative of the kind most commonly seen in heavy industrial jobs. These jobs generally are repetitive in nature, are performed frequently in congested, hot, humid, and noisy surroundings, and require only a limited exercise of higher mental reasoning. However, many elements of the stresses and organism responses encountered in such jobs result also from conditions requiring less muscular effort and greater use of mental abilities. These conditions are characteristic of modern man-machine complexes. As mentioned earlier, the effects of temperature upon human performance in these circumstances are more difficult to quantify. There are wide individual differences in reactions to stress, especially when these reactions are evaluated under conditions that necessitate reasoning and fine muscular coordination. Tasks done in the laboratory have many inherent shortcomings: artifacts are easily introduced, conditions of the tasks may be oversimplified, duplication from one situation or laboratory to the next may be incomplete, and the laboratory tasks may be so artificial that the intent of the experimenter may become obvious to the subjects.

For these and other reasons, validating laboratory findings in field studies, under actual operating conditions, is most desirable. The development of modern instrumentation has made the conduct of field investigations both feasible and convenient. However, data presently available regarding temperature effects on human performance are limited to those obtained in the laboratory. Perceptual, psychomotor and physiological measurements have been used almost exclusively to gage performance in these studies. Experimental designs have been primarily of the subject-control types, in which the above measures of performance have been made among the same subjects during exposure to various levels of temperature.

In an effort to express the combined effects of ambient temperature, humidity and air movement in a single scale, the Effective Temperature (ET) scale has been used by many investigators. This scale is based upon subjective impressions of warmth experienced upon exposure to various temperatures, humidities, and air movements, with air and walls at the same temperature. The ET scale is fixed by the temperature of still and saturated air that feels as warm as the conditions under examination. Criticism has been directed against the use of this scale for the following reasons: it requires adjustment at very high temperatures, it does not adequately account for air movements below 100 ft per minute, differences in atmospheric humidity are not adequately accounted for, and radiation is not taken into consideration when appreciable differences exist between the temperature of air and that of surrounding objects.

The so-called "normal scale" has been used for normally-dressed subjects, while the "basic scale" has been used when the subjects have been stripped to the waist. The corrected ET includes a correction factor for radiant heat, obtained when a globe thermometer reading is used in place of dry-bulb temperature.

A typical operational problem served as the basis for one of the earlier experiments to determine high temperature effects on performance. The problem was to determine the effects of very hot atmospheric conditions upon working efficiency and attitude of personnel in the confined spaces on board naval vessels operating in the tropics. Tasks included mental multiplication, number checking, following intertwined lines, and the like to simulate chart room activities. It was found that over a 4-hour work period, no adverse effects on performance were caused by an increase from 75 to 80°F ET. At 87°F ET, however, performance decreased and became more variable, and the subjects became annoyed and very uncomfortable. At 94°F ET, the subjects were unable to complete their tasks and showed signs of increased irritability, dizziness, visual blackout, and nausea (Viteles and Smith, 1946).

The most extensive investigations of human performance in hot environments were conducted by Mackworth (1946, 1947, 1948, 1949, 1950) in England and by Pepler (1953a, b, c, d, e, f, g, h, 1958, 1959) in Singapore. Pepler's earlier studies were done to evaluate the findings of Mackworth and to examine various aspects of the problems in further detail. In one comparative study, the subjects used by both investigators were young telegraphers. Mackworth acclimatized his subjects to "tropical conditions" by daily 3-hour exposures in a warm, humid environment (dry bulb temperature of 95 to 105°F) for periods of 7 to 11 weeks before the actual experimental period. In addition to the fact that Pepler's subjects were living near Singapore, they were further subjected daily to 2- and 3-hour training periods in a chamber with wet bulb/dry bulb conditions of 98/88°F.

The task of the telegraphers was to receive and write down coded messages consisting of groups of mixed letters and figures under various environmental conditions. Mackworth found a deterioration in performance, especially above 86°F ET (all ET are for the basic scale), and that this deterioration was logarithmically related to room temperature. Because of large performance differences between subjects, Pepler did not establish a common standard of accuracy and therefore did not attempt to treat his results in the same way. Pepler found less of an increase in errors at 96°F ET, and even though both investigators found that the most skilled subjects showed the least deterioration, Pepler's highly skilled subjects maintained their level of accuracy despite considerable discomfort at 96°F ET. The number of errors increased from the coolest to the warmest conditions in both studies, and Pepler found that this contrast was larger in the mornings than in the afternoons. The telegraphers living in the tropics maintained their efficiencies better than those living in England, perhaps because of their lesser distraction by profuse sweating.

In another set of similar studies, both experimenters used pursuit-meters on which subjects carried out a tracking task of continuous pointer alignment, involving a moderate amount of strenuous physical work, under various levels of environmental temperature (66 – 91.5°F ET). Significant deteriorations in accuracy occurred in both studies in the warmer environments. Average final rectal temperature and average sweat loss were found in both studies to be related to the environmental conditions, and no direct relationship was found between error score and rectal temperature. In a further analysis of his results, Pepler reported that performance in the warmer condition (84.5°F ET) was more erratic, less accurate, and more disorganized than in the cooler condition (76.2°F ET). Accurate alignment of pointers was slowed, and the pointers lagged more behind the display at 91.2°F ET as compared with 84.5°F ET. Efficiency (greater accuracy with less pointer movement) was greater at 66°F ET than at 76.2°F ET.

A later study of the same kind gave some evidence that high levels of relative humidity caused performance deterioration over a lower range of effective temperatures. In addition, subjects did not report discomfort at certain environmental temperatures, although their performance had deteriorated.

In comparing the results of corresponding studies involving a prolonged visual vigilance task, it was found that the number of missed signals increased when the environment was about $\pm 10°F$ with respect to the control temperature of 76°F ET in England, and at 67 and 92°F ET with respect to the control temperature of 82°F ET in Singapore. Performance was worse in a warm moist environment as compared with a warm dry environment with the same effective temperature. Marked deterioration of average performance occurred both in England and in Singapore over the 2-hour test period. As indicated in the previous studies, performance was not related to the physiological measures of total sweat loss and average final rectal temperature, nor were the subjects able to accurately estimate their performance, because of a tendency to relate comfort with improved efficiency.

From his work, Mackworth concluded that a critical region on the atmospheric temperature scale existed, lying between 81 and 86°F basic ET, above which acclimatized men will not work so efficiently indoors. Pepler pointed out that the critical range of Mackworth was identified by the temperature of a control climate (76°F ET, one that could be maintained in ships in the tropics using current ventilation methods) and a higher temperature at which performance became significantly worse than in the control climate. This upper temperature level was therefore relative and depended upon the control climate chosen. With this in mind, the artificially acclimatized men in England reacted much as those living in the tropics, over the common range of temperature conditions studied in both places.

The logarithmic relationship between error index and air temperature that Mackworth found in several of his experiments was obtained by Pepler in only one tracking experiment, when his experimental conditions most nearly duplicated those of Mackworth. It is believed that this emphasizes the strong dependence of evidence showing performance deterioration with environmental conditions upon the specific experimental methods and analysis used.

Mackworth had observed that skills requiring speed showed progressive deterioration with increased temperature. Pepler had men carry out a complex mental task (reporting numbers of dissimilarities between paired sets of symbols) at three different presentation speeds and in temperatures from 76 to 91°F basic ET. Failure to report comparisons (omissions) constituted the primary source of inefficiency, and these errors of omission were least frequent at the near ambient ET of 81°F, more frequent at ET of 76 and 86°F, and most frequent at 91°F ET. The fact that the climate effect was significant for errors of omission only at the slow speed of working was attributed by Pepler to the probability of other changes in this particular work situation. Proportions of comparisons at the fast speed that were reported incorrectly were significantly greater in the warm climates (86 and 91°F ET) than in the cooler climates (76 and 81°F ET), but this climate effect was not significant at medium and slow working speeds.

Errors of omission and incorrect comparisons increased significantly at the higher working speeds, and a definite practice effect was seen over the four experimental sessions. Almost all subjects felt uncomfortable at 91°F ET, and most preferred to work at the medium speed. However, the unreliability of subjective estimates when compared with measured performance was evident from the facts that all worked best at slow speed and most denied that the climates had affected their performance. Once again, total sweat loss and final rectal temperatures varied with the environmental conditions, but bore no apparent relationship to performance changes.

In a physical effort task, Mackworth found that the adverse effects of high room temperatures on performance could not be counteracted by using greater incentives. He also concluded that when an individual was directing his maximum efforts to perform well, climatic effects were most evident. Using the pursuitmeters and the task of continuous pointer alignment, as already mentioned, Pepler studied the effects of incentive and climate (ET range of 76 to 91°F). High incentive was provided by giving the subjects verbal encouragement during and after the work and telling them how they were doing; under low incentive, the subjects were given no such information or encouragement. Most accurate performance occurred at 81°F ET, with both levels of incentive. The higher incentive level was accompanied by better performance in all climates than the best performance with low incentive. Thus, incentive in this study could compensate for adverse climatic conditions to produce better efficiency. The coolest climate (76°F ET) was most frequently reported as being most comfortable and was erroneously believed to have resulted in the best performance by the subjects themselves.

The effect of two levels of incentive on a complex mental task (reporting dissimilarities between paired sets of symbols) performed at two speed levels was determined by Pepler under the same climatic conditions as just given. Errors of omission (failure to make comparisons) comprised the principal performance deterioration, and these occurred least frequently under both incentive conditions at slow speed and with the high incentive at the fast speed at 81°F ET. Accuracy for all combinations of conditions was greater at 81°F ET than at the cooler temperature of 76°F ET and the warmer temperatures of 86 and 91°F ET. Errors of omission were the same with the low incentive at the fast speed, regardless of climatic conditions. Climate effects were independent of high incentive, as found in the immediately preceding study; but the frequency of omission errors at both speeds in the warmer climates with high incentives were no greater than those with low incentives in the climate of 81°F ET. Subjective estimates of efficiency appeared to be, on the average, more accurate immediately after the subjects left the climatic chamber than those indicated by their responses to a questionnaire given after completion of the whole experiment. Pepler ascribes the latter to the influence of commonly held ideas concerning the effects of unusual climates.

Maximum performance was found to occur at about 70°F, with progressive decreases at both higher and lower ambient temperatures over the range from 50–100°F for subjects performing a visual-motor coordination task for short periods (Teichner and Wehrkamp, 1954). Performance decrement at higher ambient temperatures confirms the findings of Viteles and Smith (1946) and of Mackworth, while the decrement found at lower than comfort temperature is similar to what Pepler found in his studies. It should be noted that the conditions under which this study was conducted were much different, in many respects, from those already discussed.

Bursill (1958) suggests that study of the factor of attention, or the degree to which an operator under thermal stress conditions could successfully notice and respond to peripheral stimuli while engaged upon a continuous central task, would lead to an understanding of the mechanism of performance decrement shown to occur at ambient basic ET greater than 81–82°F. He arranged his apparatus so that the subject's attention was fixed on the central task and so that efficiency would be markedly impaired if the subject were to concentrate upon the peripheral tasks. The number and spatial distribution of peripheral visual signals missed was used to indicate the amount of attention directed to the central task (pursuitmeter). Lightly clad subjects performed in an ET of 65°F, while subjects stripped to the waist worked in a basic ET of 95°F. More peripheral stimuli were missed by most subjects in the hot environment when the central perceptual load was increased (speed of pursuitmeter increased). Bursill concluded that central attentional processes rather than mechanisms peripheral to the central nervous system were implicated. Fatigue produced by continual application to the task and reorganization of functions to deal with excessive heat seemed to be operating in combination to cause performance deterioration in the heat. Bursill suggests a common stress-responsive neuro-physiological basis for activity reduction in hot environments.

In a well-designed experiment, the effect of a wide range of temperatures (14 –104°F) on performance was studied by Russell (1957) using 72 subjects. Five dependent variables were measured: kinesthetic and tactile sensitivity, hand-grip strength, free-movement and pressure tracking, and skin temperature. As ambient and skin temperatures decreased, tactile sensitivity also decreased. It also appeared that tactile sensitivity decreased at high temperatures. Kinesthetic sensitivity was affected only at the low temperatures (below 68°F) and then after longer exposures than those required to produce a decrement in tactile performance. Decrements in hand grip strength began to appear at 50°F and lower and at 86°F and higher. Free-movement tracking, involving isotonic muscular contractions, showed signs of impairment at both ends of the temperature range, while pressure tracking, involving isometric muscular contractions, appeared to be affected only at the lower end of the temperature range. Skin temperature was found to be dependent upon the duration of exposure and ambient temperature in which the tasks were performed.

Not all the evidence presently accumulated shows the same detrimental effects on mental performance produced by exposure to high environmental temperatures as that already cited. For example, Bartlett and Gronow (1953) exposed subjects to room temperature (60–70°F), 80/70°F (dry/wet bulb), 90/80°F, and 100/90°F for 30 minutes before testing and then tested them in the same environmental temperatures for an additional 30 minutes. The tests consisted of having the subjects make decisions on the outcome of a game involving anticipatory perception and judgment. On the basis of error scores and "decision times," no effect due to heat level was found.

Pepler's experiment on the performance of a complex mental task (reporting numbers of dissimilarities between paired sets of symbols) in various environmental conditions was repeated, with certain modifications by Chiles (1958). The results of his study failed to confirm Pepler's findings of a performance decrement at environmental temperatures of ±5°F from an optimum basic effective temperature of 81°F. Chiles found that increased temperature (75–98°F basic ET) had no significant effect on the number of comparisons omitted nor on the number of errors made. At a basic ET of 109°F (two out of five subjects became nauseous and withdrew from the experiment), the subjects perspired profusely, which tended to interfere with vision, and the mean number of errors increased. Chiles felt that this level may be near the upper temperature limit for task performance by an unprotected subject.

Examination of the conditions under which the last mentioned experiments were conducted and their comparison with the results previously given provide insight into the limitations and difficulties associated with performance measurement in various environments. In Bartlett and Gronow's experiment, and those of Chiles, the subjects used were research workers in the first instance and college students in the second. In contrast, most of the previously described experiments were conducted with military enlisted men. Apparently, college-trained subjects can more readily maintain high levels of attention to detail, concentrate, and remain free from boredom, as well as devise more effective ways of attacking mental tasks, than can enlisted men in the armed services. Competence also seems to insure better performance under adverse environmental conditions. Bartlett and Gronow's work also suggests that performance involving anticipatory interpretation of static displays is less adversely affected by high-temperature conditions than performance involving current interpretation of displays that move from item to item in quick succession.

Chiles' procedures differed in several significant ways from those of Pepler, and these differences may also have contributed to the differences in results obtained. Whereas Pepler's subjects were dressed only in shorts in all environments, Chiles' subjects wore street clothes instead of shorts for the two lowest effective temperatures. Thus, Chiles tended to reduce the effect of any difference between environments. The symbols used in the comparison tasks were different in the two investigations, and Chiles did not use shields to obscure part of the display, as did Pepler. This last difference permitted Chiles' subjects to have more time for making comparisons and probably decreased their need for scanning activity.

In Bartlett and Gronow's experiment, interest was maintained at a high level by having the subjects pass from one display to the next, rather than being required to tend to a continuous operation with few or no distinct breaks. In addition, the duration of heat exposure was limited to only 30-minute periods.

In contrast to the moderately hot environments described so far, in the experiments of Blockley and Lyman (1951) four task-trained pilots were exposed for 61 minutes to 160°F, 29 minutes to 200°F and 21 minutes to 235°F (all figures represent average physiologically tolerable durations and nominal temperatures) and required to "fly" a series of flight patterns by instruments in a simulated aircraft cockpit. The subjects continued their flight task during removal from the environmental chamber and for a short time thereafter.

Deterioration of pilot performance was found to be definitely associated with the discomfort and distress of the terminal stages of heat exposure, although relatively more competent and younger subjects showed a larger proportion of nondeteriorated performance in the heat. Deterioration was found to begin from 4 to 13 minutes before the exposures were terminated for physiological reasons. Four to six minutes following heat withdrawal were necessary for performance to return to a level such as that existing just before termination of the exposure. Another 8 to 12 minutes were then required before proficiency was restored to the original, pre-exposure level. A consistent tendency toward reduced tolerance time was found for the complex flying task just described as compared with that for a relatively simple task previously run.

In a somewhat comparable study, Pepler (1959), exposed six task-trained sailors to 116/105°F, dry/wet bulb temperatures, for 30 minutes while they attempted to align a pointer with an erratically moving target mark under conditions of near-threshold visibility. Misalignment by more than a preset amount was indicated to the subject with a warning light. The results of this experiment were in substantial agreement with those of Blockley and Lyman (1951). Preterminal symptoms were similar to those experienced by Blockley and Lyman's subjects and performance was found to deteriorate most severely during the last 10 minutes or so of work, although an earlier decrement was also observed. It appeared that a break in continuous task activity could temporarily restore performance efficiency in spite of continued heat stress. Near the end of the heat exposures it appeared as though the subjects' responses became increasingly uncoordinated and more automatic.

Fraser and Jackson (1955) exposed subjects to ambient temperatures from 90 to 104°F (90–95 per cent saturation) and measured serial reaction times using a visual vigilance test. Serial reaction times were obtained by measuring the intervals between continuously and irregularly presented signals and the subject's responses. A small but significant rise in serial reaction time was found to occur under conditions of the heat stress employed.

A more recent study (Fine, *et al.*, 1960) was concerned with the effect of high humidity at high and moderate ambient temperatures upon sustained, complex mental performance. Subjects were exposed for six ½-hour periods on four successive days to 70/53°F, 70/68°F, 95/70.5°F, and 95/92°F (dry/wet bulb temperatures) with minimal wind. Tasks consisted of anagram solving and auditory discrimination. No increment or decrement in the performance of these tasks was found that could be ascribed to the environmental conditions.

Studies of cold temperature upon performance have dealt primarily with localized effects of cold upon the hands. These studies have been motivated, to a considerable extent, by the typical operational situation in which men are required to perform in a cold environment. In these cases, sufficient clothing is usually provided to assure thermal protection of the covered parts of the body. For the hands, however, the problem is complicated by the fact that at the same time that insulation must be added for thermal protection, the form and nature of the insulation must be compatible with reasonable manual dexterity.

A simple "V" test apparatus devised by Mackworth (1953) to measure finger numbness has subsequently been used by a number of other investigators. The apparatus consists of two rulers bolted together in the form of a V, and the test consists of determining the minimum gap between the ruler edges that can be distinguished by the finger. Comparisons were made between the gap discerned by the index finger tip at an ambient temperature of about 68°F with that distinguished by the same finger after 3-minute exposures to air temperatures ranging between −13 and −31°F and wind speeds from 0 to 10 miles per hour and during subsequent rewarming. The numbing effect of very low temperatures was almost tripled by the presence of a breeze, and men accustomed to working outdoors in the cold resisted finger numbness better than those accustomed to working indoors. Skin-temperature measurements showed that the fingers of the "outdoor" men remained warmer, probably because of some kind of physiological adaptation that increased hand blood flow.

In a series of tests similar to those just cited, Mills (1953) found that the minimum detectable gap increased more rapidly with lower levels of finger surface temperature, so that while the gap had to be increased by a few tenths of a millimeter to be detected when finger skin temperature dropped from 30 to 20°C, an increase in gap size of over 1.5 mm was necessary to compensate for a skin temperature drop from 15 to 5°C. Finger numbness was found to vary in intensity from one occasion to the next at low skin temperatures and was believed to be linked to current periods of vasodilation and vasoconstriction, such as are usually observed in cooled parts of the extremities. Other tests showed that the sensitivity of cooled fingers to a one-point contact force decreased, so that a force of about a gram at a skin temperature of 30°C was almost doubled to produce a threshold sensation at a skin temperature close to 0°C (Mills, 1957). The threshold for vibration perception of wrist skin increased markedly when the skin cooled, and this finding was ascribed to temperature-induced changes in receptor chemical processes rather than to changes in the mechanical properties of the cooled skin (Weitz, 1941).

In a more recent comparison (LeBlanc, *et al.*, 1960) between

Canadian fishermen accustomed to immersing their hands in cold water and control subjects from the same vicinity, the cold-water pressor response was found to be greater in the controls, while the fishermen had higher hand skin temperatures and complained less of pain during cold water immersion. Here again, adaptation of the hands to cold was accompanied by warmer temperatures. Finger numbness as measured by the V test indicated that the controls had somewhat greater numbness than the fishermen, but this difference was considered nonsignificant because of the variability of response in the two groups.

The effect of localized cold upon manual performance was studied (Clark and Cohen, 1960; Clark, 1961) by having men dressed in shorts and shoes at an ambient temperature of 70 or 75°F insert their hands into a refrigerated box and tie knots in cords while being timed with a stopwatch. It was found that slower cooling rates were associated with greater decrements in performance and that these decrements persisted even after the hands were rewarmed to precooling temperature. For the task involved (that is, one in which there is considerable movement of the hand joints), performance was unaffected at a hand-skin temperature of 60°F, while a further drop in skin temperature of 5°F was associated with critical performance decrement.

These data were unaltered by exposure duration. It appears likely, therefore, that some critical internal hand temperature must be maintained in a cold environment to prevent performance decrement of the type being discussed and that this temperature is probably around 56°F. Differences in individual susceptibility to cold, however, also play an important role in affecting performance. Subjects having bare hands but otherwise warmly dressed untied knots in an ambient temperature of −10°F. The range of times for which this repetitive task could be performed extended from a minimum of 10 minutes to a maximum of 50 minutes for the various subjects (Bader and Mead, 1951).

After reviewing much of the pertinent data, Dusek (1957) concluded that serious deterioration in hand functions occur when finger temperatures drop below 60°F, that pain and considerable loss of manual performance occur below 50°F, and that below 40°F there is a loss of tactile discrimination and ability to perform manual skills requiring fine movements.

According to Horvath and Freedman (1944), the decrease in speed of upside-down alphabet printing of warmly clothed subjects wearing mittens at an ambient temperature of −20°F can be attributed to writing inefficiency rather than to any mental deterioration. Under the same conditions, similar deterioration was observed for a gear assembly test. After sitting quietly for 3 hours in an ambient temperature of −10 to

—14°F, subjects wearing arctic clothing with mittens showed an average decrease in hand-grip strength of about 28 per cent, with no correlation between reports of the severity of hand pain and decrease in grip pressure.

Blair and Gottschalk (1947) found that performance decreased for men wearing arctic uniforms in an environment of —13 to —40°F with a wind velocity of 3–5 mph. These men had had preliminary training in operating a radar trainer, a switchboard, and a radio, but the largest deterioration in performance occurred with the radar trainer. Deterioration was also caused by contact with metal control handles of the trainer. Cold discomfort after 1½ hours at —40°F was followed by dangerous lowering of hand and foot temperatures after another hour of exposure.

Men living in a chamber maintained at 55°F were found to be less sensitive to radiant heat pain and less accurate in performing a visual-motor task (pursuit rotor) than they were when living in an ambient temperature of 75°F (Teichner and Kobrick, 1955). Impairment of visual-motor performance at the lower temperature was concluded to be the result of a lowering of the performance limit rather than a reduction in the rate or upper limit of learning.

Visual and auditory reaction times were measured by Collins and Kitching (cited in McBlair, *et al.*, 1955) in subjects in ambient temperatures of 0 and —50°F. At 0°F no significant decrease in reaction time was found, although the subjects became drowsy when initially returned to a warm room and therefore showed increased reaction times. Performance deteriorated as much as 50 per cent in the —50°F environment, and this effect was believed to be due to the discomfort of the low temperature rather than to the lowering of body temperature that occurred. No data were obtained to support the belief that the low temperature interfered with the visual process.

Attempts have been made to measure the effects of various dietary constituents on the performance of men in cold environments. Keeton, *et al.* (1946), exposed subjects to —20°C for 8 hours daily five day a week and 4 hours on Saturday. Although the men wore arctic clothing, they did not have sufficient insulation to maintain thermal equilibrium. Various visual and psychomotor tests were used to determine the effects of different diets: critical flicker fusion frequency, visual choice reaction time, speed of tapping, coordination time, and static and dynamic measures of manual steadiness. A high-carbohydrate diet was found to be better than a high-protein diet in reducing the effect of intense cold on general psychomotor functioning. Skin cooling, especially of the extremities, was slowed for those eating the high-carbohydrate diet. When the high-carbohydrate diet was compared with one having a high-fat content (Mitchell, *et al.*, 1946), the latter was more efficient in maintaining rectal temperature, and the psychomotor performance of the subjects was also improved.

Another important factor affecting performance in the cold is acclimatization. Acclimatization has been induced by exposing subjects to cold conditions for relatively short daily intervals over a period of a few weeks. Mackworth (1950) used daily exposures of 2 hours for a total of 5 weeks in a temperature of −15°C. Subjects wore winter clothing, but the hands were kept bare. Sensations of extreme cold in the hands reported after 10–30 minutes during the first week were not experienced until 1–2 hours in the second and third weeks. Blowing a 6-mile-per-hour wind on the hands during the experiments was reported to produce prolonged and intense pain initially, but this procedure became painless after sufficient cold exposure had been experienced. Apparently the increased skin temperature of the hand seen in cold acclimatized men is part of the generalized physiological response resulting in better performance.

The most recent study on this subject (Joy, *et al.*, 1962) indicates that the only common physiological change of cold acclimatization in animals and man is a decline in, or extinction of, shivering. The implication here is that some cellular biochemical changes occur that supply heat for maintaining body temperature in spite of the lack of thermogenesis due to shivering. Finally, the importance of the cortical aspect must not be overlooked. Interpretation of the cold stimulus may have a dramatic effect on performance capability and on autonomic nervous response. In fact, it is this cortical factor, rather than the limited physiological responses available, that is responsible for the greatest portion of the improvement in human performance acquired with time in cold environments.

The experimental data seem to lead to several generalizations about temperature effects on performance. Not only do these effects vary with different skills (for example, decrease of finger dexterity in the cold) that involve physical work, but tasks involving perception and reasoning, or judgment, are also affected. Certain basic elements forming a portion of the total task performance may be especially sensitive to environmental conditions. Various kinds of performance tasks may have ranges of optimal temperature conditions. In order to investigate and determine these optimal temperatures, it is necessary to include a sufficiently wide range of conditions in both field and laboratory experiments. The skill of the operator may determine how his performance will be affected by temperature, as shown so clearly in the work of Mackworth and Pepler. Again, from the work of these investigators, performance improvement in adverse ambient temperature conditions by the use of incentives was indicated. The important role in performance played by the process of environmental acclimation was pointed out, as were the subjects' sensations of temperature and their relation of these sensations to feelings of comfort and discomfort.

Our present knowledge of the interactions of man and his thermal environment has many limitations when applied to problems involving manned space-flight operations. For example, heat exchange in atmospheres of reduced pressure and unusual gaseous composition must be studied. The effects of weightlessness create problems with respect to the efficient removal of vapor and heated gases that will tend to accumulate around the body of the astronaut, especially during sleep. Once the man is outside the protective environment of the space craft, satisfactory methods must be devised to keep him from burning upon direct exposure to the sun and freezing in the shade. This problem is complicated by the changing types of thermal radiation fields that may exist and the influence of body orientation with respect to the solar system and nearby objects. Methods must also be devised to assure maximum human performance under severe temperature stress in case of equipment failure. In this connection, acclimatization is an important method to combat the deleterious effects of high temperature and may be achieved during the preflight training period by daily heat exposures.

Questions regarding the combined effect of many stresses on physiological tolerance and performance capability remain largely unanswered at the present time. The roles of nutrition and exercise during prolonged flights in confined quarters and their relation to body heat balance must be clarified. The examples of problems just given represent but a few of those relating to the important topic of temperature effects on the human component in manned space operations.

References

Adolph, E. F. *Physiology of Man in the Desert*, New York: Interscience, 1947.

Bader, M. E., and Macht, M. B. "Indirect Peripheral Vasodilatation," *J. Appl. Physiol.*, *1*:215, 1948.

———, and Mead, J. "Individual Differences in Vascular Responses and Their Relation to Cold Tolerance," *J. Appl.*, *Physiol.*, *3*:508, 1951.

Barbour, H. G., and Tolstoi, E. "Heat Regulation and Water Exchange: II. The Role of the Water Content of the Blood, and Its control by the Central Nervous System, *Am. J. Physiol.*, *67*:378, 1924.

Bartlett, D. J., and Gronow, D. G. C. *The Effects of Heat Stress on Mental Performance*, Report No. 846, Flying Personnel Res. Comm. (FPRC), August, 1953.

Bazett, H. C. "The Regulation of Body Temperatures," in L. H. Newburgh (ed.), *Physiology of Heat Regulation*, Philadelphia: Saunders, 1949, pp 109–192.

Blair, E. A., and Gottschalk, C. W. *"Efficiency of Signal Corps Operators in Extreme Cold,"* Proj. No. 57-2, Armored Med. Res. Lab., 1947.

Blockley, W. V., and Lyman, J. *"Studies of Human Tolerance for Extreme Heat: IV. Psychomotor Performance of Pilots as Indicated by a Task Simulating Aircraft Instrument Flight*, Tech. Report No. 6521, U.S. Air Force, May, 1951.

Brouha, L. *Physiology in Industry*, New York: Pergamon Press, 1960.

Bursill, A. E. "The Restriction of Peripheral Vision during Exposure to Hot and Humid Conditions," *Quart. J. Exp. Psychol., 10*:113, 1958.

Burton, A. C., and Edholm, O. G. *Man in a Cold Environment.* London: Edward Arnold, 1955.

Chiles, W. D. "Effects of Elevated Temperatures on Performance of a Complex Mental Task," *Ergonomics, 2*:89, 1958.

Clark, R. E. *The Limiting Hand Skin Temperature for Unaffected Manual Performance in the Cold*, Tech. Report EP-147, Quartermaster Res. and Eng. Command, U.S. Army, February, 1961.

—— and Cohen, A. "Manual Performance as a Function of Rate of Change in Hand Skin Temperature, *J. Appl. Physiol., 15*:496, 1960.

Cooper, K. E., Ferris, H. M., and Mottram, R. F. "Changes in Hand Blood Flow Evoked by Rapid Alteration of the Radiant Heat Exchange between the Front of the Body and the Environment," *J. Physiol., 131*:29, 1956.

Dusek, E. R. "Effect of Temperature on Manual Performance," *Protection and Functioning of the Hand in Cold Climates*, Washington, D.C.: Nat. Acad. Sci.–Nat. Res. Coun. 1957.

Fine, B. J., Cohen, A., and Crist, B. "Effect of Exposure to High Humidity at High and Moderate Ambient Temperature on Anagram Solution and Auditory Discrimination," *Psychol. Reports, 7*:171, 1960.

Fox, R. H., and Hilton, S. M. "Bradykinin Formation in Human Skin as a Factor in Heat Vasodilatation," *J. Physiol., 142*:219, 1958.

Fraser, D. C., and Jackson, K. F. "Effect of Heat Stress on Serial Reaction Time in Man," *Nature, 176*:976, 1955.

Glenn, J. H., Jr. "Pilot's Flight Report," in *Results of First U.S. Manned Orbital Space Flight, Feb. 20, 1962*, Washington, D.C.: U.S. Government Printing Office, 1962.

Hardy, J. D. "The Physiology of Temperature Regulation," *Physiol. Rev., 41*: 521, 1961.

—— and DuBois, E. F. "Regulation of Heat Loss from the Human Body," *Proc. Nat. Acad. Sci., 23*:624–631, 1937.

Hendler, E., Hardy, J. D., and Murgatroyd, D. "Skin Heating and Temperature Sensation Produced by Infrared and Microwave Irradiation," in *Temperature —Its Measurement and Control in Science and Industry*, New York: Reinhold, 1962.

―――― and Santa Maria, L. J. "Response of Subjects to Some Conditions of Simulated Orbital Flight Pattern," *Aerospace Med.*, *32*:126–133, 1961.

Horvath, S. M., and Freedman, A. *Influence of Cold upon the Efficiency of Personnel*, Proj. No. 1-11, *Armored Med. Res. Lab.*, 1944.

Joy, R. J. T., Poe, R. H., Berman, F. R., and Davis, T. R. A. "Some Physiological Responses to Arctic Living," *Arch. Environmental Health*, 4, 22, 1962.

Keeton, R. W., Lambert, E. H., Glickman, N., Mitchell, H. H., Last, T. H., and Fahnstock, M. K. "The Tolerance of Man to Cold as Affected by Dietary Modifications: Protein vs. Carbohydrates and the Effect of Variable Protective Clothing," *Am. J. Physiol.*, *146*:66, 1946.

Keller, A. D. "Thermal Regulation," *Phys. Therapy Rev.*, *30*:1, 1950.

Ladell, W. S. S. "Thermal Sweating," *Brit. Med. Bull.*, *3*:175, 1945.

LeBlanc, J., Hildes, J. A., and Heroux, O. "Tolerance of Gaspé Fishermen to Cold Water," *J. Appl. Physiol.*, *15*:1031, 1960.

McBlair, W., Rumbaugh, D., and Fozard, J. *Ventilation, Temperature, Humidity*, Contract Nonr-1268(01), San Diego College Foundation, December, 1955.

Mackworth, N. H. "Effects of Heat on Wireless Operators Hearing and Recording Morse Code Messages," *Brit. J. Med.*, *3*:143, 1946.

―――――. "High Incentives versus Hot and Humid Atmospheres in a Physical Effort Task," *Brit. J. Psychol. 38*:90, 1947.

―――――. "Definition of the Upper Limit of Environmental Warmth by Psychological Tests of Human Performance," *Roy. Soc. Emp. Conf. Rep.*, *1*:423, 1948.

―――――. "Human Problems of Work Design," *Nature*, *164*:882, 1949.

―――――. *Researches on the Measurement of Human Performance*, S.R.S. No. 268, Med. Res. Council. London: H.M. Stationery Office, 1950.

―――――. "Finger Numbness in Very Cold Winds," *J. Appl. Physiol.*, *5*:533, 1953.

MacPherson, R. K., and Newling, P. S. B. "Salt Concentration and Evaporation of Sweat," *J. Physiol.*, *123*:74P, 1954.

Mills, A. W. *"Progress Report on the Impairment of Manual Dexterity in the Cold,"* DRNL Project Report No. 1, 1953.

―――――. "Tactile Sensitivity in the Cold," *Protection and Functioning of the Hands in Cold Climates*, Washington, D.C.: Nat. Acad. Sci.–Nat. Res. Coun. 1957.

Mitchell, H. H., Glickman, N., Lambert, E. H., Keeton, R. W., and Fahnstock, M. K. "The Tolerance of Man to Cold as Affected by Dietary Modifications: Carbohydrate versus Fat and the effect of Frequency of Meals," *Am. J. Physiol.*, *146*:84, 1946.

Newburgh, L. H., and Harris, M. *Clothing Test Methods*, CAM Report 390, Ann Arbor, Mich.: Edwards Brothers, 1945.

Pepler, R. D. "A Task of Continuous Pointer Alignment—Expt. 1," *A Report to the Climatic Efficiency Subcomm. of the R.N. Pers. Res. Comm.*, T.R.U. 3/51, 1953a.

———. "A Task of Continuous Pointer Alignment—Expt. 2," *ibid.*, T.R.U. 4/51, 1953b.

———. "A Task of Morse Code Reception," *ibid.*, T.R.U. 12/51, 1953c.

———. "A Task of Prolonged Visual Vigilance," *ibid.*, T.R.U. 15/51, 1953d.

———. "A Report of the First Two Years' Psychological Experiments in Singapore," *ibid.*, T.R.U. 22/51, 1953e.

———. "A Complex Mental Task with Varying Speed Stress," *ibid.*, T.R.U. 21/52, 1953f.

———. "A Task of Continuous Pointer-Alignment at Two Levels of Incentive," *ibid.*, T.R.U. 28/52, 1953g.

———. "A Complex Mental Task with Varying Speed Stress at Two Levels of Incentive," *ibid.*, T.R.U. 33/52, 1953h.

———. "Warmth and Performance: An Investigation in the Tropics," *Ergonomics*, 2:63, 1958.

———. "Extreme Warmth and Sensorimotor Coordination," *J. Appl. Physiol.*, 14:383, 1959.

Russell, R. W. *Effects of Variations in Ambient Temperature on Certain Measures of Tracking Skill and Sensory Sensitivity*, Report 300, U.S. Army Medical Res. Lab., Fort Knox, Ky., November 1, 1957.

Teichner, W. H., and Kobrick, J. L. "Effects of Prolonged Exposure to Low Temperature on Visual-Motor Performance." *J. Exp. Psychol.*, 49:122, 1955.

——— and Wehrkamp, R. F. "Visual Motor Performance as a Function of Short Duration Ambient Temperature," *J. Exp. Psychol.*, 47:447, 1954.

Thauer, R. "Wärmeregulation und Fieberfähigkeit nach operativen Eingriffen am Nervensystem homoiothermer Säugetiere," *Arch. ges. Physiol.*, 236:102, 1935.

Viteles, M. S., and Smith, K. R. "An Experimental Investigation of the Effect of Change in Atmospheric Conditions upon Performance, *Heating, Piping and Air Conditioning*, 18:107, 1946.

Weitz, J. "Vibratory Sensitivity as a Function of Skin-Temperature," *J. Exp. Psychol.*, 28:21, 1941.

Winslow, C-E. A., Herrington, L. P., and Gagge, A. P. "The Determination of Radiation and Convection Changes by Partitional Calorimetry," *Amer. J. Physiol.*, 116:669, 1936.

Winslow, C-E. A., and Herrington, L. P. *Temperature and Human Life*, Princeton, N.J.: Princeton University Press, 1949.

9

WEIGHTLESSNESS

**J. P. Loftus, Jr.,
and Lois R. Hammer**
Aerospace Medical Research Laboratory
Wright-Patterson Air Force Base, Ohio.

INTEREST in weightlessness has been directly related to manned space flight. The focus of interest is the unusual physical stimuli of weightlessness, possible disorientation caused by conflicting or unfamiliar sensations, and the effect of prolonged weightlessness upon man's ability to tolerate the acceleration stresses of re-entry.

Three techniques have been used to study the effects of weightlessness on the human: parabolic maneuvers in aircraft, frictionless platforms, and water immersion. Each is subject to theoretical and practical difficulties that must be noted if data are to be evaluated realistically. The discussion that follows will describe the nature of weightlessness and its accompanying conditions and evaluate the experimental devices and techniques used in terms of their practicality and the limits they place upon extrapolations from the data thus obtained. The available findings are then reviewed and discussed under the general categories of orientation, psychomotor performance and physiological function.

A. Methods of Study

1. AIRCRAFT

The gravitational pull of the earth upon a body is proportional to the mass of the body and is inversely related to the body's distance from the earth. As a result, the rate of acceleration due to gravity is the same for all bodies in any particular location. When a body is not allowed to fall, its mass is evidenced by its weight. If a container, holding a few unattached objects, falls in a vacuum, the objects will possess all the properties attributable to mass but will appear to weigh nothing. That is, the objects will resist acceleration and acquire momentum if accelerated, but, if not accelerated, will register zero weight on a spring scale. Two objects of different mass will indicate zero difference on a balance because all measurements of weight depend upon opposition to the action of gravity; and in a free-fall state, the force of gravity is unopposed.

Objects in orbit have the properties expected in a continuous free fall in a vacuum. Because weight cannot be measured normally in this environment, the condition is termed "weightlessness." Objects remain

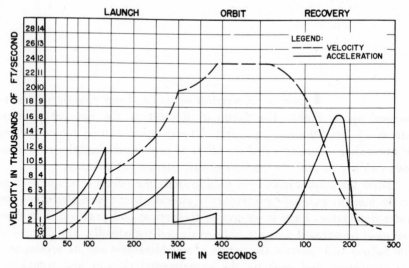

Figure 1. A typical acceleration and velocity profile of the type required for orbital flight. The peaks on the left time scale indicate burn-out of boost engines. The reentry illustrated is for a ballistic vehicle. Note that approximately fifteen g-minutes are required to achieve or return from orbit.

in circular orbit when their forward velocity is such that, as they fall, they never come closer to the surface of the earth.

The term "zero gravity" is also used to describe the condition of a body in circular orbit, since a three-axis accelerometer would indicate zero acceleration. Such devices register forces in units of acceleration of a reference mass, using the nominal acceleration due to earth's gravity as a unit.

Weightlessness never occurs without some acceleration stress. Figure 1 shows the boost acceleration and re-entry deceleration associated with an orbital flight. The duration and amplitude of the accelerations are

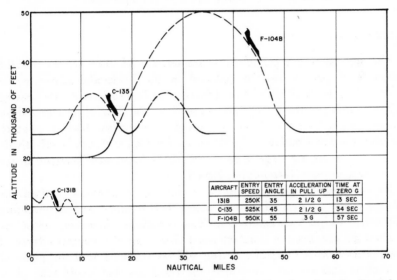

Figure 2. Typical zero gravity flight trajectories for aircraft. Partial gravity conditions may be obtained by reducing the entry angle.

determined by the power and stage characteristics of the booster and the drag characteristics and re-entry profile of the vehicle. The duration of the weightless period is indefinite if orbital velocity is attained. If less than orbital velocity is reached, the weightless period is determined by the velocity and the configuration of the trajectory.

Figure 2 indicates typical aircraft maneuver profiles and entry velocities calculated to provide periods of weightlessness for experimental purposes. Note that the duration and amplitude of the accelerations preceding and following weightlessness increase with longer periods of weightlessness. It should also be noted that the same technique can be used to produce periods of partial G.

While aircraft offer the most readily available and economic method of producing short periods of zero G, they also introduce a number of uncontrolled variables into the experimental situation. Vibration, noise, reduced pressure, and other distractions are present during the maneuver; and high acceleration is required at either one or both ends of the trajectory. The interaction of these environmental variables and the relatively long time required for many physiological systems, particularly the cardiovascular system, to adapt to changed conditions contaminates both direct physiological measures and performance measures. Subject selection may eliminate the main effect of these conditions, but no really satisfactory method for controlling them is yet available.

2. AIR-BEARING PLATFORMS

The outstanding mechanical characteristic of zero G, the inertial movement of bodies, can be induced in the horizontal plane in the presence of gravity if all frictional forces can be eliminated. Air-bearing devices, which use the air cushion created by the flow of pressurized air between two polished surfaces to provide a very low friction contact, have been used to simulate weightlessness. Friction seems to be effectively zero for the relatively large masses and forces frequently involved in the use of such devices (Dzendolet, 1960).

The air-bearing platform offers a highly economical method for studying many aspects of human motor performance and determining equipment design characteristics. Two cautions, however, must be exercised in judging the data obtained. First, all the inertial effects of forces exerted in a particular action will be reflected into the plane of free motion and are not necessarily the reactions that would take place if all axes of movement were equally free. Secondly, the gravity vector is present in the system as a component force and as a variable acting upon the operator. The effect of gravity on the neuromuscular system is not specified but is deduced from the normal muscular tone required to function in the upright position in opposition to the gravity vector. This effect should not change on the air-bearing device.

3. WATER IMMERSION

Water immersion is used to provide a physiological equivalent of the weightless condition. A body suspended in a fluid of appropriate density is subjected to equal pressure at all points, and support of the body's weight is distributed over its entire surface by the fluid. Since this condition diminishes many of the sensory cues of gravity and reduces the workload of the cardiovascular system, it is logically similar in many ways to the condition of the body while weightless (Knight, 1958; Margaria, 1958).

The effectiveness of the simulation depends in part upon the degree to which the gravity cues are eliminated and in part upon the reduction in the physical energy requirements of the body. Since, however, gravitational cues obviously cannot be completely eliminated, the simulation is necessarily imperfect. Moreover, the undesirable limitations of simulation by immersion, such as restrictions on the rate of limb movement, type of diet, and prolonged exposure of the skin to water, limit the generality of the observations. The reduction in the physical energy requirements of the passive physiological system, however, is evident, and this technique provides an opportunity to observe the functioning of these systems under a prolonged condition of reduced demand; a condition Hartman, *et al.* (1960) have termed a "hypodynamic environment."

4. SUMMARY

At present, then, the methods available for producing zero G for the study of human performance provide too brief an interval to allow satisfactory study of all the processes of interest. The simulation methods that allow prolonged observation possess a certain logical validity but have not been demonstrated to be effectively equivalent. Points of deviation from the zero G state are not easily determined solely by logical analysis. Very little information is available from the limited number of orbital and suborbital missile shots that have carried biological experiments, but the available data do coincide with the observations obtained from experimental environments.

B. Orientation

Orientation is knowledge of one's position with respect to his environment. It is based on the inputs from a variety of sensory systems (Campbell, 1951). Because gravitational force appears to be an important aspect of orientation, various writers have suggested that the absence of gravity would result in disorientation. However, disorientation has not been reported by the astronauts who have experienced several hours of weightlessness. It is possible that visual cues are adequate in such cases.

The sense of equilibrium and the postural reflexes that maintain the body in an upright position appear to depend on gravity, through the vestibular and kinesthetic senses. These mechanisms, however, concerned only with attitude or position of the body, are supplemented by certain exteroceptors, vision and the tactile sense. The latter two give information about distance and direction of both near and far objects, as well as information about the attitude of the body with respect to the rest of the visual field. These receptors should not be directly influenced by zero gravity.

Our present knowledge about orientation in a zero-gravity environment comes largely from the observations of human subjects who have been asked to report on their sensations during short periods of weightlessness, with particular attention being paid to the conditions under which people become disoriented. For example, a seated subject seems to have little, if any, difficulty. With his eyes closed, the subject may or may not become disoriented (Gerathewohl, 1957). Even when the subject floats freely in a large unconfined area, as has been done in the Aerospace Medical Laboratory's cargo aircraft, disorientation seldom occurs. When the subject tumbles or rotates in such a fashion as to lose his visual reference points, however, disorientation does ensue. Yet, vertigo produced by rotation does not seem to last as long as that occuring under normal 1-G conditions (Brown, 1959). Free floating in a dark environment, on the other hand, produces severe disorientation.

In summary, it would seem that orientation is not disturbed if one has the customary visual and tactile reference to the immediate surroundings.

1. VISUAL CUES

Orientation in the absence of surface contact is largely based on visual cues. Some subjects accept the vehicle structure as a frame of reference, while others orient to their own bodies. Simon's (1959) experiments on walking behavior revealed that with a minimum of contact a powerful reorientation has been reported by all subjects participating. The ceiling of the aircraft cabin was used as a walkway in order to observe orientation. All subjects reported that they immediately perceived the surface on which they stood as "down," with the subjective vertical defined as corresponding to the long axis of the body. This observation may refute the frequently expressed notion that a space compartment must furnish an abundance of familiar visual cues, for the foot-down orientation is based on tactile sensations that would normally be in direct conflict with vision. Simons proposes that the egocentric orientation observed in his subjects may make it possible for a crew compartment to have several floors, determined by the positions of the respective crew members.

2. VESTIBULAR CUES

A more analytical approach, although, so far, less fruitful, has been to attempt to determine the relative sensitivity of the vestibular organ and to predict its function under weightlessness as a possible disorienting factor. The vestibular otoliths, as gravity sensors, would not be expected, on a logical basis, to function normally in the absence of gravity. In fact, many investigators seem to consider weightlessness functionally equivalent to labyrinthectomy, for there is no available stimulus for the receptors. The early prediction that random movement of the endolymph would give the weightless man strongly conflicting or confusing information is not supported by the experiences of humans, as noted above. To the contrary, the lack of conflict suggests that the conscious sensations associated with weightlessness may derive, in large part, from the absence of weight of the body and relaxation of tension in the supporting skeletal muscles.

In some efforts to determine the threshold of sensitivity of the otoliths, human subjects have been submerged in water and blindfolded in order to nullify or equalize other cues which contribute to proper orientation. The weight of the body is then borne by the water, though the otoliths are still subject to 1 G stimulation (Schock, 1959a; Brown, 1961; Diefenbach, 1961).

In general, experiments of this sort have shown that there is a decreased sensitivity to body position when the subject is immersed with head downward, although, in at least one experiment, perception under water was no less accurate than on land (Margaria, 1958). In another study, perception of the gravitational vertical was found to be more accurate when head movements were permitted (Brown, 1961).

Results such as these may partially validate Quix's (1938) report of an otolithic "blind spot," noted when the head is held downward with the body supine. It has been thought by some that immersion with the body in this position should be a satisfactory simulation of weightlessness, since otolithic sensations also would be eliminated (Knight, 1958). The simulation is imperfect, however, since immersion does not completely eliminate, but only reduces many variables, such as weight of the internal organs, water resistance during movement, and hydrostatic pressure differences in the cardiovascular system. Possible partial sensitivity of the otoliths must also be considered.

Experiments on animal subjects have helped to verify the nonfunction of the vestibular sense through the observation of labyrinthine or postural reflexes under zero gravity. Labyrinthectomized animals that have learned to compensate for their loss show behavior under zero gravity that appears less disoriented than that of normal animals (Henry, *et al.*, 1952; von Beckh, 1954). The well-known labyrinthine righting reflex of cats sometimes occurred if the animals were released immediately after becoming weightless, but was delayed or failed to occur at all if the animals were held during a few seconds of weightlessness before being released (Gerathewohl and Stallings, 1958; Schock, 1959b). Labyrinthectomized cats did not right themselves at all, either on the ground or during weightless flight. Some visual adaptation appears to have taken place in the operated animals, judging from their struggling and giving evidence of confusion when they were blindfolded and subjected to zero gravity (Schock, 1959b).

The conclusion that might be drawn from such experiments is that the vestibular organ does not function as usual in the absence of gravitational stimulation. The evidence also indicates that vision may compensate for the vestibular or kinesthetic cues that normally contribute to orientation. The importance of the vestibular sense for orientation in man is still in doubt, particularly with regard to the manner in which visual stimuli supplement or are integrated with sensations from other senses.

To date, information on orientation during weightlessness has come from observations made during relatively short periods of weightlessness. The complications that may occur during a long space flight are unknown and can only be speculated upon at the present time.

3. SENSORY INTERACTION

One may reasonably question whether much of the sensory information used on earth to maintain equilibrium and orientation is of any use in an environment in which there is no gravitational vertical. Perhaps all the information required for adaptive orientation in such a reduced-sensory environment is contained within that environment, probably in the form of visual and tactile cues. As one of Gerathewohl's subjects expressed it, "I am weightless, hence I cannot fall" (Gerathewohl, 1956).

The probable importance of vision for orientation suggests an examination of certain reflex connections between the eye and the vestibular organ. The phenomenon of special interest is the so-called oculogravic illusion, an apparent movement or displacement of stationary visual stimuli as a result of linear or radial acceleration. The illusion has been extensively studied in centrifuge experiments, and a few investigators have extended the study to weightlessness during parabolic flight in aircraft. None, however, has adequately defined the direction and extent of movement when the observer is in a sub- or zero-gravity state.

During the accelerated pullup preceding weightlessness, the target appears to move down, and to move upward during the transition to weightlessness (Gerathewohl and Stallings, 1958; Schock, 1958a). Because the target stabilizes or returns to center in some cases and in others appears to oscillate slightly during zero gravity, Schock considered that the illusion may not occur at all during weightlessness, but may be strictly a function of the accelerations peculiar to the flight maneuver (Schock, 1958b).

The perception of visual vertical under altered gravitation states is also dependent upon the interaction between the eye and the vestibular apparatus. Schock found a decrement in the ability of subjects to judge visual vertical when immersed in water as compared to judgments made on land. Studies at partial G and weightlessness show that errors in the perception of vertical tend to increase as the value of G diminishes (Hammer, 1961a).

Transient weightlessness as produced in aircraft also causes some loss of visual acuity (Pigg and Kama, 1961). It is interesting that the 10 per cent decrement found is approximately that noted in studies of the effect of increased acceleration on visual acuity (White and Jorve, 1956).

There are other factors whose unknown effects could become more critical for orientation during long periods than during short-term weightlessness. If one adapts to weightlessness, as, for example, the eyes adapt to darkness, sensitivity to small transient accelerations would greatly impair one's ability to orient either himself or his vehicle when subjected to such disturbances. Long-term weightlessness may also influence orientation at a more integrated level of behavior if "time sense" is altered by the reduced physiological demands.

Data available now do not indicate that any critical problems are to be expected. One may expect rather that weightlessness may provide an ideal environment in which to study many aspects of the orientation problem.

C. Psychomotor Performance

The problem of motor performance and muscle capability in a weightless environment comprises two factors, not always easily distinguishable. In addition to a possible decrement due to changes in the musculature or nervous system, such as poor coordination or loss of muscle tonus, behavior is affected by the unaccustomed instabilities of free bodies. The former problem is more likely to be a hazard in space travel, while one might expect that the latter could be overcome by training or by restructuring behavior requirements and equipment to take into account the changed conditions.

Changes in muscle tonus during weightlessness, occurring because the skeletal muscles are no longer needed to support the body's weight, have been predicted by several writers (Balakhovskii and Malkin, 1956). In addition, lack of coordination in movements of the limbs is expected, since the limbs are weightless and only their inertia must be overcome; consequently, less than customary effort is required to move the arms or legs, assuming undiminished muscle strength.

Strughold (1949) on the other hand, has thought there should be little disturbance in coordination. Control of movements can be achieved by means of vision and the proprioceptors, which sense position and movement of the limbs. The adaptation to weightlessness shown by numerous subjects, however, seems to indicate that some experience is required in the weightless state before one's performance becomes skilled.

Soviet dogs sent on rocket flights were, according to photographs, passive during increasing G, but upon entering the weightless phase of the rocket's flight, the dogs' heads abruptly rose above the level of the cradle in which they were restrained. Galkin, *et al.* (1958), say, "This evidently is the result of the fact that the tonus of the extensor muscles of the neck and back is no longer equal to the gravitational force and the G stress."

1. AIRCRAFT EXPERIMENTS

Gerathewohl, *et al.* (1957), conducted an eye-hand coordination test in weightless flight. Subjects hit a paper target with a stylus in one quick motion, and their errors were measured. There was a tendency for subjects to cluster hits around the bull's-eye under normal gravity, to hit the target above the center during zero G, and below center during increased G. Some adjustment to the zero G condition was indicated by a steady reduction in the average upward deviation from the bull's-eye by the final (sixth) trial; responses under acceleration did not show such change. Nevertheless, absolute accuracy showed little improvement under any of the three conditions. Their conclusion was that eye-hand coordination is moderately disturbed by weightlessness, but that adaptation is possible (Gerathewohl, *et al.*, 1957).

Somewhat similar are the findings of von Beckh (1954) and Schock

(1958b). Subjects attempting to draw crosses in prearranged squares on a sheet of paper showed some inaccuracy under zero G with eyes open; but most striking was the behavior under the same condition but without visual control: crosses that should have been placed in the lower right quarter of the page drifted to the upper right. No such deviation was shown under 1 G with eyes closed, indicating the importance of vision for motor control. The direction of the error may be reasonably attributed to residual tonus in the abductor muscles.

2. DYNAMIC SIMULATION EXPERIMENTS

Lomonaco, *et al.* (1957), and Gurfinkel, *et al.* (1959), have used elevators to produce short periods of zero G rapidly alternating with increased positive G. Lomonaco found increased muscle tonus and a slight but definite motor incoordination in an aiming test, with improvement during several consecutive runs. The performance of deaf subjects without labyrinthine functions was affected to a lesser extent than was that of normal subjects.

Wade measured response times for the operation of three kinds of switches—push-button, toggle, and rotary. Mean response time, that is, time to perform a complete cycle from master push-button switch to test switch and return, increased by 15 per cent during weightlessness. The three types of response were differentially affected, with an increase of 21 per cent in time to operate the toggle switch, 15 per cent for the push-button, and 9 per cent for the rotary switch. Mean operating time for all the switches under 1 G was 0.98 sec., with the push-button having the lowest response time under both 1 G and zero G. While these differences are statistically significant, the influence of panel arrangement and response compatability were not adequately controlled, and the data cannot be compared between switches (Hammer, 1961b).

Kama tested the ability to position "weightless" objects accurately, using an air-bearing table to simulate weightlessness (Hammer, 1961b). In this case, there was a greater tendency for subjects to undershoot than to overshoot. It must be remembered that here only the objects were weightless (that is, frictionless), while the man was not weightless.

The same device was used to determine ability to discriminate masses of varying sizes (Rees and Copeland, 1960). The smallest difference in mass of weightless (frictionless) objects that could be discriminated was over twice that discernible under normal (weight) conditions.

The form of the curve for mass discrimination leads one to suspect that the judgment of mass at these values is similar to judging small weights. If such is the case, one would expect that a mass of greater value, such that an equal amount of work would be required to accelerate it, as was required for the weight stimuli in this study, might yield a better index of discrimination.

Unfortunately, the study of any long-lasting effects on or progressive deterioration of the musculature and psychomotor performance cannot be made without a period of zero G of much longer duration than has yet been obtained, and this awaits the development of a manned, orbiting laboratory.

3. WATER IMMERSION EXPERIMENTS

Hartman, *et al.* (1960), describe an exploratory study of psychomotor performance during and after prolonged water immersion, simulating weightlessness. Measures of vigilance and binary matching obtained periodically while the subject was immersed indicated a small but significant deterioration, and performance on a complex operator task also showed some decrement after the week of immersion. Changes in gross behavior after immersion were readily apparent to the investigators. They conclude that "the psychomotor effectiveness of the astronaut will be maintained at an adequate level during prolonged weightlessness, but that psychomotor behavior will be grossly disrupted upon re-entry." The restricted mobility imposed upon the subject, the use of a single subject, and the uncontrolled influence of motivation upon performance lead one to question the generality of the results.

Some estimate of the extent of the handicap man will experience in the space environment can be obtained from Table 1. Comparison of the

Table 1. A Comparison of the Discrimination Penalty for Unaccustomed Modes of Handling and Judgment. Remote Handling Requires Six to Ten Times Longer for Any Given Task (Pigg, 1961).

Basis of Judgment	Type of Handling	Difference Ratio
Weight	Direct	0.05
	Remote	0.08
Mass	Direct	0.10
	Remote	0.23

modes of handling indicates the precision penalty imposed by loss of direct contact, while comparison by basis of discrimination indicates the importance of kinesthetic feedback. The table does not indicate the time penalty incurred with the loss of gravity damping, but, as may be inferred from Wade's data this, too, is appreciable, at least for transition states.

4. LOCOMOTOR AND OTHER ACTIVITY IN WEIGHTLESSNESS

The mechanical aspect of the weightless environment that leads to lessened coordination and ineffective performance is the loss of the attractive force perpendicular to the ground, that is, gravity. This results in the loss of traction and makes it possible for the body to move away from and remain free of the surface. Several authors recognized some of the problems that could arise in attempting to move one's weightless body or perform useful work, and Hertzberg (1960) has analyzed the problem in considerable detail.

When no external forces act on a system, momentum is conserved, and the movement of bodies interacting within the system is proportional to their masses. For example, pushing an object under 1 G depends on one's traction against the ground, but in the absence of gravity the two bodies will move apart because of the action and reaction of forces. A man finds that the forces he applied on an object that caused it to move under 1 G, cause him also to move, and in the opposite direction, under zero G, unless he is anchored. The same relations make walking under zero G impossible.

Simons (1959) has experimentally studied walking under zero G conditions, using magnetic and suction cup shoes on a metal walkway to provide adhesive forces. Problems other than the need for static attachment were revealed, such as difficulty in preventing skating or sliding with the magnetic shoes and in checking the forward momentum of one's body. Later work has used Velcro material as an adhesive substance. Locomotion can be achieved in this manner, but it is inefficient and does not capitalize upon the characteristics of the environment, such as the ease of free floating from one place to another.

Simons and Gardner (1960) have tested the practicality of transporting a man through longer distances by means of a portable compressed-air propulsion device. Tumbling occurs when the line of thrust does not pass through the body's center of mass and is a serious problem. Initial efforts do indicate, however, that one may be able to learn to use such devices satisfactorily.

The law of conservation of momentum applies also to the case of the free-floating man attempting to apply torque to a fixed object, as in the use of many common tools. It has been found that under such conditions the muscular effort exerted will rotate the man's body about the point of contact with the fixed object. Dzendolet and Rievley (1959) investigated the torque that a man can exert while on an air-bearing frictionless table. A turning or tightening task is performed with maximum efficiency, that is, with minimum movement of the body, if one positions himself at right angles to the axis of rotation. Obviously, a handhold is required to keep a man in position at his work area, although short impulse forces are possible without rigid attachment (Dzendolet, 1960; Dzendolet and Rievley, 1959).

In evaluating the findings of these various experiments or in comparing one experiment with another, we must often rely on the authors' judgments of "successful" or "efficient" performance, for in many cases quantitative comparisons are not made, much less tests of statistical significance. Nevertheless, the conclusion that might be drawn is that a person firmly attached to his work place can carry out many psychomotor tasks with reasonable proficiency and that practice improves performance. If the problem of inadvertent tumbling can be avoided, familiarity with the condition also makes it possible for a free-floating man to perform many tasks adequately and to move through free space. The success of the many pilots and experimenters who have carried out zero G missions speaks as favorably in behalf of this conclusion as many of the experiments that have been reported—evidence that should not be overlooked in this area. The long-term effects and aftereffects of weightlessness on muscular capability, however, are simply unknown.

E. Physiological Functions

The fundamental obstacle to physiological research during weightlessness has been the difficulty of attaining a zero-gravity condition for a sufficient length of time. The comparatively slow adaptation of physiological functions to changed physical conditions is likely to contaminate physiological measures when the organism is subjected to rapid transitions, as of acceleration in ballistic aircraft trajectories.

1. CIRCULATORY STRESS

The most common expectation is that prolonged exposure to weightlessness will reduce the body's capacity to adapt to acceleration stress. The heart and circulatory system represent a finely adjusted mechanism capable of regulating output according to physical requirements and the condition of the system. Under high acceleration, when the demand becomes too great, the heart is unable to work against the increased pressure imposed by acceleration. Under acceleration below 1 G, on the other hand, reduced load upon the heart, lowered blood pressure, and reduction of hydrostatic pressure differences may lower heart activity to an inadequate level for adaptation to acceleration stress (Strughold, 1949), while limited use and low workload, if prolonged, tend to cause atrophy and loss of effectiveness in the musculature (Graybiel and Clark, 1960).

The seriousness of circulatory failure, should it occur, has occasioned much interest in this area. Disagreement can be found, however, as to the severity of the predicted effects. Some authors (Von Diringshofen, 1959) thought the consequences would be no more serious than with changes in body position under 1 G, which also reduce hemostatic pressure gradients. Yet a person may collapse when a sudden change is made after regulatory mechanisms have adjusted to a new body position—for instance, upon standing up after having lain in bed a long time. If this be the case, no disorders may be observed until the organism has lived for some time in the weightless state and is suddenly placed under the increased load of a positive G field; short exposure may cause no observable impairment of well-being.

A. CIRCULATORY CHANGES DURING ROCKET FLIGHT

The most successful observations of cardiac functions have been made on animals in rocket or missile flight. Burch and Gerathewohl (1960) summarized the findings from most of the known studies. American rockets have carried primates or rodents, while the Soviets have made use of their traditional laboratory animal, the dog. Even so, findings have been similar. No serious disturbances have been observed in any of the animals. The data recorded during weightlessness are not, however, clearly free of the residual effects of the high acceleration of lift-off; and the briefer the duration of weightlessness, the more likely this is to be true. Moreover, the records of conscious animals may well reflect "emotional" or startle responses to the strange environmental conditions of noise and vibration as well as weightlessness.

Anesthetized primates in V-2 and Aerobee rockets showed a slight rise in arterial pressure during lift-off, decreasing through free fall until the parachute opened. Pulse rates varied slightly, usually increasing during acceleration and dropping to initial rates during weightlessness, (Henry, *et al.*, 1952).

Subsequently, both anesthetized and conscious dogs were sent on rocket flights in the U.S.S.R. In the case of some conscious animals, pulse rate and blood pressure rose, then fell to original levels during weightlessness; in others, there was no change or arterial pressure fall. Lack of a regular pattern of response was attributed to individual differences and "diversity in force and character of the external stimuli on each separate flight" (Bugrov, *et al.*, 1958). The records of anesthetized animals showed less change; during weightlessness, pulse rate lowered and blood pressure did not change. From this fact also it was concluded that the differing reactions of the conscious animals were responses to various unusual stimuli (Galkin, *et al.*, 1958). Perhaps the most significant finding was a longer-lasting influence of acceleration after the transition to weightlessness. According to Galkin, *et al.*, a consequence of weightlessness was slower recovery from the high blood pressure and pulse rate induced by acceleration. "Laika" is reported to have undergone a sharp increase in heart rate immediately after launch of *Sputnik II*, but the return to normal rate took three times as long as in previous experiments on the centrifuge, a difference assumed due to the new experience of weightlessnss that followed, or to "changes in the functional state of the subcortical formations which regulate circulation" (Chernov and Yakovlev, 1958). This latter statement is somewhat difficult to interpret.

Individual differences again are evident among three monkey passengers in "Jupiter" nose cones. A squirrel monkey, "Old Reliable," and a rhesus monkey, "Able," showed similar sharp, brief increases in heart rate during both lift-off acceleration and entry to weightlessness, followed by a return to usual levels. Another squirrel monkey, "Baker," reacted erratically, a brief rise being followed by a prolonged fall in heart rate and then variations above and below base-line rate. These differences in response cannot be attributed either to species differences or to stimuli peculiar to each flight, since "Able" and "Baker" shared the same nose cone. During the course of the weightless phase, all three eventually established fairly steady heart rates, with fluctuations that are thought to have been caused by various startling events in the flight. Blood pressure and other measures remained normal (Graybiel, *et al.*, 1959). EKG records, when available, show no significant departure from normal.

In all the experiments described, the effects of weightlessness have not been isolated from lingering effects of acceleration or from reactions to unfamiliar stimuli other than weightlessness. Yet they represent a not unrealistic approach to tolerance for actual conditions of space flight, since, except for flights of long duration, weightlessness will not be isolated from other conditions.

It is desirable to inquire whether weightlessness and acceleration closely following one another interact to change tolerance to either condition. Von Beckh (1959) carried out this inquiry by subjecting eleven subjects to high G loads (4 to 6.5 G) before entering or after pulling out of the weightless trajectory. When transition to zero G followed high acceleration, blackout lasted longer than during the control runs (acceleration without weightlessness), and some subjects reported discomfort and pronounced disorientation. Heart rate increased during acceleration and fluctuated after entering weightlessness instead of returning to usual levels as during the control flights. The author believed that these symptoms were basically due to the failure of the cardiac mechanism to adjust immediately to the zero G state after adapted to the 1 G condition.

Similar symptoms representing lowered tolerance to the conditions occurred when acceleration followed weightlessness of 40 to 60 seconds' duration. Subjects experienced more strain and discomfort during post-weightlessness acceleration, and some blacked out at lower *g* levels than in the control runs.

Stutman and Olson tried to measure the effect on the heart of re-entry to 2½ G after weightlessness. The short duration of weightlessness (about 15 seconds) made it difficult to draw conclusions about this effect. A decided slowing of heart rate during weightlessness was noted, however, as well as a tendency toward peripheral blood pooling that was attributed to reduced cardiac output during weightlessness (Hammer, 1961b).

Data from the Russian orbital flights by Gagarin and Titov have not been made available except for minor and incomplete details. The brief ballistic flight by Shepard has, however, been reported in extensive detail (Augerson and Laughlin, 1961). In general, the trend of the data was as expected. The observation of most significance is that the relative change in pulse rate from weightlessness to re-entry acceleration was comparable to that in going from 1 G to re-entry acceleration on the centrifuge.

B. CIRCULATORY CHANGES IN WATER IMMERSION

Studies involving prolonged water immersion have been primarily concerned with the effect upon the body of reduced activity, similar to what might be encountered in weightlessness. Graybiel and Clark (1960) studied the effect of a two-week regimen of immersion and bed rest on the circulatory system and skeletal musculature of three subjects. While circulatory adjustment to changes in position was markedly affected, no change in muscular strength was found under the conditions of this study. Subjects were accompanied constantly and provided with numerous diversions in order to avoid changes attributable to sensory deprivation, and gross behavior appeared to be normal. The authors proposed that deterioration in the bone structure may occur under reduced structural load and be much harder to counteract than muscular deterioration.

Hartman, *et al.* (1960) report extensive observations from an exploratory study of a single subject who was immersed for seven days. The most significant effect was the general deterioration of the circulatory system's regulatory capacity. During the 30 min each day the subject spent out of water for clothing change, observers noted deterioration in strength, coordination, and muscle size as the experiment progressed. Simple performance tests indicated a small increase in response time each day. Several metabolic changes in white blood-cell count, urinary nitrogen, blood composition, and immunochemical responses that occurred are not readily explainable. Some of the changes may be consistent with the bone deterioration suspected by Graybiel and Clark. Unlike Graybiel and Clark's subjects, this subject experienced a reduced need for sleep but felt some of the same need for physical anchoring of the body noted in the other study.

These preliminary experiments demonstrate both the advantages and the disadvantages of simulating long-term weightlessness by immersion. They provide the opportunity for extensive physiological measurement, but the applicability of the findings is difficult to determine at the present stage of development of space vehicles. The decrements found are, in some degree at least, due to the immobility and passivity of the subject. The monotony of the experience appears detrimental to motivation and mental activity and thus to many performance measures. The elimination of psychological stresses as well as physical stresses also tends to foster deterioration of circulatory adaptive mechanisms.

Because of the reduction of stimuli in immersion studies, one might ask how much the condition called "sensory deprivation" contributed to the results. While, as Schock (1958b) notes, zero gravity may produce a state of sensory deprivation, plans for space systems in the present or foreseeable future suggest that the operator will be far from starved for sensory stimulation.

No difficulty in respiration seems likely in the weightless state, except for the problem of ventilation. The absence of convection currents with the absence of gravity could mean that exhaled air would remain in front of the nose and stifle a supply of fresh oxygen. This problem, however, seems to be a question of engineering rather than of physiology.

2. RESPIRATORY STRESS

In most of the experiments on physiological parameters during rocket flights discussed above, respiration also was measured. For the most part, no systematic changes in respiratory rate have been observed that can be considered caused by zero gravity. No other measures, such as volume of air exchanged, have been found in the published reports.

In some cases, respiratory rate rose upon transition to weightlessness, then returned to original levels (Galkin, *et al.*, 1958; Graybiel, *et al.*, 1959). In others, either a fall in rate or no significant change is reported (Graybiel, *et al.*, 1959; Pokrovskii, 1957). Again, no pattern is found in this diversity of response.

As was noted in the discussion of cardiac activity, respiratory rate also was sometimes affected by acceleration preceding weightlessness, obscuring the effects due to zero G. Less change has been observed among anesthetized than conscious animals (Galkin, *et al.*, 1958). These facts suggest that the changes that were observed signify startle reactions, of which changes in heart rate were also a part. Throughout the duration of weightlessness, there was generally a return to usual levels of activity and in no case were serious disturbances in activity observed.

3. DIGESTION AND ELIMINATION

Eating problems have been studied by Ward, *et al.* (1959). Special containers and food preparations are required to convey food to the mouth and assist ingestion, since neither fluids nor solids will remain in an open container, but no problems have occurred in the digestive cycle.

Elimination also creates a problem only in control of the waste products. It is interesting to note that in a study of urination there sometimes was a marked loss of urgency under weightless conditions, indicating that weight rather than distention of the bladder may be the stimulus (Ward, *et al.*, 1959). Graveline and Balke (1960), however, noted diuresis in a water immersion study and anticipate that this will be a symptom of adaptation to weightlessness.

4. NAUSEA

From the beginning of the study of weightlessness in flight, motion sickness has been an unexpected and recurring problem (von Diringshofen, 1959), suggesting a potential threat to the well-being of space pilots. For instance, von Beckh (1960), Loftus (1960), and Gerathewohl (1960), report vomiting in from 17 to 29 per cent of persons participating in zero G flights. When nausea is the criterion, about one-half become ill. The importance of this rate of incidence can easily be overemphasized, for it is probably a problem specific to the conditions under which research has been conducted. The high accelerations preceding and following the zero G period, anxiety, and fatigue seem to be the principal causes of the disturbance in those who are susceptible. The occurrence of sickness is rare among those accustomed to high accelerations, such as seasoned pilots; and subjects who are highly interested in the research usually adapt to the environment readily even if at first they experience some discomfort. While the consequences would perhaps be severe if motion sickness should be a genuine problem in space flight, the best solution seems to lie in the selection and training of space travelers.

The problem may not be uncommon, however, if a requirement for artificial gravity is imposed on long duration space flights by physiological considerations. Figure 3 shows an envelope of design feasibility

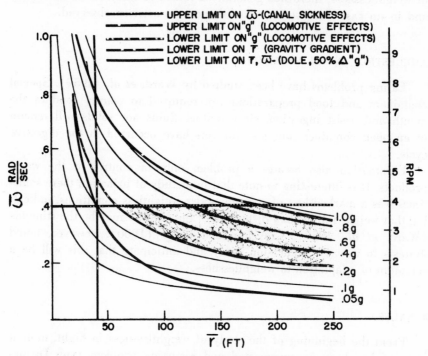

Figure 3. Human factors stress limit curves superimposed on a plot of angular velocity ($\overline{\omega}$) versus radius of rotation ($\overline{\gamma}$) to achieve various levels of artificial gravity in manned orbital satellite vehicles. (Loret)

developed by Loret (1961) for rotating space stations. The upper limit is defined as the maximum angular rate that will not produce an unacceptable incidence of motion sickness. While this limit is extrapolated from the available data, it appears to be realistic if any reasonable level of comfort is to be assured. The envelope serves to indicate how severe a penalty the requirement for artificial gravity could be. The size of a space station defined by the upper left corner of the envelope will be significantly beyond our capability for some time to come.

Conclusion

All the evidence gathered so far indicates that man can function effectively in the weightless environment. We may expect that man will play his customary roles as operator of vehicles, explorer, scientific observer, and adventurer. Unless unanticipated difficulties arise, it will be some time before space vehicles will provide opportunity for study of man's various sensory and functional attributes. Astronauts will be too active as observers and operators to serve as specimens. Psychology and physiology, however, will benefit as greatly, if not as immediately as will some other sciences, from man's activities in space.

References

Augerson, W. S. and Laughlin, C. P. "Physiological Responses of the Astronaut in the MR-3 Flight," in *Proceedings of a Conference on Results of the First U.S. Manned Suborbital Space Flight*, Washington, D.C.: National Aeronautics and Space Administration, 1961.

Balakhovskii, I. S., and Malkin, V. B. "Biological Problems of Interplanetary Flights," *Priroda*, August, 1956. Also in Krieger, F. J., *Behind the Sputniks*, Washington, D.C.: Public Affairs Press, 1958.

Brown, E. L. "Research on Human Performance during Zero Gravity," presented at the Aviation Conference, American Society of Mechanical Engineers, Los Angeles, March, 1959.

Brown, J. L. "Orientation to the Vertical during Water Immersion," *Aerospace Med.*, 32:209–217, 1961.

Bugrov, B. G., Gorlov, O. G., Petrov, A. V., Serov, A. D., Yugov, Ye. M., and Yaklovlev, B. I., "Investigations of the Vital Activity of Animals during Flights in Non-Hermetically-Sealed Rocket Cabins to an Altitude of 110 Kilometers," in Galkin, *et al.*, *Preliminary Results of Scientific Investigations Carried Out with the Aid of First Soviet Artificial Earth Satellites, Part 3, Medico-biological Investigations with Rockets*, Washington, D.C.: U.S. Joint Publications Research Service, JPRS/DC-288, Photoduplication Service, Library of Congress, October, 1958.

Burch, G. E., and Gerathewohl, S. J. *Some Observations on Heart Rate and Cardio-Dynamics during Weightlessness,* U.S. Army Medical Services, special report, November, 1959. Also *Aerospace Med., 31*:661–669, 1960.

Campbell, P. A. "Orientation in Space," in J. P. Marbarger (ed.), *Space Medicine,* Urbana: University of Illinois Press, 1951.

Chernov, V. N., and Yakovlev, V. I. "Research on the Flight of a Living Creature in an Artificial Earth Satellite," *Amer. Rocket Soc. J., 29*:736–742, 1959. Translated from *Artificial Earth Satellites,* Moscow: U.S.S.R. Academy of Science Press, no. 1, 1958.

Diefenbach, W. S. *The Ability of Submerged Subjects to Sense the Gravitational Vertical,* CAL No. OM-1355-B-1, Cornell Aeronautical Laboratory, Inc., Buffalo, N.Y., January, 1961.

Dzendolet, E. *Manual Application of Impulses While Tractionless,* WADD Technical Report 60-129, Wright Air Development Division, Wright-Patterson AFB, Ohio, February, 1960.

——— and Rievley, J. F. *Man's Ability to Apply Certain Torques While Weightless,* WADC Technical Report 59-94, Wright-Patterson AFB, Ohio, April, 1959.

Galkin, A. M., Gorlov, O. G., Kotova, A. R., Kosov, I. I., Petrov, A. V., Serov, A. D., Chernov, V. N., Yakovlev, B. I., and Popov, V. I. "Investigations of the Vital Activity of Animals during Flights in Hermetically-Sealed Cabins to an Altitude of 212 Kilometers," in Galkin, *et al.* (eds.), *Preliminary Results of Scientific Investigations Carried Out with the Aid of First Soviet Artificial Earth Satellites, Part 3, Medico-Biological Investigations with Rockets,* Washington, D.C.: U.S. Joint Publications Research Service, JOR/DC-288, Photoduplication Service, Library of Congress, October, 1958.

Gerathewohl, S. J. "Personal Experiences during Short Periods of Weightlessness Reported by 16 Subjects," *Astronautica Acta, 2*:203–217, 1956.

———. "Weightlessness," *Astronautica, 2*:32–34, 74–75, November, 1957.

———. "Personal Experiences during Short Periods of Weightlessness in Jet Aircraft and on the Subgravity Tower," presented at the Symposium on Motion Sickness in Weightlessness Research, Wright-Patterson AFB, Ohio, March, 1960.

——— and Stallings, H. D. "The Labyrinthine Posture Reflex (Righting Reflex) in the Cat during Weightlessness," *J. Aviation Med., 28*:345–355, 1957.

——— and ———. *Experiments during Weightlessness, A Study of the Oculo-Agravic Illusion,* Report No. 58-105, USAF School of Aviation Medicine, Randolph Air Force Base, Texas, July, 1958. Also *J. Aviation Med., 29*:504–516, 1958.

———, Strughold, H., and Stallings, H. D. "Senso-Motor Performance during Weightlessness, Eye-Hand Coordination," *J. Aviation Med., 27*:7–12, 1957.

Graveline, D. E., and Balke, B. *The Physiological Effects of Hypodynamics Induced by Water Immersion,* Report No. 60-88, USAF School of Aviation Medicine, Brooks Air Force Base, Texas, September, 1960.

Graybiel, A., and Clark, B. *Symptoms Resulting from Prolonged Immersion in*

Water: The Problem of Zero G Asthenia, Report No. 4, Research Project MR 005.15-2001 Subtask 1, U.S. Naval School of Aviation Medicine, Pensacola, Fla., July, 1960.

——, Holmes, R. H., Beischer, D. E., Champlin, G. E., Pedigo, G. P., Hixson, W. C., Davis, T. R. A., Barr, N. L., Kistler, W. G., Niven, J. I., Wilbarger, E., Stullken, D. E., Augerson, W. S., Clark, R., and Berrian, J. H. "An Account of Experiments in Which Two Monkeys Were Recovered Unharmed after Ballistic Space Flight," *Aerospace Med.*, *30*:871–931, 1959.

Gurfinkel, V. S., Isakov, P. K., Malkin, V. B., and Popov, V. I. "Coordination of the Posture and Movements in Men in Conditions of Increased and Lowered Gravitation," *Byulleten' Eksperimental'noi Biologii i Meditsiny* (Russian), *48*:12–18, 1959.

Hammer, Lois R. *Perception of the Visual Vertical under Reduced Gravity*, ASD Technical Report, Aeronautical Systems Division, Wright-Patterson AFB, Ohio, August, 1961a.

——. ed. *Studies in Weightlessness*, ASD Technical Report, Aeronautical Systems Division, Wright-Patterson AFB, Ohio, 1961b.

Hartman, B., McKenzie, R. E., and Graveline, D. E. *An Exploratory Study of Changes in Proficiency in a Hypodynamic Environment*, USAF School of Aviation Medicine, Report No. 60-72, Brooks Air Force Base, Texas, July, 1960.

Henry, J. P., Ballinger, E. R., Maher, P. H., and Simons, D. G. "Animal Studies of the Subgravity State during Rocket Flight," *J. Aviation Med.*, *23*:421–432, 1952.

Hertzberg, H. T. E. "The Biomechanics of Weightlessness," *Aircraft and Missiles*, *3*:52–53, 1960.

Knight, L. A. "An Approach to the Physiological Simulation of the Null-Gravity State," *J. Aviation Med.*, *29*:283, 1958.

Loftus, J. P. "Motion Sickness during a Weightless State," presented at the Symposium on Motion Sickness in Weightlessness Research, Wright-Patterson Air Force Base, Ohio, March, 1960.

Lomonaco, T., Scano, A., Strollo, M., and Rossanigo, F. "Alcuni dati sperimentali fisi-psichici sugli effetti delle accelerazoni e della subgravita previsti nell'uomo lanciata nello spazio (Some Psycho-Physical Experimental Data on the Effects of Accelerations and Subgravity as Predictors for Man in Space)," *Rivista di medicina aeronautica* (Italian), *20*:363–390, 1957.

Loret, B. J. *Optimization of Manned Orbital Satellite Vehicle Design with Respect to Artificial Gravity*, ASD Technical Report, Aeronautical Systems Division, Wright-Patterson AFB, Ohio, August, 1961.

Margaria, R. "Wide Range Investigations of Accelerations in Man and Animals," *J. Aviation Med.*, *29*:855, 1958.

Pigg, L. D. "Human Engineering Principles of Design for In-Space Maintenance," Paper No. 61-144-1838, presented at the National Institute of Aerospace

Sciences, American Rocket Society joint meeting, Los Angeles, June, 1961.
────── and Kama, W. N. *The Effect of Transient Weightlessness on Visual Acuity*, ASD Technical Report 61-184, Aeronautical Systems Division, Wright-Patterson AFB, Ohio, March, 1961.

Pokrovskii, A. V. "Vital Activity of Animals during Rocket Flights into the Upper Atmosphere," *Études Sovietique* (French), January, 1957. Also F. J. Kreiger (ed.), *Behind the Sputniks*, Washington, D.C.: Public Affairs Press, 1958.

Quix, F. H. "Un novel appareil pour l'examen du nystagmus de position (A New Apparatus for Examination of the Nystagmus of Position)," *Journal de neurologie et de psychiatrie, 3*:160, 1938.

Rees, D. R., and Copeland, Nola. *Discrimination of Differences in Mass of Weightless Objects*, WADD Technical Report 60-601, Wright-Patterson AFB, Ohio, 1960.

Schock, G. J. D. *Apparent Motion of a Fixed Luminous Target during Subgravity Trajectories*, AFMDC Technical Note 58-3, Air Force Missile Development Center, Holloman Air Force Base, N.Mex., February, 1958a.
──────. *Some Observations on Orientation and Illusion When Exposed to Sub and Zero Gravity*, unpublished Doctoral Thesis, University of Illinois, 1958b.
──────. *Perception of the Horizontal and Vertical in Simulated Subgravity Conditions*, AFMDC Technical Note 59-13, Air Force Missile Development Center, Holloman Air Force Base, N.Mex., June, 1959a.
──────. *A Study of Animal Reflexes during Exposure to Subgravity and Weightlessness*, AFMDC Technical Note 59-12, Air Force Missile Development Center, Holloman Air Force Base, N.Mex., June, 1959b.

Simons, J. C. *Walking under Zero-Gravity Conditions*, WADC Technical Note 59-327, October, 1959.
────── and Gardner, M. S. *Self-Maneuvering for the Orbital Worker*, WADD Technical Report 60-748, Wright-Patterson Air Force Base, Ohio, December, 1960.

Strughold, H., in Armstrong, *et al.* "The Aero Medical Problems of Space Travel: A Panel Meeting," *J. Aviation Med., 20*:383–402, 1949.

von Beckh, H. J. "Experiments with Animal and Human Subjects under Sub- and Aero-Gravity Conditions during the Dive and Parabolic Flight," *J. Aviation Med., 25*:235–241, 1954. Also presented at Fourth International Astronautical Congress, Zurich, Switzerland, 1953.
──────. "Flight Experiments about Human Reaction to Accelerations Which are Followed or Preceded by the Weightless State," *Aerospace Med., 30*:391–409, 1959.
──────. "A Summary of Motion Sickness Experiences in Weightless Flights Conducted by the Aeromedical Field Laboratory," presented at the Symposium on Motion Sickness in Weightlessness Research, Wright-Patterson Air Force Base, Ohio, March, 1960.

von Diringshofen, H. "From Acceleration to Weightlessness. A Space-Medicine Talk on the 'Eve' of the First Space Flight," *Medizinische* (German), No. 52, 2586–2592, 1959.

Ward, J. E., Hawkins, W. R., and Stallings, H. D. "Physiological Response to Subgravity. II. Initiation of Micturation," *Aerospace Med.*, *30*:572–575, 1959.

White, W. J., and Jorve, W. R. *The Effects of Gravitational Stress upon Visual Acuity*, WADC Technical Report 56-247, Wright-Patterson AFB, Ohio, November, 1956.

10

VIBRATION

Aaron B. Nadel

General Electric TEMPO
Santa Barbara, California

IN this chapter we are primarily concerned with the effects of vibratory forces upon biological systems, particularly the human organism. Vibratory forces are usually transmitted by the vehicle in which the man is contained. Vibration forces, if of sufficient energy, may also impinge upon the human body *via* air transmission and produce resonant responses in specific parts of the body, producing particular response patterns. Vibration may affect a portion of the human body, or the whole body. In actual studies involving the human organism, it is not possible to carry "real time" studies to the destructive level, and animals are used in place of man, with the result that experimental findings must be re-evaluated in order to ascertain their applicability to man, both as regards anatomical structure and physiological structure. From the practical viewpoint, the aspects to consider are methods of protection against the vibration motions that cannot be tolerated by man.

Vibration motions may be described as oscillations of particular amplitudes at given frequencies. An early review of the literature by

Goldman (1948) based on subjective perception of vibration over a frequency range of 1 to 70 cps, indicated that the peak acceleration on either side of a mean value must be about $10^{-2.2}$G. At about $10^{-1.1}$G, the vibration is reported to be unpleasant; when it has reached $10^{-0.3}$G, it is intolerable. McFarland (1953), whose data (prepared for use in air transport design) were found to be in close agreement with the data evaluated by Goldman, nevertheless suggested caution in interpretation, chiefly because of the subjective nature of the responses and the fact that they were compiled from a number of studies.

McFarland (1953), adapting data from several sources, has described the human responses to sinusoidal vibration. The thresholds obtained were based on determinations at single frequencies. Vibration involving more than one frequency would probably place the thresholds at about half of the values plotted.

In jet aircraft, for example, vibration of low amplitudes and frequencies has been reduced to tolerable levels. Effects from the high frequencies in jet engines are not as clearly understood, especially at ultrasonic levels, which are less tolerable than sonic frequencies of equal intensity.

Vibratory motions are best analyzed if the motion is considered as composed of the vector sum of three linear components at right angles to each other, plus three angular components. Actually, the linear component of vibration in the head-to-seat direction is of considerably greater magnitude than the other linear components in most land and air transport equipment and, as a result, has been more frequently subjected to experimental study. The predominant frequencies of mechanical vibration of land, sea, and air vehicles are generally below 50 cps. The vibratory motion found in vehicles usually has an irregular waveshape, but is most easily approached if considered as a sum of sinusoidal waves of some fundamental frequency and all integral multiples thereof, the amplitude of each sine wave being determined by Fourier analysis (Cope, 1960).

Effects of Vibration

The best known effects of vibration on man are nausea, vomiting, and dizziness, produced in large part by stimulation of the vestibular apparatus. Serious vestibular effects were seen in some of the monkeys subjected to vertical vibration of ¼- or ½-in. amplitude, at 10 cps

(Riopelle, 1958). Of more serious concern was the evident chest pain in the vibrated monkeys; and, in the case of expired monkeys, there was some evidence of hemorrhaging in the vicinity of the pericardium. Similar observations on man (White) have shown, in a few instances, sharp pain occurring in the chest, especially when acceleration exceeds 3 G. Head-to-seat vibration has been seen to cause extensive lung hemorrhaging in cats (Fowler, 1958), in mice (Roman, 1958), and in monkeys (Riopelle, 1958). No damage was found in the hearts of mice, and minimal damage was noted in the monkey hearts, whereas Fowler's cats sustained significant damage to the heart. Additionally, it was found that both mice and monkeys received severe injuries intra-abdominally, where the vibration produced intraperitoneal hemorrhage, mesenteric tears, and bleeding, along with intestinal intussusception.

In man subjected to severe vibration at 10 and 25 cps while in a sitting position, fairly severe anterior chest pain occurs within 30 seconds at the lower frequency (White). At the higher frequency, after 15 minutes' exposure, there was a moderately severe gastrointestinal bleeding, which persisted for several days. Vibration was provided at acceleration levels ranging from 3 G to 10 G at the two frequencies. Evidence of similar pathology, though of less severity, may be inferred from the rectal bleeding found in one human subject after a 15 minute exposure to vibration at 20 – 25 cps and 0.17 in. amplitude (Mozell and White, 1958) and from the constipation occurring in several subjects vibrated at 8 to 15 cps, 0.15 in. amplitude, for a 2½ minute duration. Visual acuity is also affected adversely by vibration. In a vertical vibration experiment (Mozell and White, 1958), the ability to read stationary or nonvibrating numbers is impaired. When the frequency of the vibration is increased from 8 to 23 cps, the acuity becomes highly impaired. Doubling the amplitude from 0.025 to 0.05 in. had, however, no noticeable effects.

There are other more serious effects of vibration that are injurious to man and animals. They are found chiefly in the hematological system, although evidence of other damage has been reported, for example, a brain hemorrhage immediately following vibration in one of Riopelle's (1958) monkeys.

Arising out of the work described above and other studies is the fundamental question regarding the damaging effects to certain organs during vibration at specific frequencies, when it may be stated that maximum effects seem to occur. Coermann (1939) believes that every organ with its surrounding tissue has a resonant frequency in every axis. He first presented evidence based on observations of visual acuity impairment evidently occurring maximally at certain frequencies. White noted intolerable chest pain at a lower frequency, whereas there was none at the higher frequency despite greatly increased exposure time and considerably more acceleration at the higher frequency. Roman (1958) cites similar results in support of the resonant frequency hypothesis to explain the particular types of damage occurring to particular parts of the body during whole body vibration exposure.

Experimental Studies

In order to establish human tolerance limits to mechanical vibration, experimental studies are needed both to understand the vibration force effects and to establish thresholds. Because of the hazard entailed for human subjects, animal studies are frequently done. These serve to provide useful clues of appropriate levels that may be considered safe for humans. None the less, animal studies offer definite disadvantages for possible application of findings to humans. The differences in anatomical structure, size, volume, and weight between man and other animals reflect differences in behavioral response patterns to mechanical forces between these species and man. The fact that the natural frequency of the thorax-abdomen system of a human is between 3 and 4 cps, whereas that of a mouse is found between 18 and 25 cps, indicates that maximum effect and injury will occur at markedly different vibration frequencies (Goldman, 1948).

ANIMAL STUDIES

Experimental studies have resulted in interesting and useful data. Rats exposed to severe whole-body vibration die more quickly as frequency is increased (Schaefer, *et al.*, 1959a). All subjects died at all frequencies to which they were exposed except for albinos run at 10 and 15 cps. These subjects (10 in all) were removed from the vibrator after 12 hours of steady exposure with no signs of abnormality. Other subjects (Group 1, 74 remtaining) were exposed to vibration until killed or released at 12 hours. Frequencies used were at 5 cps intervals, extending from 10 to 45 cps, and displacement (amplitude) was at 0.25 in. for all. Acceleration was not always constant, but increased as the square of frequency. None the less, the authors interpreted their results in terms of the frequency function—with the reservation that the purity of the variable was not fully established. Figure 1 shows the median dying times of these subjects.

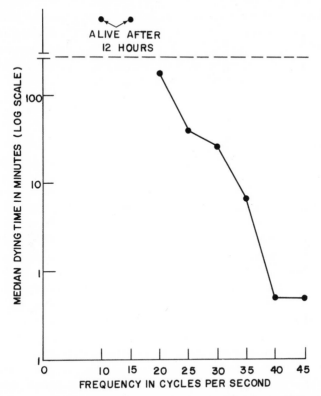

Figure 1. Median dying times of the Group 1 Subjects. (Schaefer, *et al.*, 1959a.)

A second group (Group 2) of hooded rats, totaling 55 in all, was lethally vibrated at frequencies of 25, 30, or 35 cps and at a constant risplacement of 0.25 in. The procedures used with this group followed those of the first group to obtain further lethality data on the frequency range in question and to secure more complete pathological data. A third group, totaling 23 male rats, of whom 13 were castrated, and 9 females, were also exposed to vibration forces at 30 cps and 0.25 in. displacement. Group 2 results are shown in Figure 2 with data covering sex and age differences. Using dying time data, there were differences associated both with age and sex. Younger males died more quickly than younger females at 25 and 30 cps; older females, however, died earlier than older males at all three frequencies, showing a sex reversal as age increased. On the other hand, the age effect was firm in that older females and males died faster than the younger rats at all frequencies, though reliabilities were not consistent.

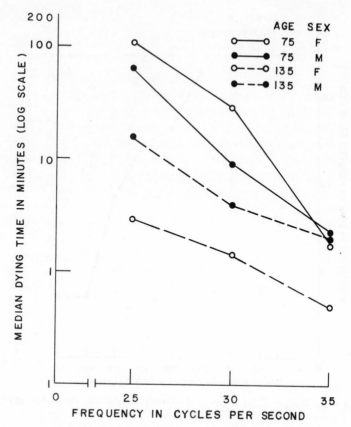

Figure 2. Median dying times of the Group 2 Subjects. (Schaefer, *et al.*,
1959a.)

With Group 3 results, castrated rats lived longer under vibration than
intact males. In fact, castrated males lived as long as the females, in
contrast to intact males.

Pathology found among the rats of Group 1 indicated significant
evidence of myocardial petechial hemorrhages, lung hemorrhage with
atelectasis, emphysema, and edema. Ossasional hemorrhage of the gastrointestinal tract was observed, whereas infrequently noted was congestion at the corticomedullary junction of the kidney. No other tissues appeared to show pathology due to vibration, nor was any pathology found
in subjects vibrated at 10 and 15 cps.

Group 2 pathological studies confirmed the myocardial and lung
hemorrhages. Other chest findings were confirmed in the younger rats,
but not in the older ones. Similarly, gastrointestinal findings were noted

only in the younger group vibrated at 25 cps. Sex appeared to play no role in pathology.

Fowler (1958), using cats, also noted the dependency on frequency, at least in part, in establishing lethal exposure time, as his animals perished more quickly at the high frequencies. Acceleration was also important in establishing lethal exposure time: 20 minutes at 10 G; 2 to 5 minutes at 15 G. Roman (1958), using mice and varying frequency from 5 to 50 cps while holding acceleration constant at 15 G, obtained a U-shaped curve, with lethal time descreasing from 5 to 20 cps, then increasing between 20 and 50 cps. Roman's method of restraint differed somewhat from those of Schaefer, *et al.* (1959a), and Fowler (1958), since his animals were supported at fewer body points and were far less rigidly restrained. The absence of central nervous system pathology in their subjects was also noted by Fowler (1958) and Roman (1958).

The work of Riopelle (1958) on behavioral decrements resulting from intense vibration indicated the primary effects of vibration to be physical and mechanical in nature with behavior decrements as a consequence of such changes. Riopelle's studies were done on monkeys. The animals were confined in chairs and subjected to a continuous course of 8 hours of vibration. Three monkeys were exposed to vibration at 10 cps at 0.25 in. peak-to-peak excursion. Of this group, one died after one hour's exposure, the remaining two survived and succeeded in a behavioral task, jumping a 5 ft barrier. Four of the animals were subjected to 8 hours of vibration at 10 cps, 0.5 in. peak-to-peak excursion. One animal expired immediately following the 8 hour exposure to vibration. The remaining three were unable to high-jump to their previbration standards. Except for one animal that died 24 hours later, the remaining two subsequently recovered to their former level of proficiency.

Hines (1958) studied the following factors in monkeys: (1) physiological changes resulting from an enforced sitting position for 8 hours; (2) physiological changes following 8 hours of intense vibration; (3) physiological changes following subcutaneous injection of 0.2 cc adrenalin hydrochloride; and (4) anatomical changes, both gross and microscopic, found after death. The major findings reported by Hines on the effects of vibration at 0.25 in. displacement included many subcutaneous hemorrhages of the legs and extreme fatigue. In each case there was an increase in heart rate and a decrease in respiratory rate and in blood pressure. Body temperature moved 0.9°C below normal in one case, 1.6°C above normal in the other. Hematological studies showed that hemoglobin rose, whereas erythrocytes fell. Although both white blood cells and neutrophiles increased in both surviving animals, the percentage increase was substantially higher for one animal rather than each showing an equal rise. The relative decrease in lymphocytes showed a similar course, whereas eosinophiles rose in one, dropped in the other.

A .05 in. displacement appeared to be far more severe. Two animals died, one immediately after vibration, the second twenty-four hours later, each with evidence of internal or subcutaneous hemorrhage. Of the two survivors, one showed subcutaneous hemorrhages, the other none. The latter, however, was extremely hypersensitive to touch. Physiological changes in the monkeys were quite marked: lowered blood pressure, very rapid heart rate. In a comparison with monkeys given subcutaneous injections, the decrease in respiratory and heart rates was in the same direction, but less than for the animals receiving intense vibration. Changes in hematology were somewhat contradictory, with the result that no common pattern was established either with this group or with those vibrated for a prolonged period.

The common findings following prolonged vibration, whether the animal expired or survived, consisted of hemorrhages and involution of lymphoid tissue, although the latter finding did not occur in all sites of lymphoid tissue. The monkeys that survived prolonged vibration, in addition, showed disintegration of white collagenic fibers in the submucosa of the gastrointestinal tract, changes in the supporting connective tissues within blood vessel walls, and an increase in connective tissue about the large blood vessels between the pericardium and the sternum that enmeshed the xiphoid process.

In other exposures of animals to vibration to ascertain physiological responses, rats were vibrated for periods of 10–40 minutes a day over several months. Vibration exposures at a frequency of 12.5 cps to an acceleration level of 15 G showed some minor behavior abnormalities (Schaefer, et al., 1959b). With accelerative levels of a few tenths of a G at 5 to 10 cps, adrenal glands showed a rapid fall in ascorbic acid content (Goldman and Von Gierke, 1960). In rabbits, following exposure to vibration for several days, changes in the reproductive cycle and growth occurred (Loeckle, 1944). Changes in respiration rates, heart activity, and peripheral circulation have been noted in men and animals as immediate and possibly transient responses to moderate vibration. Goldman (1948) also reported that certain postural reflexes appeared to be inhibited by vibratory motion.

HUMAN STUDIES

In the early studies of whole-body vibration, workers concerned themselves with subjective reports. Criteria were relatively simple, including only thresholds of perception, of unpleasantness, and of tolerance.

The results of these studies were summarized by Goldman (1948) and reproduced here in Figure 3. The data were compiled from exposures of about 5 to 20 minutes. Data are limited for long exposures involving human subjects. Very long exposures of humans at levels above threshold appear to be both irritating and fatiguing. This is similar to the findings of Riopelle (1958) with monkeys.

On short exposures of less than 5 minutes, Ziegenruecker and Magid (1959) vibrated human subjects to the criterion of intolerance, using the frequency range of 1–15 cps. Table 1 presents the results of the symptoms experienced by the subjects requesting cessation of the stress.

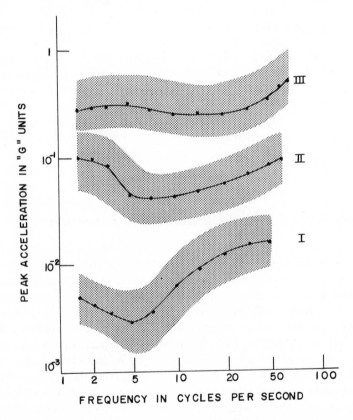

Figure 3. Average peak accelerations at various frequencies at which subjects perceive vibration (I), find it unpleasant (II), or refuse to tolerate it further (III). Exposures of 5 to 20 minutes. Shaded areas are about one standard deviation on either side of the mean. Data averaged from seven sources. (Goldman, 1948.)

It is evident that no single criterion was found although certain reactions were found more frequently than others.

Table 1.   Criteria of Tolerance

CYCLES PER SECOND	Abdominal Pain	Chest Pain	Testicular Pain	Head Symptoms	Dyspnea	Anxiety	General Discomfort
1					XXXXX XXX		XXX
2					XXXXX XXX		XXXX
3	XX	XX			XXXXX	X	XXXXX
4	XX	XX		XX	XXX	XX	XXXXX
5		XXXX				X	XXXXX X
6	XXX	XXXX		X			XXXX
7	XX	XXXXX	X	X			X
8	X	XXXX		X		XX	XXX
9	XX	XXXX			X		XXXXX
10	X	X	XXX	XX		X	
15							XXXXX XXX

Source: Ziegenruecker and Magid (1959).

Behavioral Effects of Whole-Body Vibration

The difficulties encountered in carrying experimental studies to the limits needed to ascertain the effects on behavior have restrained experimental work with human subjects. In several instances, however, objective evaluations were undertaken to determine effects of vibration. Coermann (1939) was among the first to look at performance effects. Of the variety of tasks he had his subjects undertake, only visual acuity seems to be adversely affected. Mozell and White (1958) also noted decrements in visual acuity. Their studies showed the increase in impairment to be directly related to the increase in frequency (from 8 to 50 cps). On the other hand, they reported no noticeable effects resulting from a doubling of amplitude. In a tracking study, these authors reported completely negative results. Neither amplitude, up to 0.16 in. peak-to-peak, nor frequency, between 0 and 23 cps, produced any statistically significant effects upon tracking performance. Lewis (1943), using a Mashburn apparatus, found no impairment in a sensorimotor and the ability to return to the vertical after tilting. Here, again, as in Mozell and White (1958), very low amplitudes were used measuring 4 to 6 mils at the head, at 20 cps. Loeb (1953) found considerable impairment in visual acuity. Similarly affected were tremor while holding a rifle, and tremor while holding a stylus in a small aperture. There seemed to be resonant effects here, occurring at 15 cps, with lesser impairments occurring at 25 and 35 cps.

Other investigators examined the effects of vibration on tracking tasks, with varying results. Mozell and White (1958), using heavy restraint of their subjects in a vertical vibration experiment using a nonvibrating tracking task, found essentially no decrement in performance up to 23 cps, using an amplitude of 0.05 in. Gorill and Snyder (1957) found a marked decrement in tracking tasks primarily at 30 cps, with 1.54 G acceleration. Their interpretation considered the decrement due largely to the acceleration in itself chiefly a function of frequency. The acceleration level was far less than that which was obtained in the Mozell and White (1958) study. Schmitz (1959), using similar tracking tasks, found a decrement in performance, which he also believed was related to frequency. His frequency levels were limited, however, to 2.5 and 3.5 cps, at amplitudes ranging up to 0.25 in. Fraser, *et al.* (1961), reviewing these studies, commented on the inconsistencies of these findings and interpretations. In their own exploration of these inconsistencies, Fraser, *et al.* (1961), sought especially to determine the effects of amplitude, the effect of plane of vibration, and the difference, if any, between tracking on a vibratory and nonvibratory display. Subjects were randomly exposed to 48 conditions of sinusoidal vibrations at frequencies of 2, 4, 7, and 12 cps, at amplitudes (peak-to-peak) of $\frac{1}{16}$, $\frac{1}{8}$, $\frac{3}{16}$, and $\frac{1}{4}$ in., in each of three planes. Using a minimum damping hard wooden contour seat on a specially designed shake table, subjects were exposed to a maximum peak acceleration of 3.63 G. Restraint was omitted, as was artificial damping. The performance task consisted of a display composed of a 9×9 matrix of lights on a 12×12 in. gray background. Stimuli were automatically presented in random order, and subjects manipulated a control stick that generated response signals into the display.

The results of this study, point up the author's belief that, within the range of amplitudes, frequencies, and planes examined, using unrestrained subjects, harmonic sinusoidal vibration produces a decrement in tracking performance related primarily to amplitude, although the function involved is probably modified by a dynamically varying function or functions of frequency. Complex relationships were found between amplitude and frequency. When analyzed for their individual effectiveness, an increase in either amplitude or frequency was found to be significantly related to performance decrement. When the combined effect was analyzed, amplitude was observed to be the predominant factor.

The importance of amplitude, as compared with frequency, was again observed when the combined effects of amplitude and plane and of frequency and plane were analyzed. The effects of plane alone become modified by the concurrent amplitude in that plane, with the result that a greater decrement is seen in any plane at the highest amplitude. When the effects of frequency and plane are analyzed, it is found that the decrements due to plane alone are relatively unaffected by the frequency in that plane, except at the highest frequency in the vertical plane.

Performance also varies with the plane of vibration, the greatest decrement occurring in the vertical and transverse planes. Vertical and horizontal control of the display also varied with plane of vibration. A noticeable but inconsistent decrement was observed when the display did not vibrate in conjunction with the subject. The effects were probably due to a complex interaction among the critical variables.

Protection against Vibration

Transmission of vibration through the seat is the primary means by which vehicular vibrations reach the human passenger. If a man is seated on a hard seat on a shake table that provides sinusoidal vibration in a head-to-seat direction, the vibration of the man is of the same frequency as that of the seat. If one seeks to ascertain what portion of the amplitude of seat vibration reaches the head, vibration records can be used both at head and seat points to obtain the information. Several studies along this line show the same general pattern, with any differences being due largely to differences in recording techniques and the mechanical characteristics of different subjects.

Generally speaking, the curves of Figure 4, on two subjects, show that at 0–1 cps, there is almost equal amplitude in the vibration of head and seat. As frequency increases, head vibration reaches a peak amplitude somewhere between 3 and 6 cps, the resonance frequency. At this point, head vibration is approximately 1½ and 3 times seat amplitude. Further increase of frequency beyond resonance level produces a decrease in amplitude of head vibration until it achieves the same level as seat vibration amplitude at about 10 cps. Further increase in frequency shows a progressive decrease in seat-head transmission to 70 cps, at which point only 10 per cent of the amplitude of seat vibration may be expected to

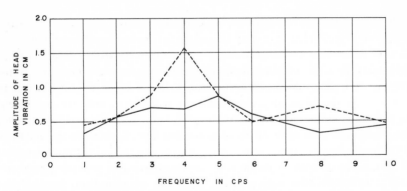

Figure 4. Amplitude of vertical vibration of head of two different subjects sitting on a shake-table (no cushion). Shake-table vibrates at an
amplitude of 0·4cm. After Müller (1939). (Cope, 1960.)

reach the head (Coermann, 1939). Several investigators have indicated
the presence of secondary resonances, evidently due to a shoulder-head
transmission resonance at 20–25 cps (Latham, 1957; Dieckman, 1958).

Cope (1960), in his analysis of this problem, suggests a theory of a
relatively simple vibration system composed of a mass isolated from a
vibrating base by a spring, after the relationship proposed by Kimball
(1932),

$$y_1 = y_2 \left[1 - \frac{m(2\pi f)^2}{K} \right]^{-1}$$

where

y_1 = amplitude of vibration of mass, cm
y_2 = amplitude of vibration of base, cm
m = mass, g
f = frequency of vibration, cps
k = elastic constant of spring in, dynes/cm

The general shape of the vibration transmission curve can be seen in
the equation for the simple system described above. Starting with 100
per cent transmission at $f = 0$, increasing f causes increasing transmission until a peak is reached at the resonant frequency. Beyond the resonant frequency, further increase in frequency causes transmission to
decrease and approach zero asymptotically.

The above equation can be used to design equipment to reduce the
transmission of vibration from vehicle to man. For instance, if a spring
or cushion is interposed between vehicle and man, the equation indicates
that for any given frequency, the percentage transmission from vehicle
to man may be reduced to any value desired by the choice of value for the

spring constant (k), simply by making the spring (or cushion) sufficiently resilient. This also has the effect of reducing the resonant frequency. By adding a shock absorber (damping) parallel with the spring, the resonance peak may be decreased at the expense of increased transmission at higher frequencies (Goldman and Von Gierke, 1960). Seat cushions can shield against vehicle vibration if their elasticity and damping constants are carefully selected. Plastic foam cushions can be designed along a range of values of these constants by varying the proportions of the ingredients.

It may be necessary to allow a certain amount of vibration to reach man in order that he may perform his tasks without decrement. If the man is not vibrating and the vehicle is, he may find interference (decrement) in reading displays accurately and in manipulating controls properly. Thus, the isolation of man from the vibrating vehicle does not automatically solve the problem of his relationship to instrumental displays or manual controls. Here this problem may either be resolved by a compromise vibratory solution between man and machine or by a design that mounts man, display panel and controls as a single unit on a spring or equivalent device to prevent motion of this unit relative to the man.

Protecting man against mechanical forces is best accomplished in one of two ways: isolation to reduce transmission of the forces to the man, and increase of man's mechanical resistance to the forces. Isolation from the vibration is achieved by the standard suspension principle of having the natural frequency of the system isolated lower than the exciting frequency at least by a factor of 2 (Goldman and Von Gierke, 1960). Both linear and nonlinear resistive elements are used for damping. Human tolerance to mechanical forces is strongly influenced by selecting the proper body position with respect to the direction of expected forces. Reenforcement of the skeleton is a necessary and important feature of seats. Mobility of the body, or the abdominal mass, can be reduced by properly designed belts and seats. Training and indoctrination are also extremely useful for producing the best use of protective equipment and for adjusting the body into the least dangerous positions during intense vibration exposure, especially for improving operator performance, reducing anxiety, and preventing man-machine resonance effects.

In the low-frequency range (below 5 cps), it is usually difficult to achieve any isolation in passenger seats by seat cushions. Actually, some amplification of the vibration may occur. The damping properties of the seat cushions are important, however, for acclimating the passenger to the frequencies above resonance, which may be important in automobile or aircraft transportation. In a severe low-frequency vibration situation, as found in tractors and related field equipments, suspension of the whole seat is far superior to the simple seat cushion. A variety of methods has been relatively successful here: hydraulic shock absorbers, rubber torsion bars, coil springs, and leaf springs. The differences among these springs are quite small. There is a difference, however, between comfort and vibration-induced stress if the seat is guided to move only in a linear direction compared with the condition where the seat pivots around a center of rotation (Dieckman, 1958). In the latter situation, there results a disconcerting and fatiguing pitching motion.

For severe vibrations around or beyond normal tolerance limits as they are likely to occur in military operations, special seats and restraints can provide maximum body support in all critical directions for the passenger, giving him the most advantageous position. Generally, for conditions as described, seat and restraint needs are the same for vibration and rapidly applied accelerations. The molded rigid enclosure developed for Project Mercury, made to the individual measurements of each astronaut, is one of the best examples of an applied solution to meet this requirement (Roman, 1958).

Since tolerance to continuous vibration depends critically on exposure time, control of duration of exposure to a vibration environment is an important protective measure. Exposure time should be reduced as much as possible to prevent cumulative permanent damage and reduce the possibility of accidents favored by vibration-aggravated fatigue.

References

Coermann, R. "Effect of Vibration and Noise on the Human Body," *Ringbuch der Luftfahrttechnic*, 5: No. 1, 1939.

Cope, F. W. "Problems in Human Vibration Engineering," *Ergon*, *3*:35–43, 1960.

Dieckman, D. "A Study of the Influence of Vibration on Man," *Ergon*, *1*:345–355, 1958.

Fowler, R. C. "Damage to Animals Due to Vibration," *Suppl. to 22nd Shock and Vibration Bulletin*, Washington, D.C.: Office of Secretary of Defense, 1958, pp. 16–19.

Frazer, T. M., Hoover, G. N., and Ashe, W. F. "Tracking Performance during Low Frequency Vibration," *Aerospace Med.*, *32*:829–835, 1961.

Gorill, R. B., and Snyder, F. W. *Preliminary Study of Aircrew Tolerance to Low-Frequency Vertical Vibration*, Boeing Airplane Co. Doc. D3-1189, July 3, 1957.

Goldman, D. E. NMRI Rept. NM 004001, Report No. 1, March, 1948.

—— and Von Gierke, H. E. *The Effects of Shock and Vibration on Man,* Lecture and Review Series No. 60-3, NMRI, Bethesda, Md., January 8, 1960.

Hines, M. *The Effects of Intense Vibration. II. Physiology and Pathology,* USAMRL Report No. 358, October 10, 1958.

Kimball, A. L. *Vibration Prevention in Engineering,* New York: Wiley, 1932.

Latham, F. "A Study in Body Ballistics: Seat Ejection," *Proc. Roy. Soc.,* B, *147*:121–139, 1957.

Lewis, D. *The Effects of Noise and Vibration on Certain Psychomotor Responses,* C.A.A. Division of Research, Report No. 8, Washington, D.C., 1943.

Loeb, M. *A Further Investigation of the Influence of Whole Body Vibration and Noise on Tremor and Visual Acuity,* USAMRL Rept. No. 165, 1953.

Loeckle, W. E. *Arbeitsphysiol, 13*:79, 1944.

McFarland, R. A. *Human Factors in Air Transportation,* New York: McGraw-Hill, 1953.

Mozell, M. M., and White, D. C. "Behavioral Effects of Whole Body Vibration," *J. Aviation Med., 29*:716–724, 1958.

Riopelle, A. J. *The Effects of Intense Vibration. I. Behavior,* USAMRL, Rept. No. 358, October 10, 1958.

Roman, J. *Effects of Severe Whole Body Vibration on Mice and Methods of Protection from Vibration Injury,* WADC Tech. Rept., 58-107, WADC, ARDC, USAF, April, 1958.

Schaefer, V. H., Link, H. J., Farrar, J. V., and Wiens, D. *Lethality in Rats as a Function of Frequency in Constant-Displacement Vibration,* USAMRL Report No. 390, 1959a.

——, Ulmer, R. G., Link, H. J., and Yost, D. H. *Some Behavioral and Physiological Studies in Vibration,* USAMRL Report No. 1389. 1959b.

Schmitz, M. A. *The Effect of Low Frequency, High Amplitude, Whole Body Vertical Vibration on Human Performance,* Proj. Rept. No. 2, Bostrom Research Lab., January 1958–January, 1959.

Selye, H. *Stress.* Montreal: Acta, 1950.

Vollmer, E. P., and Goldman, D. E. Unpublished data (Reported in Goldman, and Von Gierke, *Supra.*

White, D. C. *Preliminary Report of Whole Body Oscillations,* USNADC Report NM0011 111304.

Ziegenruecker, G. H., and Magid, E. B. *Short Time Human Tolerance to Sinusoidal Vibrations,* WADC Tech. Rept. 59-391 WADC, ARDC, USAF, July, 1959.

11

THE EFFECTS OF RADIATION
ON INTEGRATED BEHAVIOR

Paul R. Tobias
Aerospace Corporation
Los Angeles, California

Introduction: The Language and Units of Radiation

THE discovery of X-rays by Wilhelm Roentgen during a laboratory experiment in 1895 can be thought of as the start of the atomic age. Within the next three or four years, medical diagnoses were being made of radiation injuries, and the death of one of Edison's assistants was attributed to radiation overexposure. At about this same time, Becquerel became aware of a skin burn that was apparently caused by proximity to a small tube of radium and, together with the Curies, was among the earliest researchers to study the biological effects of radiation.

The following sixty years saw significant progress in nuclear theory and the understanding of the medical and biological aspects of radiation exposure. Especially was this knowledge advanced by the development of the atomic bomb during World War II and with the establishment of the Atomic Energy Commission. During this time in the United States, however, there seems to have been very little attention given to the effects of radiation on integrated behavioral performance. In contrast, as far back as 1933, the Russians have focused attention on this aspect of radiation effects. They felt that a near-lethal dose was required to produce an effect. More recent evidence suggests that lower levels of radiation can affect integrated behavior, and in some very recent work extremely low levels of radiation have been shown to affect animal and human behavior. Although it is the purpose of this chapter to review the more recent work and, specifically, the low-level radiation effects, it is desirable to provide some background material. This chapter will also deal with some very complicated problems on the types and measurement of radiation, the radiation environment of man in space and the primary biological effects of radiation. After having established the language and background knowledge, we shall proceed into the discussion of the effects of radiation on performance, as well as the specific effects of sublethal and very small doses of radiation both on the organ systems and on behavior.

TYPES OF RADIATION

Nonparticulate X and gamma radiation are classified under the heading of electromagnetic energy. This type of radiation is most familiar to the layman and is emitted by cathode-ray tubes and commercial X-ray equipment. The essential difference between gamma rays and X-rays is one of wavelength, and their primary mode of action is ionization in the mass by which they are absorbed.

The other major category of radiations is particulate radiation, which involves generally the heavy nuclei derived from some radioactive decay process. An example is the alpha particle, possessing two protons with a charge of $+2$ and having $1/30$ to $1/10$ the velocity of light. Because of the very heavy mass and double positive charge, alpha particles have tremendous ionizing power, but do not have the penetrating power of X and gamma radiations. Because of their low penetration ability, under most conditions alpha particles are not considered hazardous to biological systems.

Beta particles are another form of ionizing radiation also released in radioactive decay. They may be either negatively or positively charged, the negatively charged particles being electrons. The major difference between beta particles and other electrons is in their velocity. The energy of beta particles is from 0 to 3 Mev (million electron volts) and, in some instances, higher. As opposed to alpha particles, the beta particle has a much greater penetration, but produces only about 75 ion pairs per centimeter of travel in air. Whereas an alpha particle may be stopped by 0.06 cm of aluminum, a high-energy beta particle may traverse a centimeter of aluminum before being attenuated. In a biological system the beta particle can be most significant.

Another type of particle is the neutron, which has no charge and consequently does not ionize the tissue into which it is absorbed. Its major effect results from the radiations emitted from impact, since the collision of a neutron with any atom, whether in tissue or in a shield, produces ionizing radiations. Because of this, the effect of neutrons in tissue is greater than one would expect from comparative ionization figures. The biological effect of this particle may be 2 to 10 times as great as that of a given gamma ray. Also produced in the neutron collision is the proton, which, from a biological standpoint, is perhaps most important. Protons have a relatively high mass and charge and are extremely efficient ionizers. A proton of 115 Mev is capable of penetrating to a depth of 10 cm in aluminum, and in the last half-centimeter the ionization is approximately 16 times that at the surface of the shield.

Radiation Measurement

The roentgen (r), a unit of gamma (X) radiation per unit of time, is a measurement of the exposure dose received and can be related to the expected biological effect or injury (see Table 1). This biological effect is generally believed to result from chemical decomposition of the molecules present in organic cells. Gamma radiation produces ionization, or the changing of the stable electrical potential of a cell, thereby destroying it. The amount of ionization provides a basis for measurement that is, in turn, described by the roentgen. It is generally accepted that a single exposure of less than 25 r will produce no detectable clinical effects and that an exposure of 450 r over the whole body is fatal to 50 per cent of the individuals exposed. A whole-body exposure of 700 r or more is probably fatal in all cases.

The restriction imposed on the roentgen is that it is applied strictly to gamma (or X) radiation; further, it refers to the strength of a point source rather than to radiation absorbed by a person at that source. The roentgen is a measure of exposure dose and must be distinguished from the absorbed dose, which is measured by the rep, or *roentgen equivalent*

Table 1. Summary of Radiation Units

Symbol	Unit	Source of Radiation	Absorbing Media	Relationship to Other Units
r	Roentgen	Gamma or X-ray	1 cu cm of dry air at STP	83 ergs/gram in air 97 ergs/gram of soft tissue
rep	Roentgen equivalent physical	All nuclear (particulate) radiation	Animal tissue	97 ergs absorbed/gm of soft tissue
rad	Absorbed dose of radiation	All nuclear radiation	All material	100 ergs absorbed/gram of material
RBE	Relative biological effectiveness	All, but specified	All animal tissue	ratio — rads gamma radiation/rads specified radiation
rem	Roentgen equivalent in man	All, but specified	Human tissue	Dose in rems = RBE × dose in rads

physical. The rep is the dose of *any* nuclear radiation (for example, gamma rays, beta particles, neutrons) that results in the absorption of a specific amount of energy (97 ergs) per gram of animal tissue. Because of the difficulty in measuring the rep, another unit has been defined, the rad. The rad is the absorbed dose of any nuclear radiation that is accompanied by the liberation of a specific amount of energy (100 ergs) per gram of absorbing material.

Because different types of radiation produce different effects, a unit is required to relate all radiation to a single standard. This is the *relative biological effectiveness* (RBE). The RBE of a given type of radiation is the ratio of absorbed dose in rads of gamma radiation to that of rads of the given radiation having the same biological effect.

Another unit, the rem, or *roentgen equivalent in man,* relates the rad to the biological effect of a particular radiation absorbed. This unit is defined as the RBE times the dose in rads.

In recent years, a new unit of radiation has been advocated and adopted by many in the life sciences. This unit is the *linear energy transfer,* or LET. This designation refers to the stopping power or the retardation of a particle, especially a heavily charged particle, in terms of its kinetic energy and its distance of penetration. While the unit of LET is being used more and more in scientific publications, it is extremely difficult to relate to other units of radiation. However, some experimental investigations have linked the LET to the RBE. Specifically, the LET is the density of ionization along a particle track in terms of the rate of the linear energy transfer. Hence, protons of sufficiently high energies may have the same LET as low-energy electrons, and it has been shown that the RBE of high-energy protons is indeed similar to that of X-rays.

THE RADIATION ENVIRONMENT OF MAN IN SPACE

All of us living on the earth are exposed to a certain amount of radiation. This radiation comes from several sources: the decay processes of radioactive elements in the earth itself, the primary and secondary radiation filtering in from outer space, and man-produced radiations. When all these are combined, man yearly experiences something in the neighborhood of 0.1 to 0.2 r per year, which by the most recent figures is about 1/100 of the amount considered to be a "permissible dose."

Perhaps one of the most substantial contributors to terrestrial radiation is that filtering through from outer space. The earth's atmosphere and lines of magnetic force together form a partial shield for these space radiations. What filters through the atmospheric shield are generally the

cosmic-ray secondaries, formed by the collision of extraterrestrial pri-
maries with the atmospheric molecules. Because of this effect, and because
of the nature of man-produced radiation and earth decay radiation, the
primary earth environment of radiation is composed of ionizing radiations both of the gamma and beta types. Although the quantity of these
radiations is very small and their energies are so low that they penetrate
the human organism with great difficulty, they will play an important part
in our later discussion of the effects of very small doses on animal
behavior.

On May 1, 1958, James A. Van Allen announced the discovery of the
great radiation belts surrounding most of the earth. Further, in the
flights of the Pioneer and Explorer satellites, as well as the Russian
Sputnik and Lunik satellites, it was discovered that there are two belts
surrounding the earth and that the levels of radiation in them are certainly far from negligible. Table 2 gives Van Allen's estimates on particle

Table 2.   Van Allen's Estimates on Particle Flux

HEART OF INNER ZONE

(3,600 km on geomagnetic equator)

(a) Electrons, $E = 20$ kev: maximum unidirectional intensity:
   2×10^9 cm^{-2} sec^{-1} ster^{-1}

(b) Electrons, $E = 600$ kev: maximum unidirectional intensity:
   1×10^7 cm^{-2} sec^{-1} ster^{-1}

(c) Protons, $E = 40$ Mev: maximum omnidirectional intensity:
   2×10^4 cm^{-2} sec^{-1}

HEART OF OUTER ZONE

(16,000 km on geomagnetic equator)

(a) Electrons, $E = 20$ kev: omnidirectional intensity:
   1×10^{11} cm^{-2} sec^{-1}

(b) Electrons, $E = 200$ kev: omnidirectional intensity:
   1×10^8 cm^{-2} sec^{-1}

(c) Protons, $E = 60$ Mev: omnidirectional intensity:
   10^2 cm^{-2} sec^{-1}

(d) Protons, $E = 30$ Mev: no information

flux for the inner zone and the outer zone. This should then be compared
with Table 3, detailing the type and nature of radiation in space. With
these data it is then possible to compare some typical exposures with the
maximum permissible doses recommended by the Atomic Energy Commission. This comparison is found in Table 4.

Because of the interaction between the earth's magnetic field and the
radiation belts, there are a relatively few radiation-free trajectories by
which one might leave the earth, such as through a polar exit. Current

Table 3. Radiation in Space

Name	Nature of Radiation	Charge	Where Found
Photon	Electromagnetic	0	Radiation belts, solar radiation (produced
X-ray	Electromagnetic	0	by nuclear reaction and by stopping
Gamma ray	Electromagnetic	0	electrons)
Electron	Particle	$-e$	Radiation belts
Proton	Particle	$+e$	Cosmic rays, inner radiation belt, solar cosmic rays
Neutron	Particle	0	Vicinity of planets and sun
Alpha particle	Particle	$+2e$	Cosmic rays
Beta particle	Particle	$\pm 1e$	Cosmic rays
Heavy primaries	Particle	$+3e$	Cosmic rays

Table 4. Maximum Permissible Radiation Dosages and Some Typical Exposure Levels (in Roentgens)

Item	Amount
PERMISSIBLE EXPOSURES	
Maximum permissible dosages	0.3 r/quarter
	5.0 r/yr
Maximum permissible emergency exposure	25.0 r
TYPICAL EXPOSURES	
Normal radiation level (sea level)	0.001 r/day
Undisturbed interplanetary space (cosmic rays)	5–12 r/yr
Heart of inner belt (protons)	24 r/hr
Heart of outer belt (soft X-rays)	200 r/hr
Solar proton event (protons)	$10–10^3$ r/hr
Total exposure	2–400 r

technology, however, does not permit the use of these polar exits for all planned flight trajectories. In view of this, current planning must involve estimates of exposure risks for an astronaut, but more will be said of this at the end of this section.

Beyond the two radiation belts, there is a natural cosmic radiation environment largely produced by solar flares. As is well known, cosmic radiations are the most energetic particles known. Energies of individual particles range from a few million to several billion electron volts (Bev). The primary radiation found in interplanetary space consists of protons, alpha particles, and the nuclei of heavier elements. The protons comprise roughly 86 per cent of the radiation, 13 per cent is accounted for by the alpha particles, and the remaining 1 per cent consists of the heavier particles. There are also low energy-particles emitted by the sun. The composition and energies of these particles have not, however, been scientifically determined to an accuracy permitting them to be involved in risk calculations. More than 30 times in the past three years protons have been detected over the polar regions following a large solar flare on the sun. The high flux of protons may exist from 10 to 100 hours and of these events, six were of such intensity and duration as to have provided a lethal dose to an unshielded exposed individual in space. These solar flares or giant radiation events pose two very specific problems. The first is that although we know something about their frequency of occurrence, as yet scientists have not been able to effectively predict when and of what magnitude they will be. Secondly, because of the extremely high energies and high concentration of the protons, the particles colliding with the molecules of shielding material produce fluxes of ionizing or electromagnetic radiation within the capsule. This phenomenon of impact and scatter is known as the *Brehmsstrahlung* effect.

As yet there are only guesses as to the extent of radioactivity on extraterrestrial bodies. Fly-by probes can provide such data. Of importance may be the radiation trapped in an atmospheric environment, such as surrounds the planet Venus. Our knowledge of extraterrestrial radiation, sources, composition, and intensities is insufficient to permit more than guesses at the consequences for a shielded astronaut.

An important application of nuclear energy is in the propulsion system. In order to evaluate the human consequences from a nuclear propulsion system, one must first know the intensities and composition of radiations from a given power source, its distance from the occupants of the space vehicle, and the materials shielding the occupants from these radiations. Trapp and Konecci (1959) conducted a study to determine the probable dose for an unshielded crew. Figure 1 shows thrust in pounds versus dose rate in rem per hour for given separation distances between crew and power source. In this report Trapp and Konecci suggest that fuel and food can be arranged to provide some shielding. Trade-offs between the dose received by the crew and the weight of shielding will have to be established, and some intelligent decision will have to be made with each mission on what is a permissible dose for the crew in order to minimize this weight.

A further area where nuclear reactors must be considered is that of power supplies on an extraterrestrial body. Figures from the SNAP Programs (personal communication, 1960) show several different configurations and their shield weight for different reactor outputs in terms of kilowatts. Table 5 displays these figures. Supporting the probability of radiation exposure surrounding nuclear reactions in the recent data from the AEC station in Idaho (U.S. AEC, 1960). These figures show total

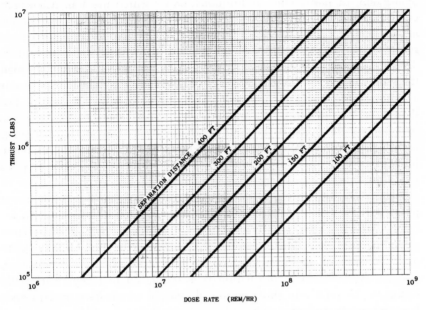

Figure 1. Dose rate at crew compartment from unshielded direct radiation. Dose rate (REM/HR)

for beta for the full year. Local materials can be used to provide shielding.

Table 5. Snap Reactors and Shield Weights

Snap	Reactor (KW$_e$)	Shield Wt (lb)
X	0.3	330
II	3.0	350
VIII	30.0	450
—	300.0	550

1960 doses to personnel to be 160 millirems for gamma and 125 millirems

All these considerations must be evaluated in terms of current knowledge at the time of planning a mission. A mission involving a two-man or three-man space vehicle is represented below.

With regard to the risk encountered in passage through the Van Allen belts, it has been found that even for a lightly shielded vehicle (1 g/cm^2 H$_2$O) the dose levels are not high. For an outbound lunar ascent trajectory ($V_o = 36,000$ ft/sec) in which no attempt is made to avoid the belts, a total integrated dose of 1.0 r is encountered. This value would, of course, be lower for typical vehicles characterized by shielding of 6 g/cm² or more. One circumstance under which the Van Allen belts could represent a hazard is in the case of an emergency return or mission abort. Then it is possible that the vehicle on its altered trajectory could reach apogee in the vicinity of the belts. In this case, where the return leg of the trajectory traverses both belts at low geomagnetic latitudes, the dose could be as high as 22.0 r. It was found, however, that generally a return route could be selected which would produce a dose of less than 12 r. For orbiting vehicles in highly elliptical orbits, extending in part beyond the belts, it was found that the desired orbit characteristics could be achieved while limiting the dose to 3–5 r per orbit. This possibility does not apply to orbits which lie entirely within the trapped radiation zones.

The solar flare problem can best be discussed from a probabilistic point of view. One can base estimates on models of the relationship between flare intensity and frequency of occurrence. The hazard represented by flares is a function of the year in which the mission takes place and probably of the time of year in which the mission occurs. Unfortunately, very little information is available on this key relationship owing to the relatively short period of time in which flare spectra have been recorded, and our guesses are necessarily crude. Flares are classified into three categories: (1) high intensity–low energy; (2) extreme intensity–low energy; and (3) high intensity–high energy. Representative of each category are the flares of (1) August 22, 1958; (2) May 10, 1959; and (3) February 23, 1956.

Because of the infrequent occurrence of the third type (five in 21 years), it is not considered in probability estimates. It then becomes a matter of assuming how many of the type 1 and type 2 flares will occur in a given year. For a year of maximum solar activity there would be 12 flares of both types occurring and perhaps three would be of the type 2 category, the remainder type 1. This assumption gives us a basis for evaluating encounter probability for a mission of known duration. Another model of flare behavior for a year of decreased activity, a few years either side of the solar maximum, would be: six flares per year, one type 2, five type 1. Using these two estimates and a mission duration of two weeks, the dose probability distribution can be determined. The results of the calculations based on the above assumptions appear in Figure 2.

These results are not very encouraging, but most factors are taken very conservatively, and it is hoped that increased knowledge of solar-flare behavior will permit less cautious estimates. It should be added that the vehicle shielding also enters into the evaluation of the dose and for the data presented a value of 7.0 g/cm² has been taken (Abel, personal communication, 1961).

Primary Biological Effects of Radiation

Two concepts must be clearly understood by the reader before we proceed with our discussion on the effect of radiation. The first is that even the smallest amount of radiation may have a very high energy level; that is, doses of gamma radiation that would not lead to observable pathology still contain energies in the thousands-of-electron-volt range. The second point to be emphasized and understood is that when discussing the effects of an environmental variable on organ systems one must accept the fact that there is tremendous variability in the response of an organ, the total organism, and even the cell. Nuclear radiation effects on living systems depend on the total dose absorbed, the rate of absorption, the composition or type of radiation, and the area of the

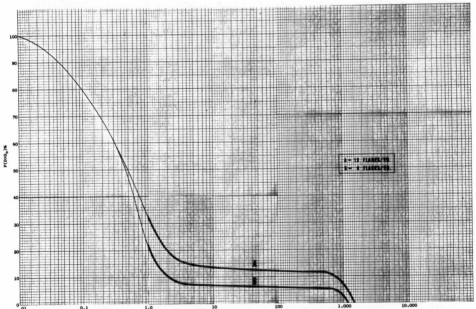

Figure 2. Integral Probability Distribution. Probability of exceeding dose D. Two week mission. Dose rate (REM/HR)

body affected. Thus, 700 r in a single dose would be fatal with whole body exposures to human beings; but when applied to localized areas over 30 years, it would not be detectable by pathological examination. Paramount in this consideration is the rate of replacement in the cells of skin, blood-forming tissues, and gastrointestinal tract. One major exception is the inability of nervous tissue to repair itself. In general, the most radio-sensitive parts are the lymphoid tissue, the bone marrow, the spleen, the reproductive organs, and the gastrointestinal tract. The skin, kidney, and liver have intermediate sensitivity; and the muscles and full-grown bones are least sensitive.

The study of the effects of radiation on human beings is facilitated by the use of observable pathology such as lesions, tumors, demonstrable genetic effects, and incidence of leukemia. To facilitate the handling of this information, a concept used extensively in pharmacology L.D. 50/30, is used. This means the dose which will yield a given effect on 50 per cent of the exposed population within 30 days.

The summary of large-dose effects due to whole-body radiation exposure is found in Table 6. The data on which this is based come from the two bomb explosions in Japan, the accident that occurred in the Marshall Islands after an atomic bomb test, and isolated accidents in various radiation laboratories. They are the same data that have led to the concept of a maximum permissible dose.

Table 6.   Expected Effects of Human Acute Whole-Body Radiation Doses

Acute Dose (Roentgens)	Probable Effect
0–50	No obvious effect, except possibly minor blood changes.
80–120	Vomiting and nausea for about 1 day in 5 to 10 per cent of exposed personnel. Fatigue, but no serious disability.
130–170	Vomiting and nausea for about 1 day, followed by other symptoms of radiation sickness, in about 25 per cent of personnel. No deaths anticipated.
180–220	Vomiting and nausea for about 1 day, followed by other symptoms of radiation sickness, in about 50 per cent of personnel. No deaths anticipated.
270–330	Vomiting and nausea in nearly all personnel on the first day, followed by other symptoms of radiation sickness. About 20 per cent deaths within two to six weeks after exposure; survivors convalescent for about three months.
400–500	Vomiting and nausea in all personnel on the first day, followed by other symptoms of radiation sickness. About 50 per cent deaths within one month; survivors convalescent for about six months.
550–750	Vomiting and nausea in all personnel within 4 hours of exposure, followed by other symptoms of radiation sickness. Up to 100 per cent deaths. Any survivors convalescent for about six months.
1,000	Vomiting and nausea in all personnel within 1 to 2 hours. Probably no survivors from radiation sickness.
5,000	Incapacitation almost immediately. Fatal to all personnel within one week.

THE EFFECTS OF RADIATION ON PERFORMANCE

This section deals with two types of studies primarily conducted within the United States. The first type of study involves the training of an animal to learn a specific task, then exposing him to a given amount of radiation, and observing the change in the progress of his learning, discrimination, or activity level. The second type of experiment deals with conditioned responses where the reaction of the animal is more reflexive. Most of these experiments involve very low doses.

LEARNING

One of the first experiments on the effect of radiation on learning was performed by Furchtgott (1951) using escape from a water maze as the learning motivation. In the first section of this experiment, 32 rats were subjected to whole-body radiation of either 200 or 300 r. Furchtgott found no difference between the control and the experimental subjects for either level of radiation, as measured on new learning and retention. In the second part of the experiment, 34 rats were subjected to 500 r, 20 rats to 400 r, and 27 rats to 300 r. It was found that retention measured by maze time was significantly poorer for the 500 r group. No effect on maze errors was found for any group.

The effects of radiation upon retention as well as other variables was studied by Kaplan, *et al.* (1951, 1952). This study deserves a fuller analysis, since it is characteristic of the majority of experiments in this area.

Eighty-seven male albino rats of the Sprague-Dawley strain were used. Sixty-one of these animals were used in the maze experiments, which used a slightly modified version of Lashley's Maze III. The radiation source was a deep-therapy X-ray machine (250 kv, 15 ma, 0.5 mm copper and 1.0 mm aluminum filters). The container did not preclude all movement by the animals, but any variations in the total air dose delivered at the tops of the animals' backs were on the order of less than ±3 per cent. Radiation was given at the rate of approximately 30 r per minute.

The animals were pretrained in the straightaway to establish a goal-seeking habit. The goal was pellets of food that the animals were permitted to eat for 30 sec. The animals received 15 trials on the maze and then the experimental group received 90, 180, 360, or 600 r. Eighteen hours later the sixteenth trial was commenced. This procedure points to a basic flaw in the experimental design. Since gastrointestinal effects of radiation are a general malaise and inability to hold down food, the effects may be due to these difficulties in the irradiated animals. Kaplan states that the only significant results were longer running times and poorer error scores for the rats receiving 600 r. This is hardly surprising, since half of the 600 r group died within 30 days. This confounding effect, using food as a goal, is common to many of the experiments covered in this review. On two of them, a delay between radiation and testing was introduced; this delay, in one case 18 months, seems sufficient to overcome the confounding effect based upon physiological examination.

Arnold (1952) used 12 rats in a maze experiment with a hunger drive to study the effect on retention of 300 r restricted to the cranium. He found no significant differences in maze errors or maze time when the radiation group was compared with a control group. In a second experiment, he used 800 r applied to the cranium, using rats with a hunger drive in a maze. Again he found no significant differences. Kaplan, *et al.* (1953), tried another approach with monkeys. He shielded the central nervous systems of the animals and studied their ability to transfer on a paired discrimination task after receiving 400 r. The monkeys receiving this dose, two whose central nervous systems were not shielded and two with shielding, showed no significant differences from controls.

Melching and Kaplan (1954), as part of the School of Aviation Medicine program, used whole-body radiation of 1,500 r on four monkeys and tested them for retention on a Y-shaped maze with a shock-avoidance motivation. Again, no significant variation was found. Rogers, *et al.* (1954), on this same project, used cumulative doses of 108 r for 12 trials on two monkeys and then tested them on tasks involving discrimination learning, retention, and transfer. No significant results were obtained.

The first positive results were reported in 1956 by Riopelle, *et al.* (1956), who divided 29 monkeys into three groups, receiving a single dose of 350 r, 10 doses of 100 r, and 10 doses of 200 r, using hunger as a drive. A significant increase in discrimination learning in the irradiated groups was observed, but no effect was noted on avoidance learning or on a direct method of delayed response. Riopelle felt that the increment in performance could be due to either an increased resistance to distraction or to increased tameness. The picture was further complicated when Blair and Arnold (1956) found an initial decrease in retention of 20 rats during maze performance after 2,500 r restricted to the cranium, but a significant later improvement in retention when the treated group was compared with a control group. He theorized that this was due to a higher hunger motivation and a decrease in exploratory drive.

What is perhaps the most complete study was reported by Fields

(1957). He used 180 and 360 r whole-body radiation on two groups of 20 rats and tested them on maze learning with a hunger drive. He reports a significant increase in straightaway and maze time for the 360 r group, but significantly fewer errors for this same group. Next he used radiation levels of 100, 200, 400, and 600 r and found that retention was significantly poorer for the 600 r group and 94 per cent of the group died within 11 days. In another part of this experiment he investigated the effects of 100, 200, and 400 r whole-body radiation on relearning after a 6-month delay. No effect was found on straightaway or maze time; there was, however, a significant increase in maze errors for the 200 and 400 r groups. A fourth section of this study tested the effect of 400, 800, and 1,000 r on hunger-motivated rats tested in a vertical maze. Although no significance was found for maze time, the 1,000 r group showed a significant increase in maze errors when compared with the 400 r, 800 r, and control groups.

The most recently reported experiment in this area was undertaken by Blair (1958). He used 5,000 r cranial radiation in 34 hunger motivated rats and found a significant decrease in both maze time and maze errors as measures of retention, substantiating his earlier results.

When the data presented here are categorized by species and lethality, it appears that there is no effect from lethal X irradiation on learning and retention of monkeys. The only indication of the effect of a sublethal dose on monkeys is an improvement of discrimination learning. Rats, on the other hand, seem to respond to a massive lethal dose with faster maze time and fewer errors. Below 350 r there seems to be no effect on rat learning in a maze, and, between 350 r and a lethal dose, evidence largely indicates a decrement in performance.

ACTIVITY AND MANIPULATION

There are four studies on the effects of X-ray on activity and manipulation. The first of these was undertaken by Leary and Ruch (1955). He used cumulative doses of 50 r on monkeys after an initial dose of either 100 or 200 r with the total dose 200, 300, or 400 r. He found no significant difference in activity between the groups or between a treated and control group. In the 400 r group, no significant change was indicated on a motivated weight-pulling task, although observed activity and manipulatory ability, as measured by a pedometer, showed significant decrease. Leary feels that these results support the hypothesis that low-motivated behavior is most susceptible to the effects of ionizing radiation.

Davis, *et al.* (1956), on a study of manipulation, found that monkeys subjected to 400 r whole-body radiation differed significantly from control animals in only two out of six tasks. There was a significant increase in failures in a bent-wire poker-chip task and there was significantly less chewing of a wood block. In this same study, Davis reports some un-published data of McDowell which indicated that, at 400 r radiation, monkeys showed a significant decrease in hand and oral manipulation.

Riopelle, *et al.* (1956), using a single dose of 250 r, 10 doses of 100 r, and 10 doses of 200 r on hunger motivated monkeys, found significantly less activity. Fields (1957) obtained similar results with 360 r radiated and hunger motivated rats on an activity drum.

Generally, it would appear from these studies that radiation, in both lethal and sublethal doses, serves to decrease activity and manipulation rates in both rats and monkeys.

CONDITIONING

Nemenov (1933) in what is perhaps the first behavioral experiment with X-ray, found a temporary slight decrease in a salivary conditioned response in dogs after 500 r. Lyman, *et al.* (1933), also of the Pavlov Laboratory, found that the salivary conditioned response in dogs tem-porarily decreased after 17,000 r radiation. In the former study, the radiation was restricted to the central nervous system.

DISCRIMINATION

Furchtgott (1952) found that brightness discrimination in rats was significantly poorer after 369 r and 490 r whole-body radiation by X-ray. Two studies by Warren and Kaplan (1954) and Warren, *et al.* (1955), represent the only experiment on discrimination using sublethal radiation sources other than X-ray. It would be well to consider in some detail the first of these studies, since it is experimentally more sound than most of the other studies discussed in this chapter.

Ten experimentally naive rhesus monkeys were studied, three of which were normal and seven irradiated. The Wisconsin General Test Apparatus was used. This is essentially a restraining cage behind a table on which a wheeled tray carrier was set, containing food wells. The stimuli were 108 different pairs of objects, differing in multiple visual dimensions. The Oak Ridge National Laboratory "Bulk Shielding" reactor was utilized as a source of fast neutron and gamma radiation. Cumulative dose procedures were utilized and the doses are listed in Table 7.

Psychological testing of the subjects was begun approximately eight months following the last radiation exposure. (This controls for the possible confounding due to gastrointestinal effects upon hunger drive.)

Table 7.   Average Radiation Dose

	GAMMA RADIATION (R)		NEUTRON RADIATION (DOSE IN REM, BASED ON NEUTRON/ GAMMA RBE OF 10)
Group	Head	Body	Head and Body
A	25	18.5	7.4
B	107	87.0	30.0
C	493	404.0	118.0

Three discrimination reversal problems were presented daily for 36 working days; thus, the total number of problems was 108, of which 18 problems were presented under each of six conditions of prereversal reinforcement.

Warren found that the performance of the irradiated group was consistently inferior to the performance of the control group. The normal monkeys averaged 68 per cent correct responses, while the irradiated group had a mean of 61 per cent. The differences between these groups was tested with the Mann-Whitney nonparametric test for ranked data and was significant at the 0.017 level.

Davis, et al. (1956) studied object discrimination of eight monkeys after receiving 400 r whole-body X-radiation. On four tests he found no significant differences.

In summary, it appears that radiation does impair discrimination processes although not all evidence is in agreement.

PERFORMANCE AFTER COSMIC RADIATION

The only study on performance after cosmic radiation reported to date is one by Harlow, et al. (1956), in which monkeys were sent in a balloon to 90,000-ft altitude. No significant differences were found on five types of discrimination problems after this exposure to cosmic radiation. It should be noted, however, that this experiment was performed in an environment not adequately controlled and that the radiation dose was not clearly established.

The Effects of Sublethal and Very Small Doses

The chief tool in the investigation of sublethal and very small doses of radiation and their effects on behavior has been conditioning. In the United States, the best examples of this type of study have come from the Navy Radiological Defense Laboratory at San Francisco. Kimeldorf (1960), in a recent review of this work, cites the saccharin-avoidance conditioning experiments performed there. In these experiments, Garcia and Kimeldorf (1960) found in rats that a neutron dose of 7.5 rad resulted in an 80 per cent reduction in preference for the saccharin fluid as compared with a control group. Further, they found that greater radiation doses gave proportionately greater preference reduction.

In Russia, the conditioning method has been used to study the effects of very small doses of irradiation on animal and human behavior. These experiments differ from the above in that some sort of reflex activity is studied instead of discrimination activity. Livanov and Kondrat'eva (1960) have reviewed this work and suggest (as Garcia has) that very small doses produce behavioral effects that can be measured by sensitive tests. These authors cite the following evidence:

1. Gorshelva, Airapetiants, and Maliukova found disturbed internal inhibition of conditioned reflexes following single total-body and head irradiation doses of 5, 10, and 20 r. Recovery occurred only after 14 to 25 days.

2. Yaroslavtseva found that three repeated doses of 10 r within a period of 5 days produced a distinct variation in conditioned reflexes, and recovery to normal did not occur for 4 months.

3. Korl'kova, in a series of experiments on rabbits, found that a single total-body dose of 5, 10, or 25 r intensifies the processes of cortical excitability as measured by increased variation of biopotentials and by increased excitability and reactivity of the cortex. Repeated irradiations at one-week intervals were less effective than the preceding.

4. Morozov and others have used near maximum permissible doses on humans. Distinct changes were detected, by means of a speech-motor conditioning method involving measures such as delayed formation of temporary bonds, prolonged latent period of conditioned reflexes, and difficulties in the alteration of reflexes.

5. Kudritskii and Fedorova, using a cumulated total-body dose of 10 r for 11 days in rabbits found changes in the flexor reflexes of the hind leg. After daily treatments of 0.1 and 0.5 r, decreases in the flexor stimulation took place within 14 days (total dose of 1.4 or 0.7 r).

6. Domshlak and others have examined persons who were systematically exposed to ionizing radiation doses of 0.05 to 0.65 r. These subjects showed a syndrome of functional disturbances in the nervous system more frequently than pathologic symptoms. The reception of gustatory and olfactory stimuli are affected early; that is, the sensitivity thresholds increase the restoration period of the thresholds following the effect

as osmic stimulation is extended, and the interaction between these two measures is affected. The original data for these six studies were not available for examination and the evidence cited is from Livanov and Kondrat'eva (1960).

Motokawa, *et al.* (1957), reported a very low-level radiation effect. For some time they had been inducing an electrical phosphene by passing a small current across the retina and having the subjects report when they saw a "bluish glow." One of his trained subjects suddenly started showing extreme variability in the threshold for this phenomenon, and Motokawa learned that this same subject was being exposed to radiation. Ten students at the university were exposed to 50-mr doses of X-radiation, and changes in the threshold of the electrical phosphene were recorded. The phosphene index was significantly higher than in a control group; the same relationship was observed for a group of X-ray technicians. In some cases the changes resulting from this low-dose exposure persisted for 10 days. Motokawa, as a result of this investigation, feels that there is a nearly linear relationship between maximum acute effect and the logarithm of the applied dose within a range from 1 to 50 mr.

Finally, the work of Miller (1960), concerning the effect of very low doses of radiation on the production of audiogenic seizures in seizure-prone rats, must be cited. This work, like that of Motokawa's, resulted from a chance observation in 1952. Miller noticed changes in the seizure threshold of her animals after moving to a new laboratory. The striking increase in seizure susceptibility was finally traced to a CO^{60} source in a neighboring laboratory that was emitting a dose of 5 to 10 times the background level (0.1 to 0.2 mrad/hour). The full investigation resulting from this discovery showed that the seizure susceptibility altered even with the increase in atmospheric radiation following the 1958 hydrogen bomb tests; and that a dose of 350 mrad experimentally administered would also significantly increase seizure susceptibility.

Summary

The present review of radiation effects on integrated behavior, while not comprehensive, leaves little doubt that sublethal and very small doses (milliroentgens) alter selected aspects of animal and human behavior. Further, there is little doubt that man venturing into space will be exposed to radiation at or beyond these levels. It is possible, from the studies reported here, that since even the smallest dose involves great energies (million electron volts), there will be some effect on organ systems if the measurement instrument is sensitive enough. That these effects can be termed deleterious is open to question and further research. Even the available data, however, suggest that it might be well to revise our thinking concerning the basis for establishing maximum permissible doses.

It is the opinion of this author that there is no dose of radiation that will not yield an effect in biological systems. In order to develop realistic standards for exposure, we must first categorize the types of dose effects. The following is a tentative classification:

1. Very small (0 to 1.0 r)
   a. Reversible effect
   b. Prolonged effect (1 to 100 days)
   c. Irreversible effect (permanent threshold changes and genetic changes)

2. Small (10 to 100 r)
   a. Reversible effect
   b. Prolonged effect
   c. Irreversible effect

3. Sublethal (species-dependent, 100 to ? r)
   a. Reversible effect
   b. Prolonged effect
   c. Irreversible effect (tumors, leukemia, etc.)

4. Lethal (species-dependent, L.D. 50/30)

5. Massive (greater than lethal)

In addition, the area of exposure, the rate of exposure, the type of radiation involved, and several other variables have to be specified.

To date all permissible dose exposures have been derived from pathological data. If man is going to take a calculated risk in such space ventures as Project Apollo, then this risk should be evaluated in terms of mission completion and human performance rather than in terms of pathology. The basing of exposure on types of effect as outlined above is perhaps a start in this direction.

Radiation is part of man's normal environment. The question of how much radiation is harmful to his goals is not answerable at our present state of knowledge, but the rapid increase in interest in this area holds the promise of some partial answers within the next few decades.

References

Arnold, W. J. "Maze Learning and Retention after X-Radiation of the Head," *J. Comp. Physiol. Psychol., 45*:358–361, 1952.

Blair, W. C., "The Effects of Cranial X-Radiation on Maze Acquisition in Rats, *J. Comp. Physiol. Psychol., 51*:175–177, 1958.
——— and Arnold, W. J. "The Effects of Cranial X-Radiation on Retention of Maze Learning in Rats," *J. Comp. Physiol. Psychol., 49*:525–528, 1956.

Claus, W. D. (ed.), *Radiation Biology and Medicine*, Reading, Mass.: Addison-Wesley, 1958.

Davis, R. T., McDowell, A. A., Deter, C. E., and Steele, J. P. "Performance of Rhesus Monkeys on Selected Laboratory Tasks Presented before and after a Large Single Dose of Whole-Body X-Radiation," *J. Comp. Physiol. Psychol., 49*:20–26, 1956.

Fields, P. E. "The Effect of Whole-body X-Radiation upon Activity Drum, Straightaway, and Maze Performance of White Rats, *J. Comp. Physiol. Psych., 50*:386–391, 1957.
Furchtgott, E., "Effects of Total Body X-Irradiation in Learning: An Exploratory Study," *J. Comp. Physiol. Psychol., 44*:197–203, 1951.
———. "The Effects of X-Irradiation on Brightness Discrimination," *J. Psychol., 34*:37–41, 1952.

Garcia, J., and Kimeldorf, D. J. "Conditioned Avoidance Behavior Induced by Low Dose Fast Neutron Exposure," *Nature, 185*:261–262, 1960.
Gubin, V. A., and Moskalev, Y. I. *Biological Effect of Small Doses of Ionizing Radiation*, Moscow: Academy of Medical Sciences, U.S.S.R., 1960 (translation: AEC-TR-4086).

Harlow, H. F., Schrier, A. M., and Simons, D. G. "Exposure of Primates to Cosmic Radiation above 90,000 Feet," *J. Comp. Physiol. Psychol., 49*:195–200, 1956.

Kaplan, S. J., and Gentry, G. "Some Effects of Sublethal Dose of X-Radiation upon Transfer of Training in Monkeys," USAF SAM Project No. 21-3501-0003, Report No. 4, December, 1953.
———, Tait, C. D., Wall, P. D., and Payne, R. E. "Behavioral Changes following Radiation: 1. Study of Retention of a Partially Learned Maze Habit," Unnumbered project, Report No. 1, USAF School of Aviation Medicine, Randolph

Field, Texas, March, 1951; 2. "Material Behavior and Maze Performance," USAF, School of Aviation Medicine, Special Report, July, 1952.

Kimeldorf, D. J. "Radiation-Conditioned Behavior," International Symposium on the Response of the Nervous System to Ionizing Radiation, Northwestern Medical School, Chicago, September, 1960.

Leary, R. C., and Ruch, T. C. "Activity, Manipulation drive, and Strength in Monkeys Subjected to Low Level Radiation," *J. Comp. Physiol. Psychol., 48*: 336–342, 1955.

Levedahl, Blaine H. "A Survey of Radiobiology for Engineers," *Human Factors, 1*: No. 3, 1–68, August, 1959.

Lindberg, R. G. "Biological Criteria for Establishing Permissible Radiation Exposures of Astronauts, Astro Systems and Research ·Laboratories," Northrop Corp., ASRL-TM-60-4, May, 1960.

Livanov, M. N., and Kondrat'eva, I. N. *Sensitivity of the Nervous System to Low Level Radiation,* Moscow: Academy of Medical Sciences, U.S.S.R., 1960 (translation: AEC-TR-4090).

Lyman, R. S., Kupalov, P. S., and Scholz, W. Effects of Roentgen Rays on the Central Nervous System, *Arch. Neurol. Psychiat., 29*:56–87, 1933.

Melching, W. H., and Kaplan, S. J. "Some Effects of a Lethal Dose of X-Radiation upon Retention: Studies of Shock Avoidance Motivation," USAF SAM Project No. 21-3501-0003, Report No. 9, August, 1954.

Miller, D. S. "Effects of Low-Level Radiation on Audiogenic Convulsive Seizures in Mice," International Symposium on the Response of the Nervous System to Ionizing Radiation, Northwestern Medical School, Chicago, September, 1960.

Motokawa, K., Kohata, T., Komatsu, M., Chichibu, S., Koga, Y., and Kasai, T. "A Sensitive Method for Detecting the Effect of Radiation upon the Human Body," *Tohoku J. Exp. Med., 66*: No. 3–4, 389–404, 1957.

Nemenov, M. I. "The Effect of Roentgen Ray Exposure of the Cerebral Hemispheres," *Radiology, 23*:86–93, 1933.

Newell, H. E., and Naugle, J. E. "Radiation Environment in Space," *Science, 132*:1465–1472, November 18, 1960.

Pogrund, Robert S. "The Spaceman and His Requirements," to be published in *Space Logistics,* New York: Wiley, 1962.

Rogers, C. M., Kaplan, S. J., Gentry, G., and Auxier, J. A. "Some Effects of Cumulative Doses of X-Radiation upon Learning and Retention in the Rhesus Monkey," USAF SAM Report No. 21-3501-0003, Report No. 11, November, 1954.

Riopelle, A. J., Grodsky, M. A., and Ades, H. W. "Learned Performance of Monkeys after Single and Repeated X-Radiations," *J. Comp. Physiol. Psychol., 49*:521–524, 1956.

Tobias, Paul. "Effects of Radiation on Performance," *Human Factors, 1*: No. 4, 8–15, 1959.

Trapp, R. F., and Konecci, E. B. *Shielding and Nuclear Propulsion*, Douglas Aircraft Co., Eng. paper No. 808, July 17, 1959.

U.S. Atomic Energy Commission, Health and Safety Division, Environmental Monitoring Data, Annual Summary for the National Reactor Testing Station, 1960.

Warren, J. M., and Kaplan, S. J. "A Study of Discrimination Learning in Monkeys with Implications for the Investigation of the Psychobiological Effects of Ionizing Radiation," USAF SAM Project No. 21-3501-0003, Report No. 6, July, 1954.

———, ———, and Greenwood, D. D. "The Solution of Discrimination Reversal Problems by Normal and Irradiated Monkeys," USAF, *Arch. Aviat. Med.*, Proj. Rep. 1955, Proj. No. 21-3501-0003 (Rep. No. 16).

12

THE DECADE AHEAD

The Editors

1. Research Implications

ALTHOUGH hundreds of studies have been reviewed in preceding chapters, this effort is merely the beginning of scientific understanding. The complexities of the aerospace environment and the subtle nuances of man's responses represent a rich and rewarding research area. Exploration of this area has started. The course for the next 10 years has officially been plotted, with the moon emerging as the first stop-over on our scientific itinerary. The official designation of a research goal, however, does little to guarantee its attainment and contributes even less to an understanding of the problems that will be encountered along the way.

The editors and contributors view our current level of knowledge as meager when compared with all that remains to be known. The decade ahead will undoubtedly advance our levels of understanding and, consequently, make us even more painfully aware of the deficits our science still suffers. In this chapter suggestions on the directions research should take during the next decade are offered.

Throughout this volume the effects of various environmental extremes on human behavior have been analyzed. Each of these stresses varies in terms of intensity, duration, frequency, and complexity. The majority of research, however, has been concerned with stress levels representative of current vehicles and mission profiles. During the next decade manned space flights will be attempted that will encounter conditions that place the human operator at the limits of his tolerance. Present research has been designed to understand the nature of environment associated with current vehicle systems and to provide protection for the occupants of these vehicles. These new demands call for a degree of sophistication all too frequently absent from today's investigations.

The first question of fundamental concern is that of defining the limits within which any stress must be maintained. Concepts such as "stress tolerance" and "tolerance limit" are often mentioned, but it is not clear whether the limit of human survival or some level below is meant. It is clear that on any manned space-flight mission the probability of successful completion will be directly contingent upon the performance level of the human operator. It is therefore important to adjust environmental parameters so that operator performance is maintained at optimal levels. From these considerations, the definition suggests itself that "tolerance limit" be used to refer to some arbitrary level beyond which performance on a given task begins to deteriorate to a level that jeopardizes mission success. More specifically, this level may be called "performance tolerance limits" and is complemented by the concept of "physiological tolerance limit," which similarly refers to the level beyond which the functioning of any physiological system is unsatisfactory. These are conservative limits. They are to be clearly distinguished from the "destructive limit," which refers to the level beyond which irreparable or irreversable damage occurs. It must be the aim of the biological scientist and human factors engineer to take every means possible to protect the operator from stresses that exceed his performance and physiological tolerance limits. The concept of the success of a mission should include that of maintaining the integrity of the total organism so that its health is not in any way permanently affected, nor its useful life shortened by exposure to environmental stresses.

Most of the stresses to which the human operator may be subjected, such as extremes of temperature, humidity, pressure, and radiation, can be controlled and maintained at acceptable levels through proper engineering. In the case of acceleration and deceleration, however, as during some re-entry and abort conditions, it is difficult to avoid degrees of stress that exceed the performance tolerance limit as defined. Fortunately, such levels of acceleration or deceleration need be maintained for only a relatively short period of time. In cases of extremely high or prolonged acceleration, it may be necessary to rely upon automatic controls during the period in which the ability of the human operator is impaired.

Certain other conditions, stressors, or precursors of stress conditions, are more difficult to evaluate. For example, there are suggestions, based on water immersion experiments and short-term orbital flights, that after even a short period of weightlessness the return to gravitational conditions stresses the cardiovascular system. This raises the extremely significant but as yet unapproachable problem of the tolerance limits that will result after a prolonged period of weightlessness. Equally unknown is whether prolonged weightlessness itself is a stressor. Other factors about which we know little are alterations in biological rhythms and changes in magnetic fields.

Thus, we see that the problem of tolerance criteria has not yet been solved. It would appear that for each of the characteristics of a stress, that is, its magnitude, duration, rate of onset, and frequency, there is a tolerance limit. These limits may be expressed for physiological systems as well as for psychological systems. At the present time, they are not clearly specified. A procedure must be developed whereby the ability of man to tolerate or withstand any attribute of an unusual environment may be specified. This work will pose a real challenge during the next decade, since it is not normally possible to measure either the physiological or the performance limits of man without risking permanent damage to the individual. Also, it appears to be increasingly clear that in many cases the study of animals does not permit accurate specifications of human tolerance limits. It may be that major methodological changes will be required during the next decade. Simulation may be used to obtain data on man's ability to withstand stresses at the upper limits of tolerance, and this technique may provide one possible solution. The use of computers to outline tolerance zones by extrapolation from available data may be another approach. There is a need for models and a need for definition within models. As the complexity of our efforts increases, it will be necessary to use terminology and models based on empirical data and exact calculations, rather than approximations. Precision in describing the components and quantities within the models will be essential.

Another basic issue is that of the interaction of various stresses. In most experiments to date a single variable has been studied to the practical exclusion of other variables. In actual conditions, of course, a number of stress vectors interact. Studies of these interactions are essential, since there are very few actual data on this critical aspect of the problem. Similarly, very few data exist on cumulative stress effects. These effects are very difficult to measure, and it appears that new instrumentation and methods will be required. For example, many of the stresses will not be those which can be duplicated on earth. An extra-terrestrial or orbiting laboratory may be required in order to study the combined effects of many stresses operating at once.

If political conditions were more stable, these problems would receive thorough, unhurried academic study. The data may even lie dormant in obscure scientific journals, awaiting a future date when segments of science and industry have progressed sufficiently to find such informa-tion useful. The conditions of the present are such, however, that the store of useful biological knowledge, so painstakingly accumulated, has been quickly depleted, and the comfortable cushion of scientific informa-tion that traditionally separated the scientist from the engineer is no longer there. The consumption of scientific data has accelerated to a frightening degree. How is the scientist, particularly the biologically involved scientist, to contend with the seemingly insatiable appetite of the data-consuming sectors of the scientific community? This general methodological problem appears to be crucial; and scientific progress, indeed the conduct of the scientific enterprise itself, may depend on how it is solved in the decade to come.

Although the methodological problems cannot be thoroughly ana-lyzed here, some aspects may be mentioned. When the conduct of the scientific enterprise today is examined, one finds that different needs exist for different kinds of information. It appears useful to classify re-search in terms of the type of need it answers. Although this classification involves a good deal of overlap between categories, its purpose is simply as an expository aid. In the first type, there is the need for information to support on-going, high-priority projects. The problem is sharply circumscribed, and the data are more in the nature of demonstrations than experimental findings. Such studies as the motor performance of a sub-ject when confined in a particular pressure suit or the design configura-tion of maximum visibility aircraft markings are examples. The need for the information is immediate, and experimental completeness may have to be sacrificed.

The second type may be characterized by the case where a mission is planned for completion some time in the future. Thorough investiga-tions of rather broad problem areas are programmed, usually with the aim of determining the best among several alternatives. The data need is rather specific, but lead times can be quite long. These problems have generally received some prior investigation, and so a compilation and analysis of the literature is necessary. Carefully controlled observations are essential. Examples of this class of research are the study of the effects of one thing on another, such as specified types of acceleration on given performance tasks, the programing of man-machine interactions on a particular mission profile, and the cure for cancer. In general the aim of the research is specified, and a target date is often fixed in this type of research.

The third and final type of research may be most readily identified as basic research. In this case there is no apparent need for the information other than as a contribution to the literature of science. Such research is not opposed to "applied" research, however, since the results may find direct application to a problem at any time. Although this type of research frequently has high "pay-off" value, this factor alone does not comprise an adequate stimulus for research. Traditionally, a personally felt need, usually to satisfy curiosity, has impelled men to spend their lives in the search. The data obtained from this source have made up the greater portion of the reservoir of scientific information referred to earlier.

It is the absence of emphasis on this third area of research that has contributed to the lack of adequate data on performance tolerance limits as well as physiological tolerance limits. Accumulating such data is, at best, a painstaking effort. The range of each of the parameters is exceedingly large because of the very nature of the aerospace environment. The many tests and measures that are used to determine the effects of exposure are, on the one hand, not powerful enough for the purpose and, on the other hand, at times preclude retesting under controlled conditions. The design for basic parametric research in each of the stress areas covered in this volume is basically the same. It involves (1) exposure of the subject to some level of stress for a certain period of time; (2) the determination of the response of the whole organism to this stress exposure; and (3) the determination of the response of one subsystem of the organism to this stress exposure.

Essentially, the questions that are being asked of the data concern stress toxicity. In pharmacology, procedures for determining toxicity are well established, but the LD_{50} for centrifuge exposure, for example, still eludes even the most competent of investigators. It should not be surprising, then, that the environmental stress scientist could well follow the experimental design procedures that have proven useful in other areas. In order to fully explore the range of effects different levels of stress administration create, a design we call "Parametric Studies with Independent Samples" should be employed. The cases where this procedure is useful are those instances where the sample (human, animal, or material) is exposed to a specified level and duration of stress and then observed. Moreover, in these instances transient or long-term changes in the sample preclude other testings at altered levels and durations of stress. In order to obtain data points for various values of a parameter, a number of subjects must be exposed to each treatment level. Following this, for experimental purposes, the subjects are discarded and not exposed to future treatment within the context of design.

The question concerning the relative importance of these three classes of research inevitably arises. In the United States, because of the exigencies of business, medicine, and war, emphasis has been greatest on types 1 and 2, with type 3 relegated to the university. This situation has been deplored by many and, to a degree, justifiably, for in a sense the store of data accumulated by such researchers is the source of intellectual and material progress. But the needs prompting types 1 and 2 research are certainly real, and the success with which problems of these types are solved is directly related with the health and even survival of many individuals. If a space capsule or the configuration of a distress signal is inadequately conceived, the survival of the men involved can be seriously jeopardized. The consequences of such research being so immediate and far-reaching, it is reasonable to demand that the best available scientific minds be used. This conclusion may seem paradoxical, since we are so accustomed to thinking of "eggheads" being above ordinary daily needs and activities. We are also used to thinking that the "practical" man is the expert on such problems, but clearly this is not necessarily the case. Such individuals have in many cases made important contributions, but in view of the complexities of the contemporary world, science must replace intuition.

In many cases the need for a bit of information becomes acute only because of poor planning. In the frenzied drive toward technological supremacy, very few people have the time or the background to think about and define over-all needs. Great gaps in knowledge, instead of being properly surveyed and filled, are hurriedly patched over. Not only does such a procedure frequently result in ineffective information, but if carried on too long, the structure of science, instead of growing in scope and depth, may crumble into discrete, sterile heaps. Long-range planning and thorough long-range experimental programs are needed not only to preserve the fabric of science, but to assure the success of many current and contemplated missions and projects. Particularly in the field of bioastronautics are thorough parametric studies of human performance under extreme environmental conditions essential. Only through such comprehensive investigations will the safe limits of operator tolerance become known in terms of data that are useful to the designer and engineer. The conduct of research in the decade ahead will determine the human cost of the conquest of space.

2. Societal Implications

The next decade will witness man's continuing attempt to dominate the unusual environment of space. Highlighting these efforts will be the manned trip to the moon and return. In order to help reach this goal, the United States, for example, is committing billions of dollars and enlisting the efforts of a sizable proportion of the country's scientific and technical skill. In the process of making a successful lunar flight, changes in all aspects of human society, which have become evident with the advent of the space age, will make themselves even more apparent. Historically, such changes have usually been accompanied by some painful experiences. Members of the scientific and technical community cannot remain unconcerned about the nature of these changes.

Profound modifications in man's concept of himself and the role he plays in a greatly expanded universe will occur. The possibility that rational life forms, different from those we know, exist on a multitude of other planets will require reinterpretations of some currently accepted religious beliefs. In the political sphere, the gradual influx of scientists who have a part in directing the efforts of large governmental agencies controlling the expenditure of large sums of money will probably continue. This may well alter the public's image of the kind of people they consider to be best qualified to serve in the government.

The actual steps leading to a manned lunar landing within ten years have been publicized by NASA. Three unmanned lunar landings are scheduled to precede Project Apollo. The first, designated "Ranger," is designed to provide close-up visual information on the moon's surface and, after a "hard" landing, seismological information. The second, "Surveyor," will "soft" land on the moon an instrument package that will televise detailed information on the moon's surface, analyze the composition of the moon's crust, and make other physical measurements. Finally, "Prospector" will land a mobile device capable of exploring the surface of the moon within a 50-mile radius of its impact point. A sample of lunar crust will be automatically returned to earth in a small rocket. In addition to these probes designed to assess the lunar environment, instruments and supplies to be used by lunar explorers will be landed on the moon before the three-man Apollo crew arrives.

Doubts concerning the need for lunar explorations may increase, particularly as casualties begin to rise. It may be instructive to review some of the reasons that have been offered to justify the tremendous burdens involved. First, survival as a nation depends to a large degree upon the ability at least to match the technological levels of potential adversaries. Second, valuable scientific discoveries will be made as a result of detailed studies of extraterrestrial environments. Third, space exploits are important in terms of national prestige. Fourth, the technology necessary to support a space program indirectly produces other material benefits. Fifth, satellites can be used directly for communications, weather forecasting, and navigation. Finally, it is the nature of man to accept any challenge. The challenge of space is irresistible.

INDEX

In order to facilitate finding material through the use of this Index, each major entry offers a breakdown of relevant content. This organization is added to the usual alphabetical listings of authors. The italicized page numbers indicate the reference; other page numbers indicate citations in the text. Cross references are employed to guide the reader to related topics and double listings are often given for the same content to increase the probability of locating the desired material.

Subjects

Acceleration:
  behavioral oscillations, 275
  centrifuge description, 206, 251, 285, 295
  coriolis effect, 230, 372
  devices, 207, 247
  disorientation, 219, 229, 264, 357
  dynamic training devices, 299
  effects on: closed-loop tracking, 253; control forces, 233, 237, 257; higher mental abilities, 263, 269, 291; learning and performance, 240, 245, 293; memory, 271; mobility, 236; motor performance, 237; personality, 279; psychomotor performance, 232, 289; reaction times, 238, 243; response sequences, 242; sensitivity, 219; side-arm controllers, 257; space station design, 232, 237; time perception, 270; tracking, 246; training, 292, 295; vestibular senses, 219
  environment descriptions, 204
  error characteristics, 274, 288
  illusions, 230
  impact, 210
  nomenclature, 195
  oculoagravic illusion, 230
  oculogravic illusion, 230
  oculogyral illusion, 231
  oculomotor effects, 225
  physiological tolerance, 208, 213
  protection and restraint, 213, 248, 262, 290
  psychological factors, 289
  sensation, mechanisms of, 218
  static training devices, 298
  vertigo, 265
  visual loss, 223
Acclimatization, 92, 348
Air-bearing platforms, 356
Anxiety, 44, 142, 280, 291

Apollo, 284, 293, 425
Astronaut maneuverability, 365
Attention, 41, 101, 137
Audiogenic seizures, 413
Auditory reaction times, 226, 244
Autonomic nervous system, 49, 156, 158

Balloon flights, 134, 135, 137, 154, 411
Biochemical measures:
  ACTH, 48, 51
  adrenaline, 35, 50, 53
  adrenal steroids, 51
  aldosterone, 332
  catecholamines, 29, 35, 50, 183
  eosinophiles, 103, 386
  hydroxycorticosteroid, 51, 91, 114
  iodine uptake, 52
  noradrenaline, 35, 50, 53
  steroid hormones, 48
  thyroid activity, 52
Biological rhythms, 29, 43, 183, 421
Blacky test, 48
Bourdon-Wiersma Stipple Test, 44
Brain stem (see also Reticular activating system), 48, 173
Bremsstrahlung effect, 402

Cardiovascular system:
  acceleration, blood pressure, 9, 35
  arterial pressure, 6
  blood pressure, 7, 53, 103
  blood vessel wall, 7
  brady cardia, 130
  diastolic blood pressure, 9
  EKG, 52, 128
  Fourier analysis, 7
  heart rate, 52, 335
  pressure wave, 5
  stress, 5, 35, 128
  thermal stress, 11
  vasoconstriction, 13

Cardiovascular system (*cont.*)
 volume, 53
 weightlessness, 366, 368
Catecholamines (*see also* Biochemical
 measures), 29, 35, 50, 183
Centrifuge (*see also* Acceleration), 204
Chemoreceptors, 27
Cognitive tests, 43
Concept formation, 43
Confinement:
 consensual validation, 180
 definitions, 170
 drive reduction, 177
 morphological effects, 176
 perceptual problems, 142, 179
 personal interaction, 143, 170
 physiological effects, 176
 prisoners of war, 180
 problem-solving, 179, 181
 psychopharmacology, 183
 neurophysiological basis, 172
Control coding, 240
Coriolis effect, 230, 372
Cosmic radiation (*see* Radiation)
Critical flicker fusion, 41, 101, 347

Disorientation (*see also* Orientation),
 219
Diurnal variation (*see also* Biological
 rhythms), 43, 95, 143, 183
Dynamic training devices, 299, 363
Dyna-Soar, 284, 293

Edwards Personal Preference Schedule,
 46
Electrophysiological measurements:
 electrocardiogram (EKG), 128
 electroencephalogram (EEG), 55,
 158, 160
 electromyogram (EMG), 54, 235
 galvanic skin response (GSR), 29,
 45, 52, 101, 115, 128, 155, 160
 techniques, 130, 137, 138, 159, 160,
 162
Exercise, 334

Factor analytic technique, 104, 106,
 116, 119
Figure drawing, 48
Functional deafferentation, 176

G forces (*see* Acceleration)
Gemini, 293
General Adaptation Syndrome, 48
General Classification Test (GCT), 110
Golay detector, 14
Group cohesiveness, 75, 96, 187

Hypodynamic environment (*see* Confinement)
Hypothalamic function (*see also* Autonomic nervous system), 157

Intelligence tests, 41
Ionizing radiation (*see* Radiation)
Isolation (*see also* Confinement),
 171

Keplerian Trajectory (*see* Weightlessness)
Knowlis Mood Scale, 46

Life support systems, 143, 187
Lunar missions, 425

MacKinney Reporting Test, 155
MacQuarrie Test, 102
Magnetic fields, 29, 421
Manhigh II flight, 134, 153
Manhigh III flight, 137
Man's role in space, 150, 187
Mathematical models:
 computor simulation, 61
 man-machine model, 66
 pseudo-random numbers, 72, 83
 simulation sequence, 73
 team cohesiveness, 75
Mercury flights, 133, 251, 284, 293,
 296, 300, 393
Minnesota Manual Dexterity Test, 102
Minnesota Multiphasic Personality In-
 ventory, 46, 111
Minnesota Paper Form Board Test, 44
Motor tests, 42, 91, 102
MR-3 flight (*see also* Mercury flights),
 133

New London Inventory, 111
NRC-Neurotic Inventory, 111
Number Facility Task, 43
Nutrition, 347
Nyquist diagram, 20

Ohm's Law, 323
Orientation (*see also* Disorientation):
 sensory interaction, 360
 vestibular cues, 359
 otoliths, 359
 visual cues, 358
 postural reflexes, 357
Otoliths, 219
Otis Self-Administering Test, 109

Pacinian corpuscles, 219
Pain threshold, 18

Perceptual integrating system, 175
Perceptual-motor tests, 43
Perceptual retention, 41
Perceptual speed, 41
Perceptual tests, 40
Performance errors, 301
Performance tolerance limits, 289
Personality characteristics:
　anxiety, 44, 142, 280, 291
　claustrophobia, 93, 111
　conformity, 97
　emotional response, 44
　expectancy, 38
　flexibility, 44
　gratification, 39
　moods, 46, 104
　problem-solving, 43
　projective techniques, 111
　rigidity, 44
Physiological selectivity, 49
PSI apparatus, 43
Psycho-motor performance:
　coordination, 42, 91, 347
　discrimination, 42
　MacQuarrie Test, 102
　Minnesota Manual Dexterity Test, 102
　motor tests, 42, 91, 102
　perceptual-motor tests, 43
　reaction time, 43, 347
　steadiness, 42, 91, 101, 347
　tapping, 347

Q-sort, 116

Radiation:
　behavioral activity, 409
　Bremsstrahlung effect, 402
　cosmic radiation, 411
　dose classification, 414
　electrical phosphenes, 413
　exposure in submarines, 92
　learning & retention, effects of, 407, 410
　lethal dose, 397
　measurement, 397
　outer space, 401
　permissible dose, 399
　sickness, 406
　SNAP reactors, 403
　solar flares, 404
　Soviet studies, 412
　sublethal doses, 411
　tolerance, 397
　types, 396
　Van Allen Belts, 400
　vehicle shielding, 403

Regulatory behavior, 3, 34
Research needs, 421
Respiratory system:
　anoxia, 43
　carbon dioxide production, 90
　carbon dioxide stress, 25, 103
　hyperventilation, 24
　positive pressure breathing, 226
　respiratory stress, 24, 54
　weightlessness, 370
Reticular activating system, 48, 52, 152, 157, 171, 186
Role behavior, 98, 169, 187
Rorschach Test, 47, 111
Rotating room, 231, 237

Self-ratings, 46, 91, 104
Sensory deprivation (*see also* Confinement), 171
Skin resistance (*see* Electrophysiological measurements, [TSR])
Sleep, 185
SNAP reactors, 403
Societal implications, 425
Space cabin simulators, 43, 141, 146
Space flight simulation, 282, 300
Space stations, 232, 237, 372
Space tools, 365
Spin recovery, 242
Static training devices, 298
Stress:
　definitions, 34, 89, 115, 127
　fatigue, 133
　indices, 39
　interaction, 421
　physiological measures, 128
　psychological measures, 40
　psychophysiological, 128
　respiration, 24
　tolerance, 420
　vision, 17
Submarines:
　atmosphere, 90
　confinement, 93
　exteroceptive input, 93
　Fleet Ballistic Missile (FBM), 96, 104
　group cohesiveness, 96
　human engineering aspects, 100
　leadership, 99
　morale, 96
　odors in, 94
　personality assessment, 111
　radiation, 92
　role behavior, 98
　selection of personnel, 108
　sound level in, 93

Submarines (*cont.*)
  submariner motivation, 113
  time estimation,
  visual impairment, 93

Taylor Manifest Anxiety Scale, 46
Temperature:
  acclimatization, 348
  and complex mental tasks, 340
  curvature effect, 329
  effective temperature (ET) scale, 337
  and exercise, 334
  infrared energy, 11
  and kinesthetic sensitivity, 342, 345
  and nutrition, 347
  pain receptors, 15
  pain thresholds, 18
  and performance, 137, 334
  physical factors of, 322
  physiological factors of, 327
  shivering, 13
  and stress, 336
  thermal comfort zone, 13, 137
  thermal energy, physical factors of, 322
  thermal stress, 11
  tolerance, 16, 140
Thematic Apperception Test (TAT), 111
Time estimation, 95, 184, 228

U-shaped curve, 49, 174, 177

Van Allen Belts, 400
Vertigo, 265
Vibration:
  definition, 379
  equipment design, 391
  physiological effects, 386
  protection, 390, 392
  secondary resonances, 391
  subcutaneous hemorrhage, 385
    tolerance, 382
    tracking, 389
    vigilance, 41, 101, 136, 153, 175, 179
    visual effects, 388
    whole-body, 386
Vision:
  acceleration, effects of, 220
  dark adaptation, 19
  flash blindness, 4, 19, 20, 21, 22, 23
  flicker fusion, 40, 347
  illusions, 230
  positive pressure breathing, effects of, 226
  vibration, effects of, 388
  visual stress, 17

Weightlessness:
  air-bearing platforms, 356
  aircraft experiments, 362
  animal experiments, 367
  circulatory changes, 366, 369
  definitions, 354
  digestion, 371
  Keplerian trajectory, 132, 264, 269, 299, 300, 355, 362
  long-term, 361, 366
  maneuverability, 365
  motor behavior, 365
  nausea, 371
  orientation, 357
  physiological measures, 128
  proprioceptive input, 188
  respiratory stress, 370
  transient, 361
  visual acuity, 361
  water immersion, 229, 356, 359, 369
Wisconsin Card Sorting Task, 43
Work-rest schedules, 144, 146

X-15 data, 130, 284

Zeigarnik technique, 95

Authors

Adams, O. S., 146, 147, 148, 149, 150, 151, 153, *162*
Adams, R. M., 130, *164*
Ades, H. W., 408, 410, *416*
Adolf, E. F., 332, *349*
Alexander, H. M., 178, *189*
Allen, S. C., *313*
Alves, D., 103, 114, 115, *125*
Alvis, H. J., 93, *119*
Andrews, T. G., 41, *58*
Andrews, W. H., 256, 269, *314*

Antonitis, J. J., 178, *190*
Armstrong, H. G., 230, 231, *304*
Armstrong, N. A., 256, 269, *314*
Arnold, W. J., 408, *415*
Ashe, W. F., 248, 249, *304*, *311*, 389, *393*
Atkinson, J. W., 47, *59*
Augerson, W. S., 133, *162*, 225, 226, 227, 270, *304*, *307*, *310*, *315*, 368, 369, 371, *373*, 375
Auld, F., 111, *121*
Auxier, J. A., 408, *416*

Ava, C., 57
Ax, A. F., 48, 54, 56

Backer, P. W., 270, 298, 299, 318
Bader, M. E., 331, 346, 349
Baer, D. M., 183, 189, 190
Bairstow, L., 199, 304
Balakhovskii, I. S., 362, 373
Baldes, J., 234, 236, 259, 315
Baldwin, H. W., 170, 188
Balke, B., 371, 374
Ballinger, E. R., 269, 304, 360, 367, 375
Bamford, H. E., 167, 188
Band, R. I., 42, 56
Barbour, H. G., 332, 349
Barr, N. L., 368, 371, 375
Bartlett, D. J., 342, 350
Bartlett, N. R., 110, 111, 119, 120, 121
Basowitz, H., 42, 49, 56, 57
Bates, G., 204, 304
Bazett, H. C., 329, 350
Beach, E. L., 108, 120
Beckman, E. L., 211, 221, 225, 226, 227, 230, 244, 246, 304, 305, 307, 310
Beeding, E. L., 137, 138, 164, 210, 304
Behnke, A. R., 103, 120
Beischer, D. E., 368, 371, 375
Benson, V. G., 225, 226, 227, 304, 305
Bermack, J. E., 57
Berman, F. R., 348, 351
Berman, M. L., 35, 56
Berrian, J. H., 368, 371, 375
Berrien, F. K., 94, 120
Berry, R. N., 110, 121
Bevan, W., 227, 232, 285, 305
Bexton, W. H., 175, 176, 180, 181, 188, 192
Bitterman, M. E., 40, 57
Blair, E. A., 347, 350
Blair, W. C., 408, 409, 415
Blanchard, W. G., 215, 305
Blethrow, J. G., 208, 318
Blitz, B., 44, 59
Blockley, W. V., 16, 30, 343, 344, 350
Board, F., 51, 56
Boardman, W. K., 228, 311
Boettcher, C. A., 235, 239, 245, 248, 249, 254, 314, 316
Bombard, A., 168, 175, 188
Bond, G. L., 110, 120
Bondurant, S., 208, 215, 305
Bowden, J., 48, 58
Bowlby, J., 183, 188
Box, G., 78, 84, 85
Briggs, D. L. A., 111, 120
Brinkley, J. W., 210, 313
Brody, E. B., 51, 56, 187, 188

Bronk, D. W., 30
Brouha, L., 336, 350
Brown, B. P., 252, 253, 305
Brown, C. W., 240, 305
Brown, D. V. L., 19, 30
Brown, E. L., 358, 373
Brown, F. A., 186, 188
Brown, J. L., 3, 42, 56 187, 188, 219, 223, 224, 225, 227, 228, 229, 230, 232, 233, 235, 238, 241, 242, 244, 248, 250, 252, 253, 254, 259, 261, 266, 279, 280, 285, 293, 297, 305, 306, 310, 313, 359, 373
Brozek, J., 41, 56
Bryan, G. L., 238, 306
Buckley, E. P., 112, 123
Buckner, D. N., 110, 122
Bugrov, B. G., 368, 373
Buhrlen, L., 221, 236, 259, 306
Burch, G. E., 54, 56, 367, 374
Burch, N. R., 47, 52, 55, 56, 57, 132, 160, 161, 163
Burke, R. E., 223, 224, 225, 229, 230, 238, 244, 266, 305
Burmeister, H., 225, 238, 243, 266, 306
Burney, C., 167, 168, 169, 188
Burns, N. M., 42, 44, 47, 56, 170, 181, 184, 185, 188, 189, 190, 228, 306
Buros, O. K., 40, 56
Bursill, A. E., 341, 350
Burton, A. C., 328, 329, 350
Burwell, R. B., 142, 164
Butler, R. A., 178, 189
Byars, G. E., 138, 163
Byford, G. H., 223, 314
Byrd, R. E., 167, 168, 169, 175, 176, 189
Byrnes, V. A., 19, 30

Callaway, E., 42, 56
Campbell, D. T., 99, 120
Campbell, P. A., 357, 374
Candland, D. K., 42, 59
Canfield, A. A., 225, 226, 228, 233, 236, 238, 243, 266, 306, 307, 316, 319
Carmault, R. J., 270, 310
Cattell, R. B., 117, 119, 120
Ceran, S. J., 237, 312
Chaffee, J. W., 307
Chambers, A. N., 120
Chambers, R. M., 218, 225, 226, 227, 228, 229, 233, 235, 237, 244, 245, 246, 250, 252, 254, 257, 259, 260, 264, 266, 268, 270, 272, 279, 285, 289, 292, 293, 297, 304, 305, 307, 308, 309
Champlin, G. E., 368, 371, 375
Channell, R. C., 100, 120

Charland, P. V., 267, *318*
Cheatham, D. C., 254, *310*
Cherniak, N. S., 247, 285, *308*
Chernov, V. N., 362, 368, 371, *374*
Chichibu, S., 413, 416
Childers, H. E., 47, 55, *56*, 160, 161, *163*
Chiles, W. D., 4, *30*, 146, 147, 148, 149, 150, 151, 153, *162*, 342, *350*
Chow, K. L., 176, *189*
Christensen, K. K., 219, *308*
Cibis, P. A., 19, *30*
Clark, B., 230, 231, 237, *308*, *312*, 367, 369, *374*
Clark, C. C., 197, 199, 201, 203, 208, 215, 219, 230, 233, 234, 237, 241, 252, 263, 270, 281, 285, *308*, *312*, *313*, *318*
Clark, R. E., 346, *350*, 368, 371, 375
Clark, W. G., 221, 225, 234, 236, 259, *308*, *315*
Clarke, N. P., 247, 285, *305*, *308*
Clarke, R. S., 176, *189*
Claus, W. D., *415*
Coburn, K. R., 225, 226, 227, 244, 246, *304*, *305*, *307*
Cochran, L. B., 222, 238, 241, *309*
Code, C. F., 221, 236, 259, 265, *309*, *319*
Coermann, R., 381, 388, 391, *393*
Cohen, A., 344, 346, *350*
Cohen, E., 268, *316*
Cohen, S. I., 49, *59*, 236, *319*
Cohn, A. E., 54, *56*
Cole, J. O., 183, *192*
Collins, C. C., 42, *56*, 230, 235, 248, 252, 259, 293, *306*, *309*, *310*
Comrey, A. L., 225, 228, 233, 236, 238, 243, 266, *306*
Comroe, J. H., 24, *30*
Conkley, J. D., *57*
Conrad, E., 51, *58*
Cook, E. B., 111, 114, *120*
Cooper, D. Y., 26, *30*
Cooper, K. E., 331, *350*
Cooperman, N. R., 43, *56*
Cope, F. W., 227, 228, 244, 245, 268, *309*, 380, 391, *393*
Copeland, N., 363, *376*
Cordes, F. C., 19, *30*
Coser, R. L., 99, *120*
Cramer, E. H., 144, *163*
Cramer, R. L., 237, *312*
Creer, B. Y., 211, 214, *309*, *317*
Crissy, W. J. E., 97, 112, *120*, *123*
Crist, B., 344, *350*
Cronbach, L. J., 116, *121*
Crosbie, R. J., *30*, 197, 199, 201, 203,

230, 231, 235, 254, 259, *308*, *309*, *312*, *315*
Crowell, J. W., 27, *30*
Culver, J. F., 270, *314*

Darrow, C. W., 101, *121*, 186, *189*
Davis, J. F., *58*
Davis, R. C., 49, 53, *56*
Davis, R. T., 409, 411, *415*
Davis, T. R. A., 348, *351*, 368, 371, *375*
Davson, H., 21, *30*
Day, R. E., *309*
Dean, W. F., 180, *189*
Deese, J., 40, *58*
DeForest, R. E., 225, 226, 227, *304*
Delhagen, J. E., 177, *190*
Den Breeijen, A., 51, *58*
Dennis, J. P., 248, *309*
De Silva, H., *57*
Deter, C. E., 409, 411, *415*
Dews, P. B., 228, *309*
Dickerman, D., 248, *309*
Dieckman, D., 391, 393, *393*
Diefenbach, W. S., 359, *374*
Dill, D. B., *57*
Dixon, F., 197, 201, *309*, *310*
Doane, B. K., 176, 177, 180, 181, *189*, *190*, *192*
Doerfel, H. V., 252, 254, 285, *307*
Douglas, W. K., 270, *310*, 314
Drolette, M. E., 45, 49, 53, *57*
Drury, D. R., 221, 225, 233, 234, 236, 259, *308*, *315*
Duane, T. D., 211, 221, 225, 227, 230, *304*, *310*
DuBois, E. F., 326, *350*
Duff, I. F., 88, 90, 93, 94, 96, 99, 102, 108, 113, *121*
Duffner, G. J., 93, 96, 111, *121*
Duffy, E., 174, *189*
Dusek, E. R., 346, *350*
Dyson, G. W., 113, *121*
Dzendolet, E., 356, 365, 366, *374*

Ebaugh, F. G., 11, *30*
Ebersole, J. H., 90, 92, *121*
Edelberg, K., 267, *310*, *318*
Edelberg, R., 52, *57*, 223, 247, *316*
Edholm, O. G., 328, 329, *350*
Edwards, M. W., 25, *31*
Eggleston, J. M., 229, 254, 270, 285, *307*, *310*
Eiband, A. M., 207, 208, 211, *310*
Ellis, W. H. B., 280, *306*
Elmadjian, F., 48, 51, *57*
Elwood, M. A., 248, *309*
Emmel, G. R. J., 26, *30*

English, H. B., 47, *57*
Enoch, J. M., 222, *310*
Eron, L. D., 111, *121*
Essen, K. W., 90, 103, *121*
Evarts, E., *189*

Fahnstock, M. K., 347, *351*
Farrar, J. V., 382, 383, 384, 385, *394*
Farrow, R. L., 7, *30*
Faubert, D. A., 208, *308*
Faucett, R. E., 91, 93, 101, 102, 103, *121*
Feigl, E., 7, *30*
Fenichel, R. L., *315*
Ferris, H. M., 331, *350*
Fetherstonhaugh, M. L., 176, *189*
Fiedler, F. E., 99, *121*
Fields, P. E., 408, 410, *415*
Fine, B. J., 344, *350*
Fischer, C. F., 252, *310*
Fiske, D. W., 175, 177, *189*
Fleishman, E. A., 292, *310*
Fletcher, D. E., 248, 293, *310*
Flinn, D. E., 144, *163*
Forbes, W. H., *57*
Forgays, D. C., 176, *189*
Forgus, R. H., 183, *191*
Forlano, G., *57*
Fowler, R. C., 381, 385, *393*
Fox, R. H., 330, *350*
Fozard, J., 347, *351*
Frankenhaeuser, M., 222, 228, 229, 236, 243, 268, 270, *310*
Franks, W. R., 150, *163*, 243, *315*
Fraser, D. C., 344, *350*
Fraser, T. M., 249, *311*, 389, *393*
Frazer, J. W., 294, *311*
Fredricson, E., 176, *192*
Freedman, A., 346, *351*
French, J. D., 172, *189*
French, J. W., 41, 43, *57*
French, R. L., 96, 97, *121*
Fuller, J. L., 176, *192*
Funkenstein, D. H., 45, 48, 49, 53, *57*
Furchtgott, E., 407, 410, *415*
Fuster, J. M., 174, 178, *189*
Futterweit, A., 254, *315*

Gaddis, T. E., 180, *189*
Gagge, A. P., 325, *352*
Gaito, J., 228, *313*
Galambos, R., 264, 265, 266, *311*
Galkin, A. M., 362, 368, 371, *374*
Gallant, R. P., 248, 263, 285, *317*
Garattini, S., 183, *189*
Garcia, J., 412, *415*
Gard, P. W., 222, 309

Gardner, M. S., 365, *376*
Garner, J. D., 208, *318*
Gauer, O. H., 196, 197, 203, 208, 211, 213, 221, 223, 231, *311*
Gelb, A., 176, *189*
Geldard, F. A., 218, *311*
Gellhorn, E., 157, *163*
Gentry, G., 408, *415*, *416*
Gerathewohl, S. J., 218, 231, 269, *311*, 358, 360, 361, 362, 367, 371, *374*
Getline, G. L., 254, *311*
Gewirtz, J. L., 171, 183, *189*, *190*
Ghetti, V., 183, *189*
Gifford, E. C., 42, 44, *56*, 170, 181, 184, *188*, *189*, 228, *306*
Gildenberg, B., 137, 138, *164*
Girdner, J. B., 177, *190*
Glenn, J. H., 334, *350*
Glickman, A. S., 113, *122*
Glickman, N., 347, *351*
Glickman, S. E., 178, *190*
Goldberger, L., 47, *57*
Goldfarb, W., 183, *190*
Goldman, D. E., 248, *311*, 380, 382, 386, 387, 392, *393*, *394*
Goldstein, K., 176, *189*
Goldstein, M. S., *56*
Goldstone, S., 228, *311*
Gorlov, O. G., 362, 368, 371, *373*, *374*
Gorill, R. B., 249, *311*, 389, *393*
Gottschalk, C. W., 347, *350*
Gouras, P., 7, *30*
Graham, C. H., 110, 111, *121*
Grand, D. A., 42, *58*
Graveline, D. E., 357, 364, 369, 371, *374*, *375*
Gray, J. S., 24, *30*
Gray, R. F., 215, 219, 225, 230, 231, 234, 235, 237, 254, 259, 263, 270, 280, 285, *306*, *308*, *309*, *311*, *312*, *313*, *318*
Graybiel, A., 219, 225, 230, 231, 232, 237, 270, 300, *308*, *310*, *312*, *314*, 367, 368, 369, 371, *374*, *375*
Greely, P. O., 221, 234, 236, 259, *308*
Green, G. A., 236, 238, *306*, *319*
Greenbaum, L. J., 88, 90, 111, *122*
Greene, L. C., *30*
Greenwood, D. D., 410, *417*
Greiner, T. H., 52, *57*, 132, 160, *163*
Grinker, R. R., *56*
Grissom, V. I., 251, 270, 293, 295, 298, *312*
Grodins, F. S., 24, *30*
Grodsky, M. A., 408, 410, *416*
Gronow, D. G. C., 342, *350*
Gubin, V. A., *415*

Guedry, F. E., 219, 230, 231, 232, 237, 300, *312*
Guignard, J. C., 248, *312*
Gulick, W. L., 42, *59*
Gulliksen, H., 95, *121*
Gurfinkel, V. S., 363, *375*
Gussack, H., *56*
Guyton, A. C., 27, *30*

Haber, H., 231, *311*
Hagen, D. H., 144, *163*
Hall, R. A., 230, *312*
Hallenbeck, G. A., 224, 264, *313*
Ham, G. C., 229, 230, *313*
Hamburg, D. A., 51, *56, 57*
Hammer, L. R., 361, 363, 369, *375*
Hanes, L. F., 167, *188*
Hanna, T. D., 228, *313*
Hardy, J. D., 13, 14, *30*, 197, 199, 201, 203, 219, 233, 237, 252, 270, 281, 285, *308, 313*, 326, 327, 329, 333, *350, 351*
Harlow, H. F., 178, *189*, 411, *415*
Harris, J. D., 93, *122*
Harris, M., 330, *351*
Hartman, B. O., 144, *163*, 357, 364, 369, *375*
Hauty, G. T., 42, *57*, 141, 142, 143, 153, *163, 164*
Hawkins, W. R., 142, *164*, 371, *377*
Headley, R. N., 210, 313
Hebb, D. O., 49, *57*, 174, 176, 178, *189, 190*
Henderson, R. L., 177, *190, 191*
Hendler, E., 333, 334, *351*
Henriques, F. C., 15, 19, *30*
Henry, C. E., 101, *121*, 186, *189*
Henry, J. P., 221, 223, 234, 236, 247, 259, *308, 310, 311, 313, 316*, 360, 367, *375*
Heron, W., 94, *122*, 175, 176, 177, 180, 181, *188, 189, 190, 192*
Heroux, O., 345, *351*
Herrington, L. P., 325, 326, *352*
Hertzberg, H. T. E., 365, *375*
Hess, E. H., 183, *190*
Hessberg, R. R., 205, 206, 210, *304, 305, 313*
Hiatt, E. P., *305*
Hildes, J. A., 345, *351*
Hill, J. H., 238, 241, 242, *313*
Hilton, S. M., 330, *350*
Hines, M., 248, *316*, 385, *394*
Hixon, W. C., 232, *316*, 368, 371, *375*
Hoff, E. C., 88, 90, 111, *122*
Hoffman, J., 179, *192*
Holleman, E. C., 256, 269, *314*
Holmes, R. H., 368, 371, *375*

Holt, R. R., 47, *57*
Holtzman, W. H., 40, *57*
Hoover, G. N., 249, *311*, 389, *393*
Hope, J. M., 48, *57*
Hopkins, C. O., 152, *164*
Hornick, R. J., 235, 239, 245, 248, 249, 254, *314*
Horowitz, L., 177, *190*
Horst, P., 116, *122*
Horvath, F. E., 40, *57*
Horvath, S. M., 346, *351*
Howard, P., 223, *314*
Howarth, D., 176, *190*
Hunter, H. N., 211, 221, 227, 230, 238, 241, 242, *304, 310, 314*
Hupp, D. I., 231, *312*
Hussman, T. A., 41, *58*
Hyde, A. S., 247, 285, *308*

Innis, R. C., 247, *317*
Irving, A., *30*, 248, *312*
Isakov, P. K., 363, *375*

Jackson, C. B., 270, *314*
Jackson, K. F., 344, *350*
Jacobs, H. I., 237, 238, 254, *314, 316*
Jasper, H., 178, *192*
Jensen, R., 227, 228, 244, 268, *309*
Jerison, H. J., 41, *57*
Johnson, G. E., 160, *163*
Johnson, H. I., 252, 253, *305*
Johnson, L., 219, *308*
Johnson, W. H., 230, 231, 232, *312, 314*
Jones, E. R., *314*
Jones, M. B., 167, *190*
Jones, R. W., 24, *30*
Jorve, W. R., 222, *319*, 361, *377*
Joy, R. J. T., 348, *351*

Kaehler, R. D., 236, 237, 239, 240, 250, 259, *314*
Kahn, A. R., 130, *164*
Kama, W. N., 361, *376*
Kaplan, S. J., 407, 408, 410, *415, 416, 417*
Karmiol, E. D., 150, *163*
Kassai, T., 413, *416*
Keeton, R. W., 347, *351*
Keighley, G., 225, *315*
Keller, A. D., 327, *351*
Kennedy, R., 230, 231, 232, *312*
Kennedy, W. A., 243, *315*
Keough, R. H., 26, *30*
Kerr, R., 226, *307*
Kerr, W. K., 238, 243, 264, 280, *315*
Kety, S. S., 50, *57*
Keys, A., 41, *56*
Kimball, A. L., 391, *394*

Kimeldorf, D. J., 412, *415*, *416*
Kimura, D., 184, *190*
King, A. L., 6, *30*
King, B. C., 236, 237, 238, *315*
King, B. T., 93, 97, 110, 111, *122*
King, S. H., 45, 49, 53, *57*
Kinsey, J. L., 93, 97, 99, 110, 111, *122*, 167, *190*
Kipnis, D., 113, *122*
Kirshner, N., 51, *59*
Kish, G. B., 177, 178, *190*
Kistler, W. G., 368, 371, *375*
Kleitman, N., 43, *56*
Kling, J. W., 177, *190*
Knauff, P. R., 150, *163*
Knight, L. A., 357, 359, *375*
Knoblock, E. C., 270, *310*, *314*
Kobrick, J. L., 347, *352*
Koella, W. P., 237, *312*
Koga, Y., 413, *416*
Kohata, T., 413, *416*
Kohl, J. W., 108, *124*
Komatsu, M., 413, *416*
Kondrat'eva, I. N., 412, 413, *416*
Konecci, E. B., 167, *190*, 402, *417*
Korchin, S. J., 42, *56*
Kornhauser, M., 208, *315*
Kosov, I. I., 362, 368, 371, *374*
Kotova, A. R., 362, 368, 371, *374*
Krugman, H. E., 41, *57*
Kuehnel, H., 254, *315*
Kupalov, P. S., 410, *416*
Kydd, G. H., *30*, *315*

Lacey, B. C., 49, *58*, 155, 156, 157, 158, 159, 160, 161, *163*
Lacey, J. I., 49, 50, 52, 53, *58*, 155, 156, 157, 158, 159, 160, 161, *163*
Ladell, W. S. S., 331, *351*
La Gaipa, J. J., 113, *122*
Lambert, E. H., 221, 225, 234, 236, 259, 265, 280, *309*, *313*, *315*, *319*, 347, *351*
Lambertson, C. J., 26, *30*
Lamson, E. T., 48, *57*
Lansberg, M. P., 232, *315*
Last, T. H., 347, *351*
Latham, F., 391, *394*
Lathrop, R. G., 250, 266, 272, *307*
Laughlin, C. P., 133, *162*, 270, *304*, *310*, *315*, 369, *373*
Lawton, R. W., *30*
Lazarus, R. S., 40, *58*
Leary, R. C., *416*
Le Blanc, J., 345, *351*
Lechner, M., 279, 280, 297, *306*
Leopold, N. F., 169, 171, 180, *190*
Levedahl, B. H., *416*

Leverett, S. D., 208, 215, *315*
Levine, A. S., 96, 101, 113, *122*
Levine, R. B., 146, *162*
Levy, E. Z., 48, *59*, 160, *163*, 167, *190*
Lewin, K., 95, *122*
Lewis, D., 388, *394*
Lewis, S. T., 210, *315*
Lewisohn, P., 42, *58*
Lhamon, W. J., 228, *311*
Lifton, R. J., 180, *190*, *191*
Lilly, J. C., 169, 171, 179, *191*
Lindberg, R. G., *416*
Lindsley, D. B., 48, *58*, 172, 174, 178, *191*
Link, H. J., 382, 383, 384, 385, 386, *394*
Lipkin, M., *30*
Livanov, M. N., 412, 413, *416*
Loeckle, W. E., 386
Loeb, M., 388, *394*
Loftus, J. P., 270, *315*, 371, *375*
Lokatos, G., 210, *313*
Lombard, C. F., 233, *316*
Lomonaco, T., 363, *375*
Lorenz, K. Z., 183, *191*
Loret, B. J., 372, *375*
Lubin, A., 175, *192*
Luchins, A. S., 183, *191*
Lund, D. W., 223, 243, 266, *318*
Lyman, J., 343, 344, *350*
Lyman, R. S., 410, *416*

McBlair, W., 347, *351*
McClure, D., 137, 138, 152, *164*
McCormick, E. J., 199, *316*
MacCorquodale, K., *308*
McCutchan, J. W., 16, *30*
McDowell, A. A., 409, 411, *415*
MacEwan, C., 116, *122*
McFadden, E. B., 208, *318*
McFarland, R. A., 43, *58*, 135, *163*, 380, *394*
McGill, T. E., 42, *59*, 179, *192*
Macht, M. B., 331, *349*
Maciolek, J. A., 223, *310*
McKenzie, R. E., 144, *163*, 357, 364, 369, *375*
Mackie, R. R., 110, *122*
Mackworth, N. H., 41, *58*, 175, *191*, 337, 345, 348, *351*
MacPherson, R. K., 331, *351*
Maddi, S. R., 175, 177, *189*
Magid, E. B., 387, *394*
Magoun, H. W., 48, *58*, 157, *163*, 184, 186, *191*
Mahatoo, W., 177, *189*
Maher, P. H., 360, 367, *375*
Malkin, V. B., 362, 363, *373*, *375*

Malmo, R. B., 53, 54, *58, 59,* 174, *191*
Managan, R. F., 210, *313*
Mandler, G., 41, *58*
Margaria, R., 357, 359, *375*
Maroc, J., 51, *58*
Martin, E. E., 221, *316*
Marx, M. H., 177, *191*
Mason, J. W., 51, *58*
Mead, J., 346, *349*
Meehan, J. P., 236, 237, 238, 239, 240, *314, 316*
Melching, W. H., 408, *416*
Melzack, R., 176, *191*
Miller, D. S., 413, *416*
Miller, H., *305*
Miller, I., 268, *316*
Miller, J., 110, *120, 122,* 247, *316*
Miller, J. G., 34, *58*
Mills, A. W., 345, *351*
Mintz, A., 169, *191*
Mitchell, H. H., 347, *351*
Molish, H. B., 91, 92, 97, 98, 113, 114, 117, *122, 125*
Monroe, J. T., 144, *163*
Montague, E. K., 230, *312*
Montgomery, K. C., 178, *191*
Moore, F., 215, *305*
Moore, J. W., 27, *30*
Morehouse, L. E., 233, 235, *318*
Morgan, T. E., *163*
Morris, G. O., 175, *192*
Morrow, D. J., 236, 237, 238, *315*
Morse, W. H., 228, *309*
Moruzzi, G., 48, *58,* 184, 186, *191*
Morway, D. A., 226, 244, 246, *307*
Moskalev, Y. I., *415*
Mosley, J. D., *304*
Motokawa, K., 413, *416*
Mottram, R. F., 331, *350*
Mozell, M. M., 249, *316,* 381, 388, 389, *394*
Mueller, C. G., 110, *121*
Muenzinger, K., *123*
Muller, A., 78, *85*
Muller, M., 78, 84, *85*
Mullin, F. J., 43, *56*
Mungall, R. G., 252, 253, *305*
Murgatroyd, D., *351*
Murphree, H. B., 93, 111, *122*
Murphy, J. P., 157, *163*

Nall, M. L., 88, *123*
Naugle, J. E., *416*
Nelson, D. H., 51, *58*
Nelson, J. G., 257, 285, 289, 297, *308*
Nemenov, M. I., 410, *416*
Neumann, C., 54, *56*

Newburgh, L. H., 330, *351*
Newell, F. W., 176, *189*
Newell, H. E., *416*
Newling, P. S. B., 331, *351*
Newman, P. P., 91, 93, 101, 102, 103, *121*
Nicholson, F. T., 252, 254, *310, 315*
Ninow, E. H., 91, 98, 112, 113, *122, 123*
Niven, J. I., 232, *316,* 368, 371, *375*
Norins, A. L., 24, *30*
Norsworthy, M. E., 222

Oken, D., *56*
Ormiston, D. W., 167, *191*
Osler, S. F., 40, *58*
Owens, W. A., 110, *122*

Pace, N., 103, *120*
Parker, J. W., 93, 100, 113, 114, 115, *123, 125*
Parry, C. H., 51, *58*
Pashalian, S., 97, 112, *123*
Patterson, J. L., 197, 201, 230, *309, 310, 312*
Payne, R. B., 42, *57*
Payne, R. E., 407, *415*
Pearson, R. G., 138, *163*
Peck, L. H., 241, *313*
Pedigo, G. P., 368, 371, *375*
Pepler, R. D., 42, *58,* 337, 344, *352*
Persky, H., 51, *56, 58*
Peterson, L. H., 5, 7, *30*
Petrov, A. V., 362, 368, 371, *373, 374*
Pettitt, J. A., *56*
Pidcock, G. B., 235, *306*
Pigg, L. D., 361, *375, 376*
Pi Suner, A., 28, *30*
Poe, R. H., 348, *351*
Pogrund, R. S., *416*
Pokrovskii, A. V., 371, *376*
Popov, V. I., 362, 363, 368, 371, *374, 375*
Preston, T. H., 247, *316*
Preusser, P. B., *120*
Price, D. B., 51, *58*

Quix, F. H., 359, *376*

Rapaport, D., 45, *58*
Rees, D. R., 363, *376*
Reeves, E., 294, *311*
Riehl, J. L., 160, *163*
Riesen, A. H., 176, *189, 191*
Rievley, J. F., 365, 366, *374*
Riggs, L. A., 110, *121*
Riley, M. B., 223, 236, *319*
Riopelle, A. J., 248, *316,* 381, 385, 387, *394,* 408, 410, *416*
Ritch, T. G., 95, 101, 103, *123, 125*

Ritchie, M. L., 167, *188*
Ritter, C., 169, 176, *191*
Roberts, C. L., 177, *191*
Rogers, C. M., 408, *416*
Rohrer, J. H., 98, 99, *123*
Roman, J. A., 130, *164*, 381, 382, 385, 393, *394*
Roos, B. M., 42, 44, *58*
Roscoe, T., 88, 99, *123*
Rose, B., 294, *316*
Rose, H. W., 19, *30*
Rosen, A. C., 40, *58*
Rosenbaum, J. R., 267, *318*
Ross, M. O., 228, *316*
Ross, S., 41, *58*, 183, *192*
Rossanigo, F., 363, *375*
Rowen, G., 130, *164*
Rubacky, E. P., 270, 299, *316*
Rubenstein, M., 215, *318*
Rubin, B., 113, 114, 115, *123*
Ruch, T. C., *416*
Ruff, G. E., 48, *59*, 160, *163*, 167, *190*, 270, *314*
Ruff, S., 221, *311*
Rumbaugh, D., 347, *351*
Rupel, J. W., 42, *58*
Russell, R. W., 342, *352*
Russell, W. A. M., 238, 243, 264, 280, *315*

Salzman, E. W., 223, 247, *310*, *316*
Samuels, I., 172, *192*
Samuels, L. T., 51, *58*
Sandberg, N. E., 93, *123*
Santa Maria, L. J., 334, *351*
Sarason, S., 41, *58*
Satter, G. A., 110, *123*
Scano, A., 363, *375*
Schaefer, K. E., 90, 95, 103, *123*
Schaefer, V. H., 382, 383, 384, 385, 386, *394*
Schafer, G. E., 219, 230, 231, *316*
Schanche, D., 135, *164*
Schein, E. H., 180, *192*
Schlosberg, H., 40, 41, *59*
Schmitz, M. A., 248, 249, *316*, 389, *394*
Schock, G. J. D., 280, *317*, 359, 360, 361, 362, 370, *376*
Scholz, W., 410, *416*
Schrier, A. M., 411, *415*
Schriever, B. A., 150, *164*
Schubert, G., 232, *317*
Schwartz, I., 93, *123*
Scott, E. L., 98, 99, *123*
Scott, J. P., 176, *192*
Scott, T. H., 175, 176, 177, 180, 181, *188*, *189*, *190*, *191*, *192*

Selye, H., 34, 38, 48, 51, *59*
Senders, J., 227, 232, 285, 299, *305*, *317*
Serov, A. D., 362, 368, 371, *373*, *374*
Serrano, J., 160, *163*
Shagass, C., 54, *59*
Sharpless, S., 178, *192*
Shepard, A. B., 251, 270, 293, 298, *317*
Shepard, R. B., 7, *30*
Shilling, C. W., 108, 113, *121*, *124*
Shmavonian, B. M., 49, 54, *59*
Shroeder, K. R., 24, *30*
Siegel, A., 85, *86*
Siegel, A. I., 112, *123*, 176, *192*
Sieker, H. O., 221, *317*
Silverman, A. J., 49, 51, *59*, 236, *319*
Silverman, R. E., 41, 44, *59*
Simon, G. B., 268, *316*
Simons, A. K., 235, 239, 245, 248, 249, 254, *314*, *316*
Simons, D. G., 134, 135, 137, 138, *164*, 167, *192*, 228, *317*, 360, 367, *375*, 411, *415*
Simons, J. C., 358, 365, *376*
Slayton, D. K., 293, 295, 298, *317*
Slocum, J., 168, *192*
Smedal, H. A., 211, 214, 247, 248, 263, 285, *309*, *317*
Smith, B. J., 264, *308*
Smith, E. E., 98, *124*
Smith, J. B., 230, *314*
Smith, K. R., 44, *59*, 337, 341, *352*
Snyder, D. L., 184, *190*
Snyder, F. W., 249, *311*, 389, *393*
Snyder, R. Z., 242, 269, *317*
Solomon, R. L., 110, *121*
Spector, W. S., 21, *30*
Spitz, R. A., 183, *192*
Stacy, R. W., 7, *30*
Stallings, H. D., 360, 361, 371, *374*, 377
Stapp, J. P., 207, 208, 210, *315*, *317*
Stark, L., *30*
Steele, J. P., 409, 411, *415*
Steinkamp, G. R., 142, *164*
Stella, G., *30*
Stennet, R. G., 54, *59*, 174, 178, 180, *192*
Stevens, S. S., 40, *59*
Stewart, W. K., 219, *317*
Stinnett, G. W., 247, 248, 263, 285, *317*
Stoll, A., 15, *30*, 211, 212, 223, *318*
Stullken, D. E., 368, 371, *375*
Strughold, H., *30*, 362, 367, *374*, *376*
Stullken, D. E., 368, 371, *375*
Sullivan, J. A., 230, *314*
Svenson, D. W., 238, *306*
Swearingen, J. J., 208, *318*
Sykes, G. M., *192*

Tagiuri, R., 100, *124*
Tait, C. D., 407, *415*
Taylor, C. L., 16, *30*
Taylor, J. A., 44, *59*
Teichner, W. H., 42, *59*, 341, 347, *352*
Thaler, M., 51, *58*
Thaler, V. H., 48, *59*, 160, *163*, 167, *190*
Thauer, R. J., 11, *30*, 327, *352*
Theron, P. A., 54, *59*
Thompson, W. R., 176, 178, 183, *190*, *191*, *192*
Tiira, E., 169, *192*
Tinbergen, N., 183, *192*
Tobey, S., 148
Tobias, P., *417*
Tolstoi, E., 332, *349*
Tolcott, M. A., 100, *120*
Trapp, R. F., 402 *417*
Trumbull, R., 227, 232, 285, *305*

Ulmer, R. G., 386, *394*
Ulvedal, F., *163*

Van Allen, J. A., 400
Van Bockel, J. J., 270, 298, 299, *318*
Vandenberg, J. D., *318*
Van Deventer, F. M., *57*
Vernon, J. A., 42, *59*, 179, *192*
Verplanck, W. S., 110, *121*
Viteles, M. S., 337, 341, *352*
Voas, R. B., 251. 270, 293, 295, 298, 299, *318*
Vollmer, E. P., 236, 237, 238, *315*, *394*
Von Beckh, H. J., 128, 130, *164*, 269, 270, 360, 362, 368, 371, *376*
Von Diringshofen, H., 367, 371, *377*
von Gierke, H. E., 248, *311*, 386, 392, *394*
Vykukal, H. C., 248, 263, 285, *317*

Walker, E. L., 47, *59*
Wall, P. D., 407, *415*
Wang, G. H., 52, *59*
Ward, J. E., 142, *164*, 371, *377*
Ware, R. W., 130, 132, *164*
Warner, H., 7, *31*
Warren, B. H., 130, *164*
Warren, J. M., 410, *417*
Warren, N. D., 233, 238, *306*, *316*
Warrick, M. J., 223, 243, 266, *318*
Weaver, A. B., 215, *318*
Weaver, J. A., 230, *312*
Webb, M. G., 241, 242, 280, *306*, *312*, *313*
Webb, P., 16, *31*
Wehrkamp, R. F., *59*, 341, *352*
Weiss, H. S., 238, 241, 242, 267, *314*, *318*

Weitz, J., 240, *318*, 345, *352*
Welch, B. E., 144, *163*
Welham, W. C., 103, *120*
Wells, J. G., 233, 235, *318*
Westheimer, G., 225, *319*
Weybrew, B. B., 89, 90, 91, 92, 93, 95, 97, 98, 100, 101, 103, 104, 110, 112, 113, 114, 115, 116, 117, *122*, *124*, *125*
Wheaton, J. L., 170, 179, 181, *192*
Wherry, R. J., 111, 114, *120*
White, D. C., 249, *316*, 381, 388, 389, *394*
White, W. A., 103, *120*
White, W. J., 222, 223, 225, 227, 285, *319*, 361, 377
Whiteside, T. C. D., 24, *31*
Whitney, R. J., 54, *59*
Whitney, R. U., 215, *315*
Wilbarger, E., 368, 371, *375*
Wiens, D., 382, 383, 384, 385, *394*
Williams, A. C., 152, *164*
Williams, H. L., 175, *192*
Williams, M., *59*
Willmon, T. L., 95, 103, *125*
Willmorth, N. E., 236, 238, *306*, *319*
Wilson, C. L., 110, *122*
Wilson, R. C., 225, 226, 228, 233, 236, 238, 243, 266, *306*, *319*
Wilson, S. E., 167, *188*
Wing, S., 41, *57*
Wingrove, R. C., 211, 213, *309*, *317*
Winslow, C. E. A., 325, 326, *352*
Wolf, A., 176, *192*
Wolf, J., 85, *86*
Wood, E. H., 221, 234, 236, 259, 265, *309*, *313*, *315*, *319*
Woodling, C. H., 252, 285, *308*
Woodward, L. K., 235, *306*
Woodworth, R. S., 40, 41, *59*

Yakovlev, B. I., 362, 368, 371, *373*, *374*
Yamamoto, W. S., 25, 26, *31*
Yost, D. H., 386, *394*
Youniss, R. P., 97, 113, 114, 117, *125*
Youtcheff, J. S., 150, *163*
Yugov, Ye. M., 368, *373*

Zarriello, J. J., 230, *312*
Zedekar, R. G., 270, 298, 299, *318*
Ziegenruecker, G. H., 387, *394*
Ziegler, J. E., 211, 221, 227, 230, *304*, *310*
Ziegler, R. B., 47, *56*
Zimmerman, W. S., 238, 243, *307*
Zuidema, G. D., 196, 203, 208, 211, 213, 215, 223, 236, 247, *310*, *311*, *313*, *315*, *316*, *317*, *319*